JEAN BOSSY

Professor of Anatomy
Faculty of Medicine
University of Montpellier, France

Atlas of

Neuroanatomy

and

Special Sense Organs

W. B. SAUNDERS COMPANY · *Philadelphia* · *London* · *Toronto*

W. B. Saunders Company: West Washington Square
Philadelphia, Pa. 19105

12 Dyott Street
London, WC1A 1DB

833 Oxford Street
Toronto 18, Ontario

Atlas of Neuroanatomy and Special Sense Organs   ISBN 0-7216-1875-8

Print No.:   2   3   4   5   6   7   8   9

Preface

This schematic atlas of neuroanatomy and the special sense organs is neither a textbook nor a formal manual. It is intended as a teaching aid to facilitate correlation of the theoretical and practical studies of the nervous system and the special sense organs, for the express purpose of clarifying clinical and pathological manifestations of disorders and dysfunctions.

Some diagrams may appear to have a paucity of detail while others are seemingly overcomplicated. The latter are by no means intended to be memorized; they are included with the hope of enhancing comprehension. If parts of the atlas become handy references, one of the chief goals in the preparation of this book will have been realized.

The morphological drawings approximate nature as closely as possible in order to facilitate practical study but, where necessary, subtle simplification has been introduced to aid understanding.

International nomenclature has been used throughout the atlas but the most frequently encountered alternative names are also listed.

To the entire staff of the Department of Anatomy of the St. Louis University School of Medicine I express my sincere appreciation for their assistance in helping me to learn English anatomical terminology, which was indispensable for the preparation of this book.

I am especially indebted for the benevolent assistance of the Chairman of that department, Dr. R. O'Rahilly, as well as for that of Dr. Vidić and Miss L. Soleman.

It is a pleasure to take this opportunity to acknowledge the highly competent and meticulous care with which Mrs. Marie Courtine has executed the many drawings in this atlas.

I am also deeply grateful to Mr. J. Alan Shnapier for reviewing the manuscript.

Finally, the encouragement of this endeavor by Vigot Frères and the W. B. Saunders Company deserves mention. Without the kind cooperation and understanding provided by Mr. Jean-Paul Vigot for the French edition and Mr. John L. Dusseau and his colleagues for the English version, this atlas would never have been undertaken. Any success this book may achieve is due to these people, to whom I am indeed grateful.

JEAN BOSSY

Contents

PART FOUR Cranial Nerves and Special Sense Organs

PART FIVE Autonomic Nervous System

Part One

General Considerations of the Nervous System

Definitions

The *nervous system* consists of nerve and associated cells organized into the brain, brain stem, spinal cord, nerves, ganglia and parts of receptor organs which correlate and regulate the internal reactions of the body and control its adjustment to the environment.

We can distinguish:

Centers, a collection of nerve cell bodies (or perikaryon)

Pathways, extensions of the nerve cells which conduct impulses

Neuroglia (or glial tissue), a supportive tissue of the nerve cells, the function of which is not only support but also the dynamic nutrition of the cells

Vessels, which supply the various components of the nervous system

Sheaths (or coverings), which protect the nerves

The brain and the spinal cord comprise the *central nervous system*. The ganglia and the nerves outside the brain and spinal cord form the *peripheral nervous system*, which is divided into *spinal* and *cranial* parts.

There is also the *autonomic (or vegetative) nervous system*, which includes centers and pathways in both the central and the peripheral nervous systems.

The central nervous system is protected by *osseous coverings*, the skull for the brain and the vertebral canal for the spinal cord. It is surrounded by the *meninges* and bathes in the *cerebrospinal fluid*.

The *peripheral nervous system* is distributed throughout the body. The *epineurium*, collagen and connective tissue sheath surrounds the nerves; the *perineurium* is a lamellar connective tissue sheath surrounding the bundles or fascicles of peripheral nerves; the *endoneurium*, interstitial connective tissue, separates individual nerve bundles and fibers.

According to the polarity of the nerve cells (or neurons), a fiber which conducts a nerve impulse toward a center is called *centripetal*, or *afferent*; a fiber is *centrifugal*, or *efferent*, if it conducts a nerve impulse away from a center.

A *receptor* is a more or less specialized organ, always including nerve termination, the function of which is to change a stimulus into a nerve impulse. An *effector* is a nerve end-organ which, when it receives a nerve impulse, produces an external or internal dynamic response.

Divisions

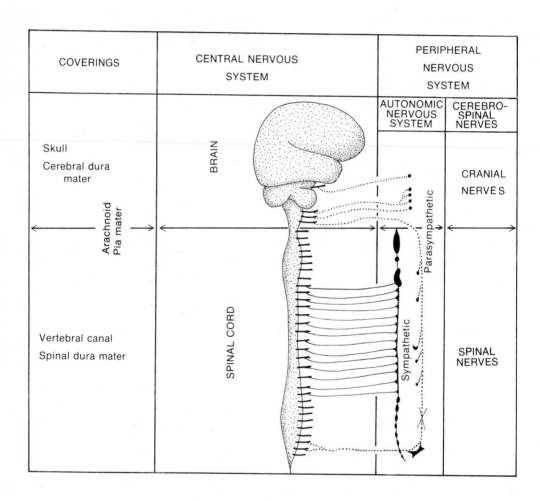

COVERINGS	CENTRAL NERVOUS SYSTEM	PERIPHERAL NERVOUS SYSTEM	
		AUTONOMIC NERVOUS SYSTEM	CEREBRO-SPINAL NERVES
Skull Cerebral dura mater	BRAIN		CRANIAL NERVES
Arachnoid Pia mater		Sympathetic · Parasympathetic	
Vertebral canal Spinal dura mater	SPINAL CORD		SPINAL NERVES

Nerve Cells

Primitive ganglion cell   Neuron   Neurosecretory cell

DIAGRAM OF A TYPICAL NEURON

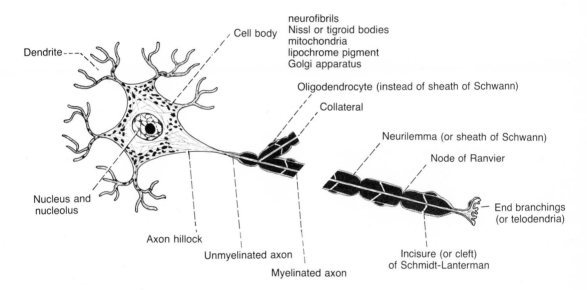

Dendrite

Cell body
- neurofibrils
- Nissl or tigroid bodies
- mitochondria
- lipochrome pigment
- Golgi apparatus

Oligodendrocyte (instead of sheath of Schwann)

Collateral

Neurilemma (or sheath of Schwann)

Node of Ranvier

End branchings (or telodendria)

Nucleus and nucleolus

Axon hillock

Unmyelinated axon

Myelinated axon

Incisure (or cleft) of Schmidt-Lanterman

SHEATHS OF NERVE FIBER

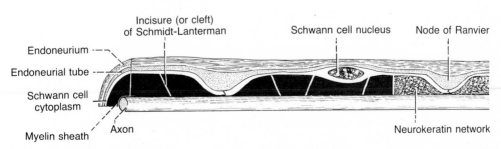

Incisure (or cleft) of Schmidt-Lanterman

Schwann cell nucleus

Node of Ranvier

Endoneurium

Endoneurial tube

Schwann cell cytoplasm

Myelin sheath

Axon

Neurokeratin network

(Modified from Ham, A. W.: Histology. Ed. 5, Philadelphia, J. B. Lippincott Company, 1965, p. 554.)

Ultrastructure of a Node of Ranvier*

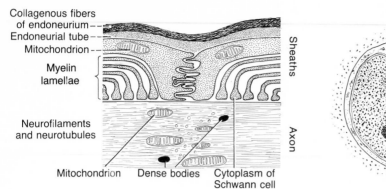

Collagenous fibers
of endoneurium
Endoneurial tube
Mitochondrion

Myelin
lamellae

Sheaths

Neurofilaments
and neurotubules

Axon

Mitochondrion — Dense bodies — Cytoplasm of
Schwann cell

Unmyelinated Nerve

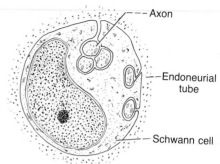

Axon

Endoneurial
tube

Schwann cell

Some Shapes of Neurons

Multipolar Neurons

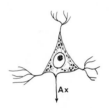   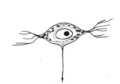

Ax

Pyramidal cell
of motor cortex

Mitral cell
of olfactory bulb

Purkinje cell
of cerebellar
cortex

Cell with oppositopolar dendrites
and a lateral axon, in the central
autonomic centers

Bipolar Neuron

Pseudounipolar Neuron

Unipolar Neuron

Cell of vestibular
ganglion

Cell of
spinal ganglion

Cell of mesencephalic
nucleus of V

*Adapted from Robertson, J. D.: The ultrastructure of nodes of Ranvier in frog nerve fibers. J. Physiol., 137:8P and 9P, 1957.

Organization of the Nervous System

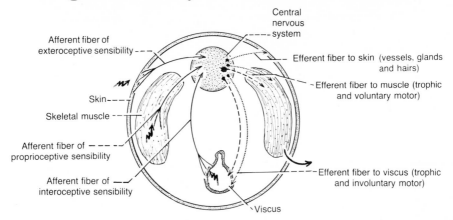

The body reacts to three types of stimuli (heavy broken arrow 〰〵), originating from the external environment, from the viscera and from the somatic system (namely, bones, joints and skeletal muscles).

The central nervous system receives impulses corresponding to these three kinds of stimuli by way of afferent neurons. After adjustment, it responds through efferent neurons by sending (1) voluntary motor impulses to skeletal muscles which are acting upon the external environment (heavy arrow ⟶), (2) involuntary motor impulses to smooth muscles of the viscera and the hairs, and to the glands, and (3) trophic impulses to most of the structures of the body.

SINGLE (OR MONOSYNAPTIC) REFLEX ARC

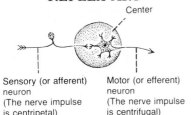

DIAGRAM OF AN ELEMENTARY REFLEX IN THE HUMAN SPINAL CORD

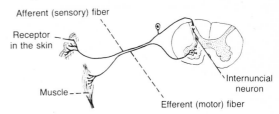

DIAGRAM OF THE GENERAL ORGANIZATION OF A NERVOUS CENTER IN THE SPINAL CORD

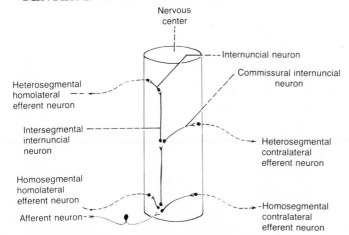

DIAGRAM OF AN AXON REFLEX AND ANTIDROMIC CONDUCTION

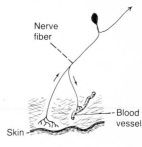

The efferent, afferent and internuncial neurons are defined in relation to a definite spinal level.

NEURONAL CIRCUITS

DIAGRAM OF NEURONAL CONVERGENCE AND SPATIAL FACILITATION

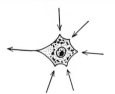

Besides the spatial summation, there is a temporal summation of excitations

SHOWERS OF TRANSMISSIONS

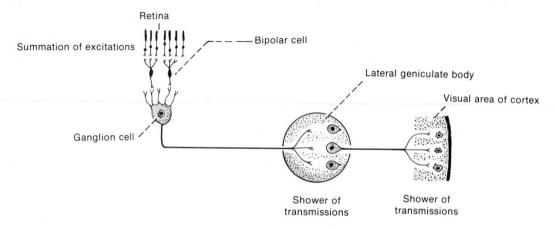

Retina

Summation of excitations

Bipolar cell

Lateral geniculate body

Visual area of cortex

Ganglion cell

Shower of transmissions

Shower of transmissions

MANIFOLD NEURONAL CHAIN

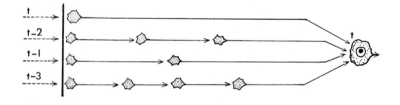

In order that different impulses reach one cell at the instant "t," it will be necessary that they start from their different centers at the instants "t-1," "t-2" or "t-3," according to the number of synapses they must pass through before reaching this cell.

PATHWAY SWITCHING

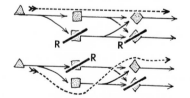

R: refractory period

To connect one cell to another, the impulse (passing through a neuronal chain) may follow various paths, depending on the refractory conditions of the synaptic links.

SYNAPSE

End-Feet (or End-Bulbs) on the Surface of a Neuron

Diagram of Electron Microscopic Appearance of a Synaptic Junction[*]

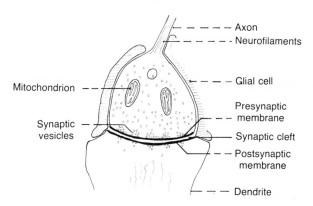

Axon

Neurofilaments

Mitochondrion

Glial cell

Presynaptic membrane

Synaptic vesicles

Synaptic cleft

Postsynaptic membrane

Dendrite

Types of Synapses

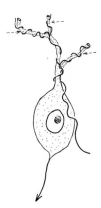

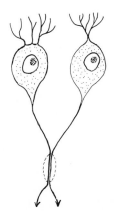

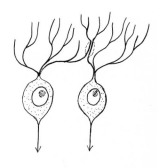

Axosomatic synapse (end-feet and basket)

Axodendritic synapse (climbing fiber upon dendrite of Purkinje cell)

Axoaxonic synapse (or ephapse)

Hypothetical dendrodendritic synapse

[*]Adapted from Palay, S. L.: The morphology of synapses in the central nervous system. Exp. Cell Res. (suppl.), 5:275-293, 1958; and De Robertis, E.: Submicroscopic changes of the synapses after nerve section in the aortic ganglion of the guinea pig. J. Biophys. Biochem. Cytol., 2:503-512, 1956.

Organogenesis

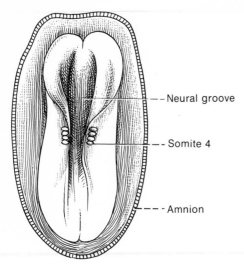

DORSAL ASPECT OF A 1.2 MM. HUMAN
EMBRYO; ABOUT 21 DAYS; 4 SOMITES
(MODIFIED FROM KEIBEL AND MALL)

Neural groove

Somite 4

Amnion

SCHEMATIC TRANSVERSE
SECTION OF A 1.5 MM.
HUMAN EMBRYO; ABOUT
22 DAYS

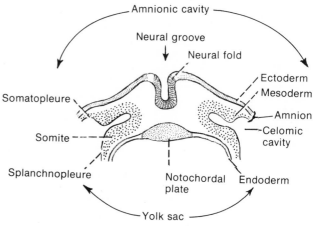

Amnionic cavity

Neural groove

Neural fold

Somatopleure

Ectoderm
Mesoderm
Amnion
Celomic
cavity

Somite

Splanchnopleure

Notochordal
plate

Endoderm

Yolk sac

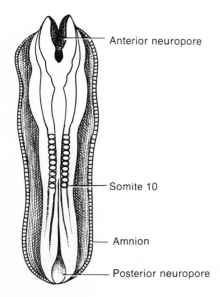

Anterior neuropore

Somite 10

Amnion

Posterior neuropore

DORSAL ASPECT OF A 2 MM. HUMAN
EMBRYO; ABOUT 23 DAYS; 10
SOMITES (IN PART FROM KOLLMAN)

Two Brain–Vesicle Stage (Very Short Stage, 8 to 20 Somites) 2.4 mm. Human Embryo; 11 Somites; About 23 Days

Lateral Aspect

Anterior neuropore
flanked by the neural folds

Forebrain
Hindbrain

Spinal cord

Transverse Section

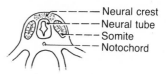

Neural crest
Neural tube
Somite
Notochord

Three Brain–Vesicle Stage (20 to 30 Somites) 3.2 mm. Human Embryo; About 28 Days

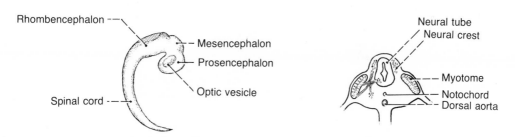

Rhombencephalon

Mesencephalon
Prosencephalon

Optic vesicle

Spinal cord

Neural tube
Neural crest

Myotome
Notochord
Dorsal aorta

Five Brain–Vesicle Stage 7 mm. Human Embryo; About 32 Days

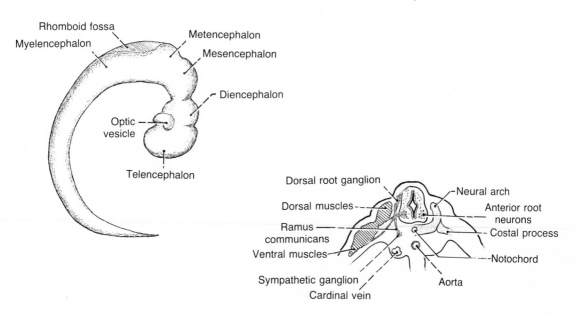

Rhomboid fossa
Myelencephalon

Metencephalon
Mesencephalon

Diencephalon

Optic vesicle

Telencephalon

Dorsal root ganglion
Dorsal muscles
Ramus communicans
Ventral muscles
Sympathetic ganglion
Cardinal vein

Neural arch
Anterior root neurons
Costal process
Notochord
Aorta

Drawing of an 8 mm. Human Embryo; About 38 Days; Right Lateral Aspect after Clearing

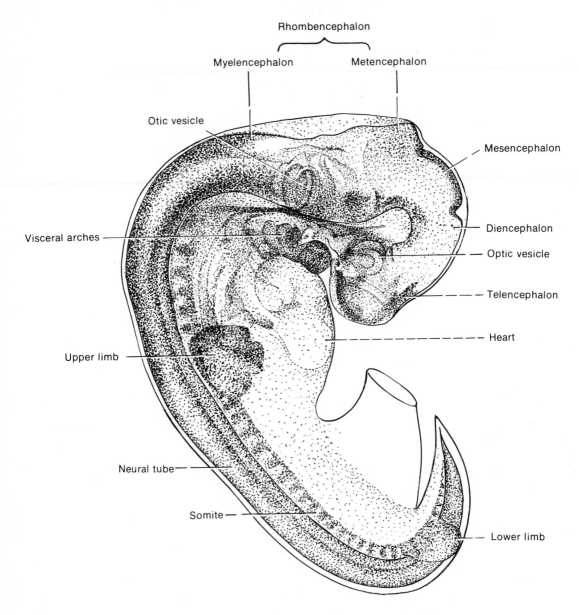

Rhombencephalon

Myelencephalon

Metencephalon

Otic vesicle

Mesencephalon

Visceral arches

Diencephalon

Optic vesicle

Telencephalon

Heart

Upper limb

Neural tube

Somite

Lower limb

General Considerations of the Peripheral Nervous System

The peripheral nervous system includes:

The spinal nerves emerging from the spinal cord and passing through the intervertebral foramina

The cranial nerves emerging from the brain and passing through the skull

Only a part of the autonomic nervous system

The peripheral and the autonomic nervous systems include ganglia and nerves. The ganglia, groups of cell bodies, are either of cerebrospinal or autonomic type.

A *cerebrospinal ganglion* shows the following characteristics: larger size, no synapses, pseudounipolar cells, many satellite cells. *An autonomic ganglion* shows: synapses, multipolar cells, few satellite cells (see page 14).

The nerve fibers are grouped in fasciculi which, emerging from the cerebrospinal axis, are called *roots*. The merging of a dorsal and a ventral root forms a *spinal nerve* at the spinal level; in the cranial region, two or more roots form a *cranial nerve* (see page 20).

Spinal nerves may exchange fibers, forming a *plexus* with its trunks and cords. The *peripheral nerves* from these plexuses give rise to muscular, cutaneous, articular, osseous and vascular *branches*.

These peripheral nerves may exchange some fibers through *rami communicantes* (see page 17). According to the Nomina Anatomica, the term ramus anastomaticus (anastomosis) must be discarded as a designation for a connection between two nerves. The term *ramus communicans,* formerly reserved for the rami connecting the cerebrospinal and the autonomic nervous systems, is used for all branches which connect nerves to one another.

DIAGRAM OF THE FORMATION OF A SPINAL NERVE

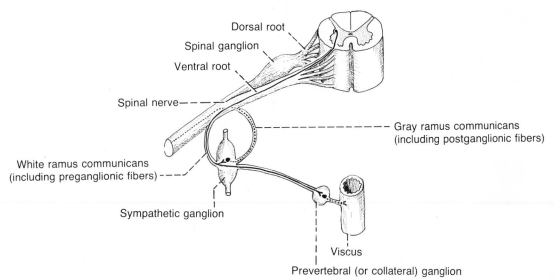

MICROSCOPIC DATA

STRUCTURE OF A PERIPHERAL NERVE

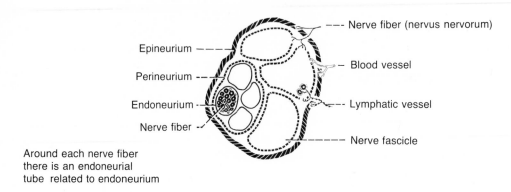

Epineurium
Perineurium
Endoneurium
Nerve fiber

Nerve fiber (nervus nervorum)
Blood vessel
Lymphatic vessel
Nerve fascicle

Around each nerve fiber
there is an endoneurial
tube related to endoneurium

COMPARISON BETWEEN:

| SPINAL GANGLION | AND | AUTONOMIC GANGLION |

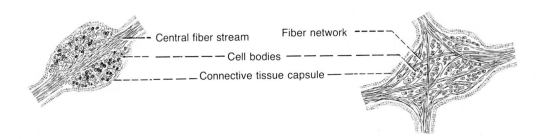

Central fiber stream
Cell bodies
Connective tissue capsule

Fiber network

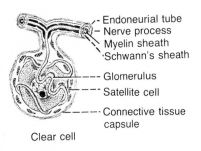

Endoneurial tube
Nerve process
Myelin sheath
Schwann's sheath
Glomerulus
Satellite cell
Connective tissue
capsule

Clear cell

Dark cell

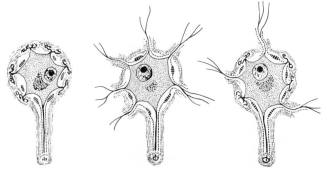

Cajal's type I cell
(with short dendrites
ramifying into the
capsule)

Cajal's type II cell
(with slender and long
dendrites piercing
the capsule)

Cajal's type III cell
(with short and
long dendrites)

SPINAL NERVES

The *spinal nerves* emerge from the vertebral canal through the *intervertebral foramina.*

Each is formed by the fusion of two *spinal roots.* The ventral root is motor; the dorsal one is sensory and presents a spinal ganglion.

When the dorsal root of the first cervical nerve exists, its ganglion is located on the neural arch of the atlas. A similar location on the neural arch of the axis is constant for the second cervical nerve. The other spinal ganglia lie inside the intervertebral foramina, except the last ones, which are enclosed within extensions of dura mater and located in the epidural space.

Just after emerging from the vertebral canal, each spinal nerve divides into a *dorsal ramus* and a *ventral ramus.*

The *dorsal ramus* shows a segmental arrangement. It is distributed to the deeper (or proper) muscles of the back and to the skin located on each side of the line of the spinal processes. This ramus divides into a medial branch and a lateral branch.

The *ventral ramus* does not have a segmental arrangement, except in the thoracic region. The ventral rami form the various plexuses and provide for the innervation of muscles of the limbs and the walls of the body. Their cutaneous areas are irregular, implying a plexiform arrangement. In the trunk, where the nerves are of the segmental type, each nerve gives rise to a lateral and an anterior cutaneous ramus.

A *plexus* is formed by several ventral branches, which exchange fibers in a variable manner. In a plexus there are, separately and distinguishably: (1) a vertebral, or spinal, portion; (2) an intermingling, or intermediate, portion; and (3) a peripheral portion corresponding to the origin of the various peripheral nerves.

In the brachial plexus, the intermediate portion includes a trunk portion, formed by the union of the ventral rami or plexus roots, and a cord portion, resulting from an exchange of fibers between the trunks.

The *peripheral nerves* divide into *branches* or *rami.* These different elements may be mixed (sensory and motor nerves), cutaneous (cutaneous nerve), vascular (vascular nerve), or articular (articular nerve).

Each spinal nerve gives rise to a *meningeal ramus* (or sinuvertebral nerve). This ramus has a spinal root and an autonomic root. It originates as soon as the spinal nerve emerges from the intervertebral foramen and immediately detours back after receiving its autonomic root.

Division of a Spinal Nerve After Passing Through an Intervertebral Foramen

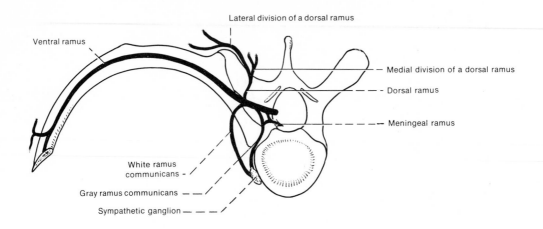

Lateral division of a dorsal ramus

Ventral ramus

Medial division of a dorsal ramus

Dorsal ramus

Meningeal ramus

White ramus communicans -

Gray ramus communicans — — —

Sympathetic ganglion — — — —

Arrangement of the Various Fibers in a Spinal Nerve

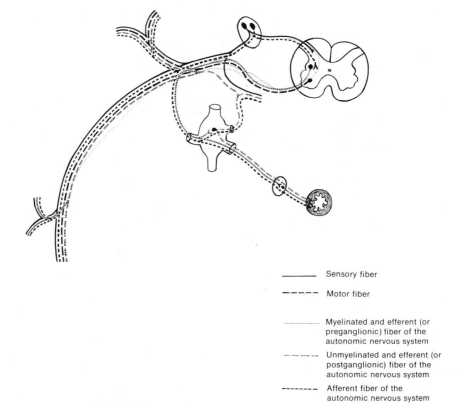

—————— Sensory fiber

- - - - - Motor fiber

················· Myelinated and efferent (or preganglionic) fiber of the autonomic nervous system

·— ··· — ··· Unmyelinated and efferent (or postganglionic) fiber of the autonomic nervous system

- - - - - - Afferent fiber of the autonomic nervous system

FIBER EXCHANGES THROUGH COMMUNICATING BRANCHES

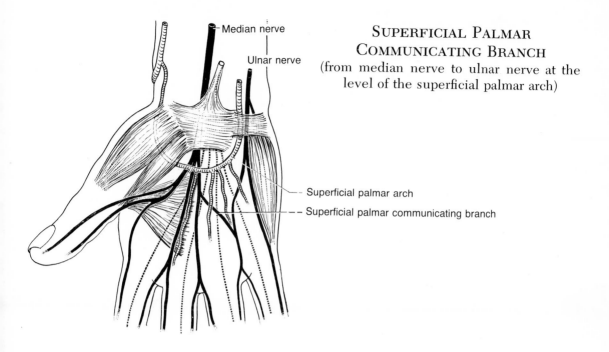

SUPERFICIAL PALMAR COMMUNICATING BRANCH
(from median nerve to ulnar nerve at the level of the superficial palmar arch)

Median nerve

Ulnar nerve

Superficial palmar arch

Superficial palmar communicating branch

BRACHIAL PLEXUS

Communicating branches between the various roots, trunks and cords form the peripheral nerves.

The fibers from the 2nd thoracic nerve to the skin of axilla may directly join the brachial plexus and participate in the formation of the medial brachial cutaneous nerve, or follow the course of the 2nd thoracic nerve, emerge with its lateral branch and join the medial brachial cutaneous nerve.

C5

C6

C7

C8

T1

T2

Radial nerve

Musculocutaneous nerve

Median nerve

Ulnar nerve

Medial antebrachial cutaneous nerve

Medial brachial cutaneous nerve

SPINAL ROOTS

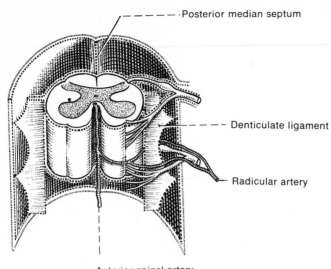

ANTERIOR ASPECT OF A
SPINAL SEGMENT WITH ITS
COVERINGS, SHOWING THE
EMERGENCE OF THE SPINAL
ROOTS

CROSS SECTION OF THE VERTEBRAL CANAL AND ITS CONTENTS

Section Passing Between Two Intervertebral Foramina

Section Passing Through an Intervertebral Foramen

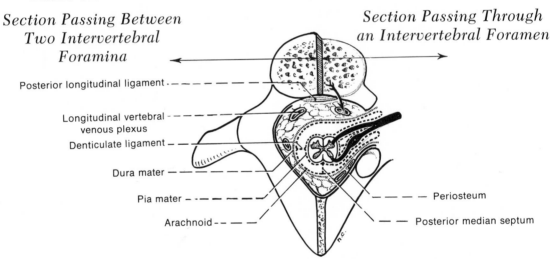

RELATIONSHIPS OF A SPINAL NERVE IN AN INTERVERTEBRAL FORAMEN

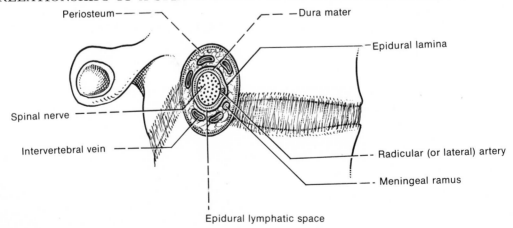

Spinal Roots and Spinal Ganglia— Courses and Relationships

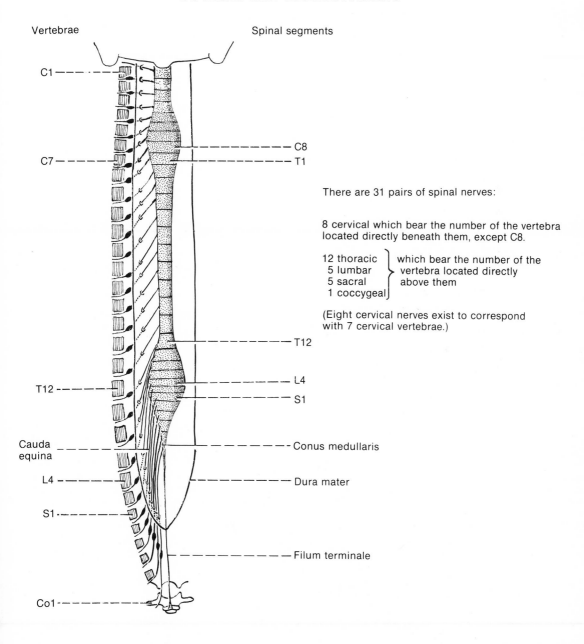

Vertebrae

Spinal segments

C1

C7

C8
T1

There are 31 pairs of spinal nerves:

8 cervical which bear the number of the vertebra located directly beneath them, except C8.

12 thoracic
5 lumbar
5 sacral
1 coccygeal
} which bear the number of the vertebra located directly above them

(Eight cervical nerves exist to correspond with 7 cervical vertebrae.)

T12

T12

L4

S1

L4

Cauda equina

Conus medullaris

S1

Dura mater

Filum terminale

Co1

Page 19

CRANIAL NERVES

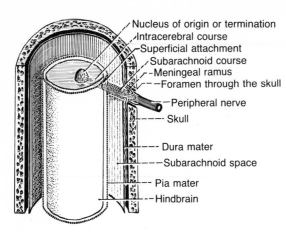

Nucleus of origin or termination
Intracerebral course
Superficial attachment
Subarachnoid course
Meningeal ramus
Foramen through the skull
Peripheral nerve
Skull
Dura mater
Subarachnoid space
Pia mater
Hindbrain

DIAGRAM OF THE VARIOUS PARTS OF A CRANIAL NERVE

CLASSIFICATION OF THE CRANIAL NERVES ACCORDING TO THEIR ORDER OF EMERGENCE

I. Olfactory nerves
These are the nerve twigs passing through the cribriform plate of the ethmoid; the olfactory tract, joining the olfactory bulb to the brain, should be considered as a cerebral white bundle

II. Optic nerve
This is not a true nerve; it should be considered a cerebral expansion

III. Oculomotor nerve
A motor nerve which includes the parasympathetic fibers from the autonomic nucleus of the oculomotor nuclear complex

IV. Trochlear nerve
A motor nerve

V. Trigeminal nerve
A mixed nerve

VI. Abducent nerve
A motor nerve

VII. Facial nerve

The motor root of this includes the parasympathetic fibers from the lacrimopalatonasal nucleus
Intermediate nerve (of Wrisberg)
The sensory root of the facial nerve which includes the parasympathetic fibers from the superior salivatory nucleus

VIII. Vestibulocochlear nerve
A sensory nerve

IX. Glossopharyngeal nerve
A mixed nerve which includes the parasympathetic fibers from the inferior salivatory nucleus

X. Vagus nerve
A mixed nerve which includes the parasympathetic fibers from the dorsal motor nucleus of the vagus nerve

XI. Accessory nerve
A motor nerve which consists of two parts: bulbar and spinal roots

XII. Hypoglossal nerve
A motor nerve

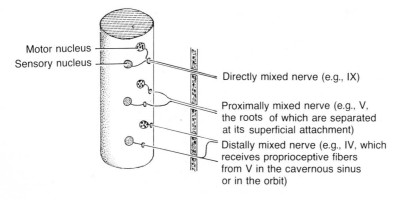

Motor nucleus
Sensory nucleus

Directly mixed nerve (e.g., IX)

Proximally mixed nerve (e.g., V, the roots of which are separated at its superficial attachment)

Distally mixed nerve (e.g., IV, which receives proprioceptive fibers from V in the cavernous sinus or in the orbit)

STRUCTURE OF A MIXED CRANIAL NERVE (ACCORDING TO WINCKLER)

General Considerations of the Central Nervous System

The *gray matter* of the central nervous system includes the cortex (or pallium), located at the periphery of cerebral hemispheres and cerebellum, and centers which form either *nuclei*, if they are well individualized and harmoniously proportionate, or *columns*, if one dimension greatly exceeds the other two.

The *white matter* of the central nervous system is formed by the processes of the neurons.

The *funiculus* has only a topographic significance.

From a descriptive and functional point of view, it is possible to distinguish:

tract, a bundle of nerve fibers having a precise origin and termination, and a definite function (e.g., corticospinal tract)

fasciculus, a bundle of nerve fibers, morphologically well defined (e.g., arcuate fasciculus)

lemniscus, more or less flat and ribbonlike band of nerve fibers (e.g., medial lemniscus)

Pathway is both a general and a functional term (e.g., auditory pathways).

A *decussation* is the crossing of nerve fibers inside the central nervous system (e.g., corticospinal decussation).

Chiasma (from the greek letter χ) is used for the crossing of optic fibers.

The term *projection fibers* is used for all the axon fibers, either corticifugal or corticipetal, which connect the cerebral cortex with the brain stem or the spinal cord.

The *association fibers* connect the various cortical areas or centers of the same side (e.g., cingulum), whereas the *commissural fibers* cross the median plane of the central nervous system, connecting structures of similar or differing function (e.g., anterior commissure.

DRAWING OF A SAGITTAL SECTION OF THE HEAD SHOWING THE VARIOUS PARTS OF THE BRAIN AND THEIR RELATIONSHIPS WITH CRANIOFACIAL ELEMENTS

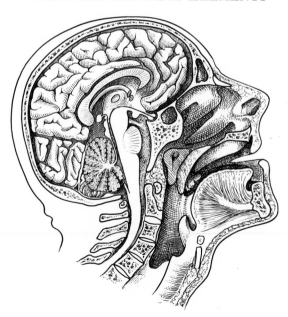

Schematic Diagram of the Nervous Centers and Their Main Pathways

As a general rule, the great intracerebral pathways are crossed, these crossings being called decussations.

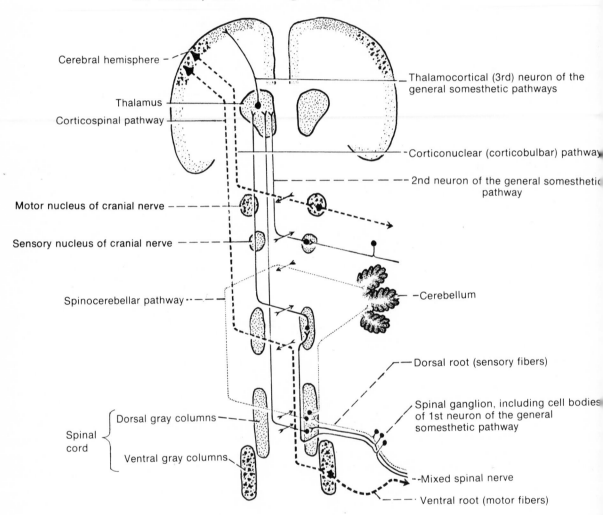

Small arrows indicate decussations.

General Considerations of the Autonomic Nervous System

Definitions

Communicating rami (rami communicantes)

The communicating rami are nerve rami uniting the various elements of spinal or cranial nerves to sympathetic trunks. Macroscopically, we can distinguish oblique and transverse rami, and lateral and medial communicating rami. Microscopic study permits classification into gray communicating rami (including, above all, postganglionic nonmyelinated fibers) and white communicating rami (formed by a majority of preganglionic myelinated fibers). The white communicating rami exist only from T1 to L2; they are the most lateral according to Winckler, the most oblique according to Botar.

Ganglia

The paravertebral sympathetic trunk is formed by ganglia joined with cords of fibers (interganglionic rami). The ganglia have various shapes, depending on the level: conglomerate or elongated in the cervical region, triangular on the thorax, fusiform at the lumbar and sacral levels.

In the embryo there is one ganglion for each metamere; in the adult, several ganglia may merge (e.g., stellate ganglion).

Besides these paravertebral ganglia, there are prevertebral (collateral, previsceral) ganglia. Their size is variable and they are located close to the viscera. Although they are peripheral sympathetic centers, these prevertebral ganglia receive some parasympathetic fibers; they send fibers only to viscera.

Fibers and synapses

Schematically the fibers originating from spinal centers follow the spinal roots and nerves and emerge from the vertebral canal. After passage through the intervertebral foramina, these fibers leave the spinal nerve by a white communicating ramus and reach a ganglion of the sympathetic trunk.

At this point, there are three possibilities:

(1) They may synapse in the ganglion, leaving it by a gray communicating ramus and reaching the corresponding spinal nerve. Such is the case for autonomic fibers distributed to blood vessels, glands of the skin and erector pili muscles in the area of this spinal nerve.

(2) They may synapse in another ganglion of the sympathetic trunk and, as in the first case, reach a spinal nerve located above or below the ganglion.

(3) They may pass through the sympathetic trunk, leaving the trunk by a splanchnic nerve and reaching a prevertebral ganglion, where they synapse before ending in a viscus.

Plexuses

The autonomic fibers arising from various ganglia may form a network near or on the organs innervated. These network arrangements are called plexuses.

Sometimes plexuses, located close to a ganglionic mass, may result from the intermingling of preganglionic and postganglionic fibers and clusters of ganglion cells. Such plexuses are called ganglionic plexuses.

Splanchnic nerves

The nerves connecting the sympathetic trunk to prevertebral ganglia are called (largo sensu) splanchnic or visceral nerves. As a general rule a splanchnic nerve originates from that part of the sympathetic trunk located above the visceral level to which it is distributed; for instance, the cervical sympathetic trunk gives rise to the splanchnic (visceral) nerves which go to some thoracic viscera.

Divisions

The autonomic nervous system may be divided according to its origin or its termination.

At the origin we distinguish the sympathetic and the parasympathetic components which correspond to different pathways and centers, and which act either in opposition or in a complementary way.

At the termination we must separate (1) the autonomic components going to somatic elements, the fibers of which pass through the gray communicating rami, reach the spinal or cranial nerves and follow the same distribution, and (2) the visceral components, which follow the splanchnic nerves, reach peripheral centers (i.e., prevertebral ganglia) and are distributed to the viscera.

Diagram of the Autonomic Nervous System on a Transverse (or Metameric) Plan

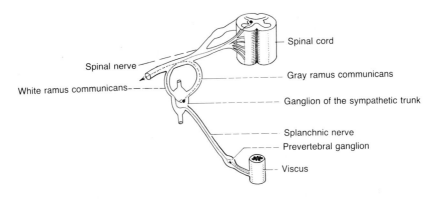

- Spinal cord
- Spinal nerve
- Gray ramus communicans
- White ramus communicans
- Ganglion of the sympathetic trunk
- Splanchnic nerve
- Prevertebral ganglion
- Viscus

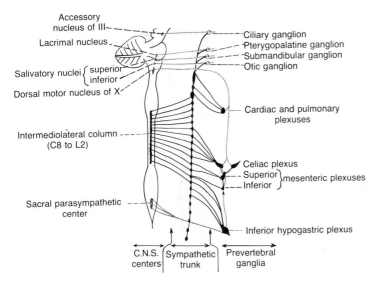

- Accessory nucleus of III
- Lacrimal nucleus
- Salivatory nuclei { superior / inferior }
- Dorsal motor nucleus of X
- Intermediolateral column (C8 to L2)
- Sacral parasympathetic center
- Ciliary ganglion
- Pterygopalatine ganglion
- Submandibular ganglion
- Otic ganglion
- Cardiac and pulmonary plexuses
- Celiac plexus
- Superior / Inferior } mesenteric plexuses
- Inferior hypogastric plexus

| C.N.S. centers | Sympathetic trunk | Prevertebral ganglia |

Longitudinal Diagram of the Autonomic Nervous System

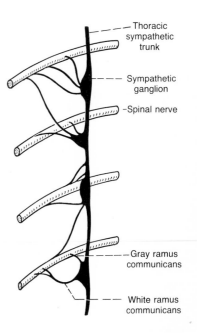

- Thoracic sympathetic trunk
- Sympathetic ganglion
- Spinal nerve
- Gray ramus communicans
- White ramus communicans

Rami Communicantes of the Thoracic Sympathetic Trunk

(From Winckler, G., Arch. Anat. Histol. Embryol., 44:37-58, 1961.)

Sensory Nerve Endings

Intra-epithelial endings in contact with the external environment		Intra-epithelial endings, but not in direct contact with the external environment		Immediately subepithelial endings		Encapsulated formations		
Chemical sensibility	Tactile sensibility	Chemical sensibility	Tactile sensibility	Protopathic sensibility	Trichoesthetic (in part epicritic) sensibility	Epicritic sensibility	Thermal sensibility	Pressure

Olfactory cells

Free epithelial endings (corneal and visceral epithelium)

Taste bud

Free endings

Hederiform endings

Tactile discs of Merkel

Unmyelinated subepithelial plexus

Myelinated subepithelial plexus

Papillary tuft

Glomerulus (thermal sensibility)

Peritrichal nerve endings

Corpuscle of Meissner

Corpuscle of Krause: cold

Corpuscle of Ruffini: warmth

Corpuscle of Golgi

Pacinian corpuscle

Epithelium

Basement membrane

Dermis

Fat

Trophic?

Trophic?

======= Myelinated fiber

——— Unmyelinated fiber

Stimulus must traverse multiple specialized formations before reaching sensory organs	Stimulus originates from inside the body	Stimulus originates from a vessel	Stimulus originates from a gland or a viscus
	Proprioceptive sensibility	Visceral sensibility	
	Equilibration Muscular sense	Barosensibility Chemosensibility	
Teloreceptivity			

Special sense organs

Visual sensibility (retina) — Auditory sensibility (cochlea) — (Vestibule of the ear) Maculae and ampullary crests — (Skeletal muscle) Pacinian corpuscle Neuromuscular spindle Free endings — Neurotendinous organ of Golgi Pacinian corpuscle (into the interfascicular connective tissue) — (Intima) Free endings — (Media) Free endings ? — (Adventitia) Free endings and corpuscles — Cylindrical corpuscle and free endings Endocrine gland — Peri- and intraglandular free endings Exocrine gland — (Adventitial membrane) Corpuscles (Muscular coat) Free endings (Mucous membrane) Free endings Viscus

From a functional point of view it is necessary to consider:

General somesthetic sensibility
- Exteroceptive sensibility
  - Epicritic sensibility
    - Tactile
    - Trichoesthetic (in part)
  - Nociceptive sensibility
    - Thermal Protopathic (Head and Rivers*)
    - Pain Trichoesthetic (in part)
- Vibratory sensibility
- Proprioceptive sensibility
- Interoceptive or visceral sensibility

Special sense organs
- Vision: teloreceptivity
- Audition: teloreceptivity
- Olfaction and gustation: chemical sensibility
- Equilibration: correlated with proprioceptive sensibility

*Head, H., Rivers, W. H. R., and Sherren, J.: The afferent nervous system from a new aspect. Brain, 28:99-115, 1905.

RECEPTORS
General Structure of the Receptors

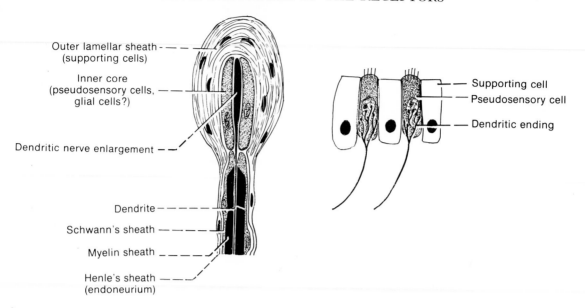

Outer lamellar sheath (supporting cells)

Inner core (pseudosensory cells, glial cells?)

Dendritic nerve enlargement

Dendrite

Schwann's sheath

Myelin sheath

Henle's sheath (endoneurium)

Supporting cell

Pseudosensory cell

Dendritic ending

Noncapsulated Nerve Endings

Intra-epithelial Free Nerve Endings

Peritrichal Nerve Endings*

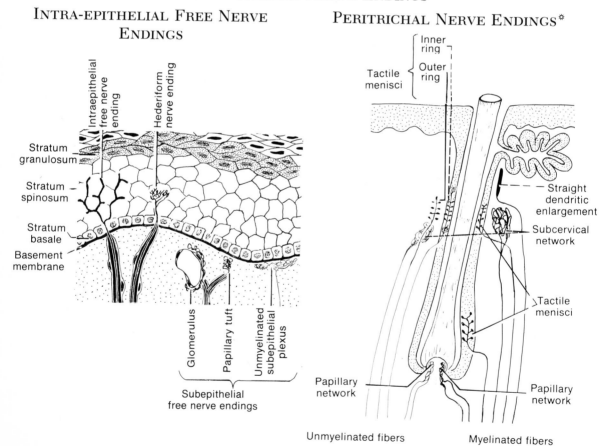

Intraepithelial free nerve ending

Hederiform nerve ending

Stratum granulosum

Stratum spinosum

Stratum basale

Basement membrane

Glomerulus

Papillary tuft

Unmyelinated subepithelial plexus

Subepithelial free nerve endings

Tactile menisci

Inner ring

Outer ring

Straight dendritic enlargement

Subcervical network

Tactile menisci

Papillary network

Papillary network

Unmyelinated fibers

Myelinated fibers

*(From Dubreuil, G., and Canivenc, R.: Manuel Théorique et Pratique d'Histologie. Vol. 2. 6th ed. Paris, Vigot Frères, 1967, p. 402.)

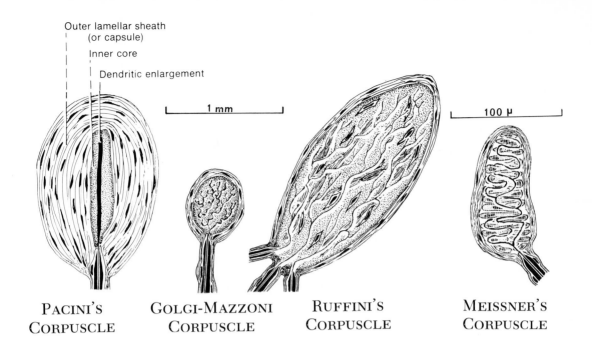

Outer lamellar sheath
(or capsule)
Inner core
Dendritic enlargement

|← 1 mm →|

|← 100 µ →|

PACINI'S
CORPUSCLE

GOLGI-MAZZONI
CORPUSCLE

RUFFINI'S
CORPUSCLE

MEISSNER'S
CORPUSCLE

NEUROMUSCULAR SPINDLE

ELECTRON MICROSCOPIC CROSS
SECTION OF A PACINIAN
CORPUSCLE°

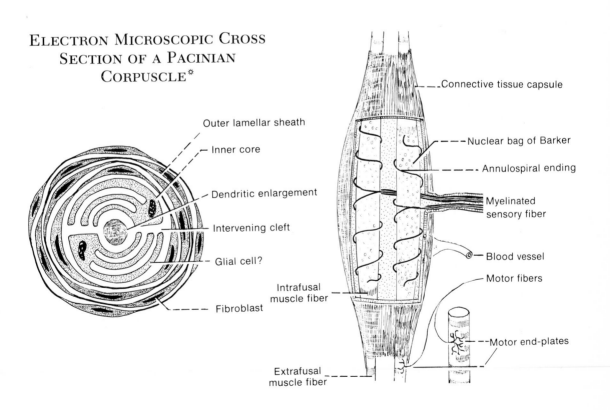

Outer lamellar sheath

Inner core

Dendritic enlargement

Intervening cleft

Glial cell?

Fibroblast

Connective tissue capsule

Nuclear bag of Barker

Annulospiral ending

Myelinated
sensory fiber

Blood vessel

Motor fibers

Intrafusal
muscle fiber

Motor end-plates

Extrafusal
muscle fiber

°(From Pease, D. C., and Quilliam, T. A.: Electron microscopy of the Pacinian corpuscle. J. Biophys. Biochem. Cytol., 3:331-342, 1957.)

Motor Nerve Endings
MOTOR END-PLATE OF SKELETAL MUSCLE
Light Microscopy

GENERAL ASPECT OF A MOTOR
END-PLATE

DIAGRAMMATIC SECTION OF A
MOTOR END-PLATE

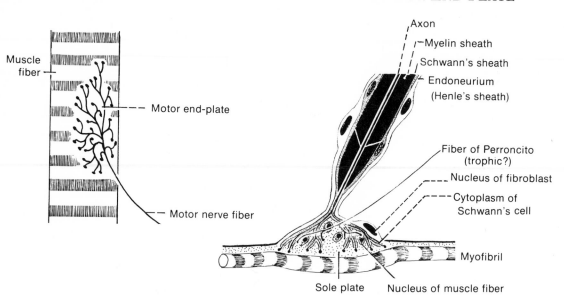

Muscle
fiber

Motor end-plate

Motor nerve fiber

Axon
Myelin sheath
Schwann's sheath
Endoneurium
(Henle's sheath)
Fiber of Perroncito
(trophic?)
Nucleus of fibroblast
Cytoplasm of
Schwann's cell
Myofibril
Sole plate   Nucleus of muscle fiber

Electron Microscopy*

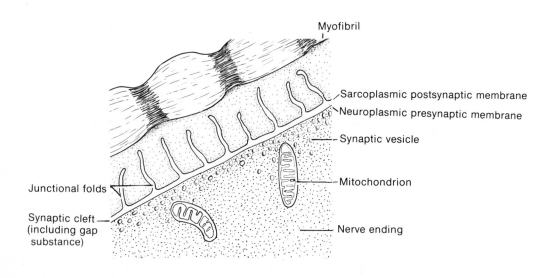

Myofibril

Sarcoplasmic postsynaptic membrane
Neuroplasmic presynaptic membrane
Synaptic vesicle
Mitochondrion

Junctional folds

Synaptic cleft
(including gap
substance)

Nerve ending

*(Modified from Rhodin, J. A. G.: An Atlas of Ultrastructure. Philadelphia, W. B. Saunders Company, 1963, p. 30.)

DIAGRAM OF SMOOTH MUSCLE INNERVATION

Light Microscopy

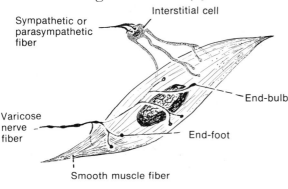

- Sympathetic or parasympathetic fiber
- Interstitial cell
- End-bulb
- Varicose nerve fiber
- End-foot
- Smooth muscle fiber

DIAGRAM OF CARDIAC MUSCLE INNERVATION

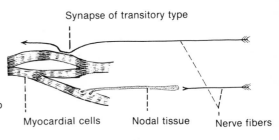

- Synapse of transitory type
- Myocardial cells
- Nodal tissue
- Nerve fibers

Electron Microscopy

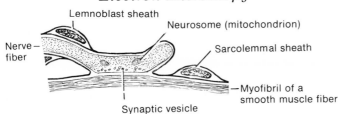

- Lemnoblast sheath
- Neurosome (mitochondrion)
- Sarcolemmal sheath
- Nerve fiber
- Myofibril of a smooth muscle fiber
- Synaptic vesicle

GLANDULAR FIBERS* (EXCITOSECRETORY)

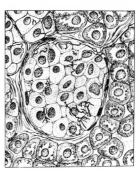

Nerve Fiber Relationships with the Pancreatic Cells in Cats

EFFERENT APPARATUS TO THE VESSEL

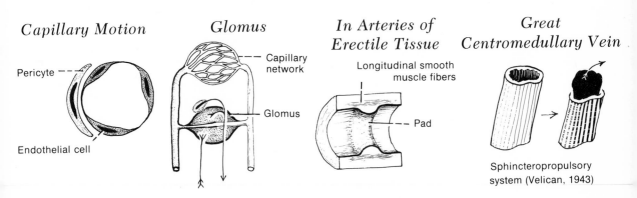

Capillary Motion
- Pericyte
- Endothelial cell

Glomus
- Capillary network
- Glomus

In Arteries of Erectile Tissue
- Longitudinal smooth muscle fibers
- Pad

Great Centromedullary Vein
- Sphincteropropulsory system (Velican, 1943)

From Richins, C. A.: The innervation of the pancreas. J. Comp. Neurol., 83:223-236, 1945.

Diagrams of Organ Innervation

SKELETAL MUSCLE

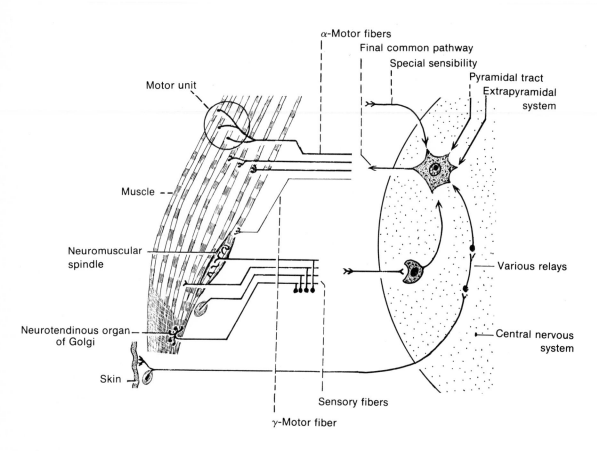

Motor unit = 1 axon + x muscle fibers
(x = 1 to 100)

GLANDS

Exocrine Gland

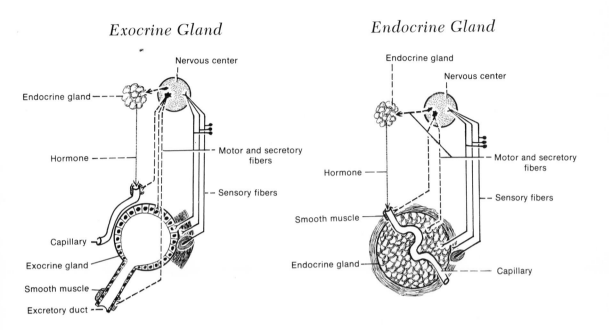

Nervous center

Endocrine gland ---

Hormone ---

Capillary

Exocrine gland

Smooth muscle

Excretory duct

Motor and secretory fibers

Sensory fibers

Endocrine Gland

Endocrine gland

Nervous center

Hormone ---

Smooth muscle

Endocrine gland

Motor and secretory fibers

Sensory fibers

Capillary

VISCUS

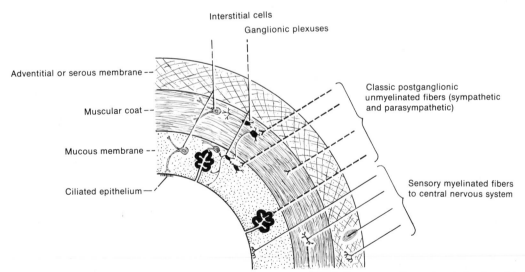

Interstitial cells

Ganglionic plexuses

Adventitial or serous membrane --

Muscular coat --

Mucous membrane --

Ciliated epithelium --

Classic postganglionic unmyelinated fibers (sympathetic and parasympathetic)

Sensory myelinated fibers to central nervous system

Free endings or smooth muscle spindles (Larsell and Dow)

Neuroglia

EPENDYMAL CELLS

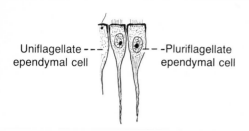

Uniflagellate --- ependymal cell

-Pluriflagellate ependymal cell

SCHEMATIC ELECTRON MICROSCOPE ASPECT OF A CHOROID VILLUS*

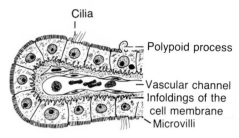

Cilia

Polypoid process

Vascular channel
Infoldings of the cell membrane
Microvilli

MACROGLIA†

Protoplasmic Astrocyte

Fibrous Astrocyte

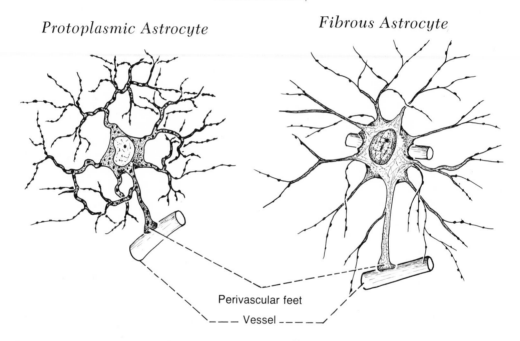

Perivascular feet
--- Vessel ---

OLIGODENDROGLIA†

Interfascicular Oligodendrocyte

Perineuronal Oligodendrocyte

MICROGLIA†

Microglial Cell

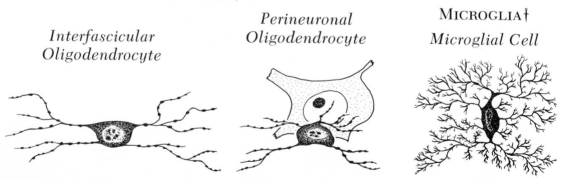

*From Maxwell, D. S., and Pease, D. C.: The electron microscopy of the choroid plexus. J. Biophys. Biochem. Cytol., 2:467-474, 1956.

†Penfield, W.: Neuroglia, normal and pathological. In Penfield, W. G. (ed.): Cytology and Cellular Pathology of the Nervous System, Vol. 2, New York, Paul B. Hoeber, Inc., 1932, pp. 423-479.

Part Two

Spinal Nerves

Dorsal Rami of the Spinal Nerves

Cutaneous Branches of the Dorsal Rami of the Spinal Nerves

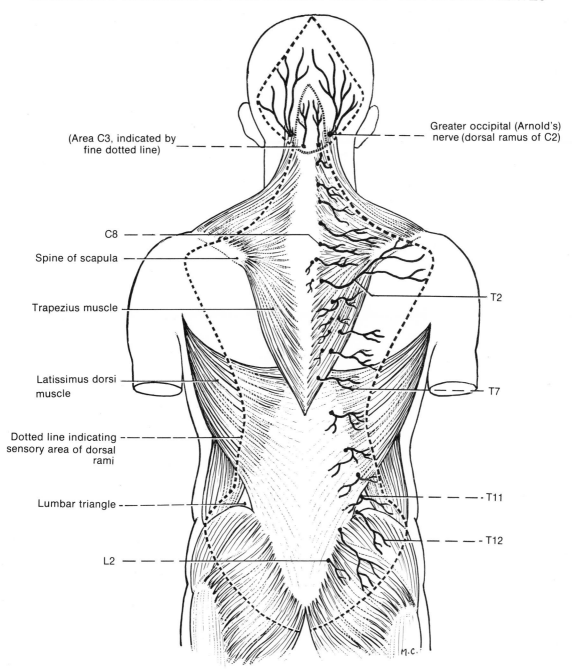

(Area C3, indicated by fine dotted line)

Greater occipital (Arnold's) nerve (dorsal ramus of C2)

C8

Spine of scapula

Trapezius muscle

Latissimus dorsi muscle

Dotted line indicating sensory area of dorsal rami

Lumbar triangle

L2

T2

T7

T11

T12

All the dorsal rami of the spinal nerves have a quota of motor fibers which are distributed to the deeper muscles of the back; they maintain a type of distribution which may be considered metameric.

Usually there is no sensory root for C1.

There are some fiber exchanges be-tween the 2nd, 3rd and 4th cervical dorsal rami which form the posterior cervical plexus (Cruveilhier).

Trolard described a posterior sacral plexus formed by the first four sacral dorsal rami.

SUPERFICIAL COURSE OF THE GREATER OCCIPITAL (ARNOLD'S) NERVE

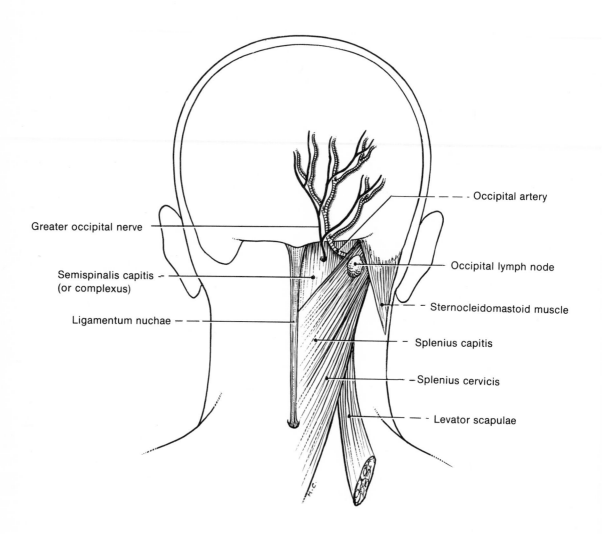

Greater occipital nerve

Semispinalis capitis (or complexus)

Ligamentum nuchae

Occipital artery

Occipital lymph node

Sternocleidomastoid muscle

Splenius capitis

Splenius cervicis

Levator scapulae

DORSAL RAMI OF THE FIRST THREE SPINAL NERVES

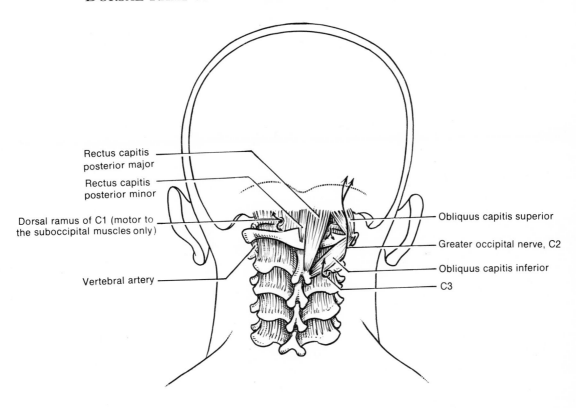

Rectus capitis posterior major

Rectus capitis posterior minor

Dorsal ramus of C1 (motor to the suboccipital muscles only)

Vertebral artery

Obliquus capitis superior

Greater occipital nerve, C2

Obliquus capitis inferior

C3

Meningeal Rami of the Spinal Nerves

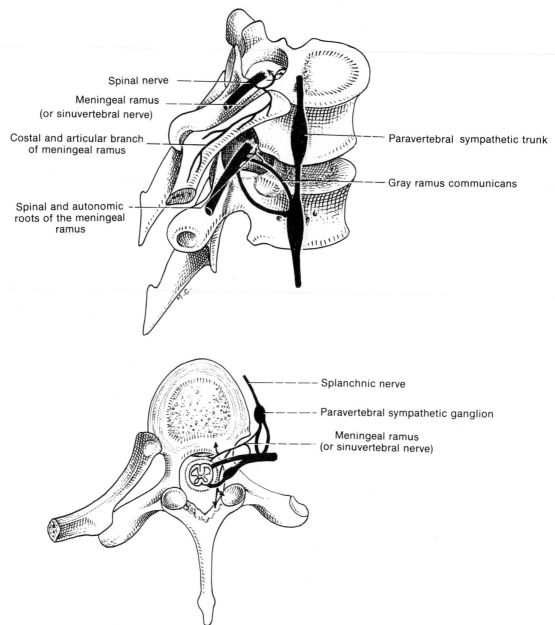

Spinal nerve

Meningeal ramus
(or sinuvertebral nerve)

Costal and articular branch
of meningeal ramus

Spinal and autonomic
roots of the meningeal
ramus

Paravertebral sympathetic trunk

Gray ramus communicans

Splanchnic nerve

Paravertebral sympathetic ganglion

Meningeal ramus
(or sinuvertebral nerve)

The meningeal rami (or sinuvertebral nerves) are formed by the junction of a spinal root and an autonomic root; this latter originates from the gray ramus communicans or the nearby sympathetic ganglion. The nerve, so formed, enters the intervertebral foramen, anterior to the spinal nerve. This meningeal ramus gives rise to one extravertebral branch, which supplies the costovertebral joints and the periosteum of the neck of the rib, and to one intravertebral branch, which supplies the vertebral body, the vertebral arch, the posterior longitudinal ligament, the dura mater, the intervertebral joints, and the vessels of the vertebral canal.

Cervical Plexus

ORIGIN AND LOCATION OF THE CERVICAL PLEXUS

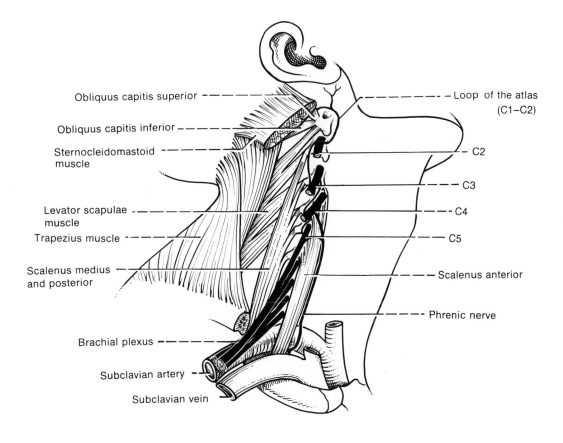

Obliquus capitis superior — Loop of the atlas (C1–C2)

Obliquus capitis inferior

Sternocleidomastoid muscle — C2

C3

Levator scapulae muscle — C4

Trapezius muscle — C5

Scalenus medius and posterior — Scalenus anterior

Phrenic nerve

Brachial plexus

Subclavian artery

Subclavian vein

Page 41

SUPERFICIAL BRANCHES OF THE CERVICAL PLEXUS

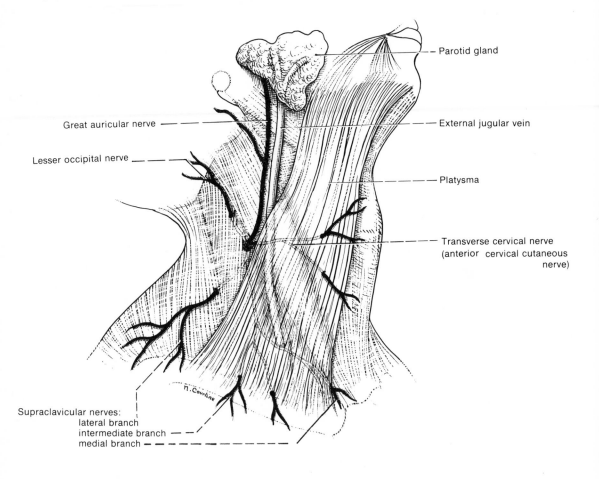

Parotid gland

Great auricular nerve

External jugular vein

Lesser occipital nerve

Platysma

Transverse cervical nerve
(anterior cervical cutaneous
nerve)

Supraclavicular nerves:
lateral branch
intermediate branch
medial branch

MUSCULAR BRANCHES OF THE CERVICAL PLEXUS

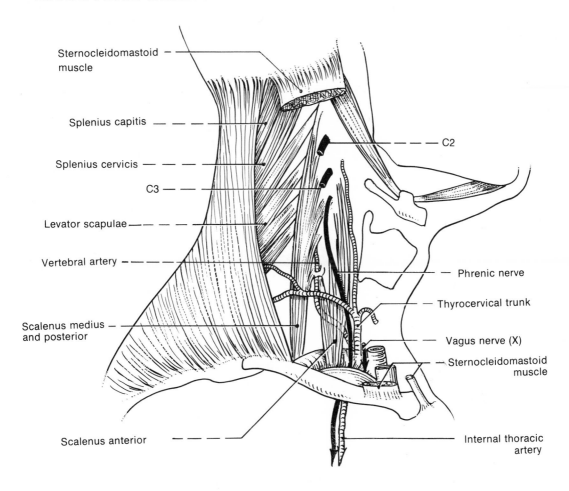

Sternocleidomastoid muscle

Splenius capitis

Splenius cervicis

C3

Levator scapulae

Vertebral artery

Scalenus medius and posterior

Scalenus anterior

C2

Phrenic nerve

Thyrocervical trunk

Vagus nerve (X)

Sternocleidomastoid muscle

Internal thoracic artery

Muscular branches arising from cervical plexus:

Phrenic nerve: C4 (+ C3 and C5)
Nerves to levator scapulae: C2, C3, C4, and dorsal scapular nerve
    (or nerve to the rhomboids)
Nerves to the intertransverse muscles: C2, C3, and C4
Nerves to the rectus capitis anterior and lateralis
Nerves to longus capitis and longus cervicis
Nerves to the scaleni; according to Hovelacque, at the cervical
    level there is only one branch from C4 to the scalenus medii

INTERCONNECTING BRANCHES OF
THE CERVICAL PLEXUS

Interconnection with the Accessory Nerve (XI)

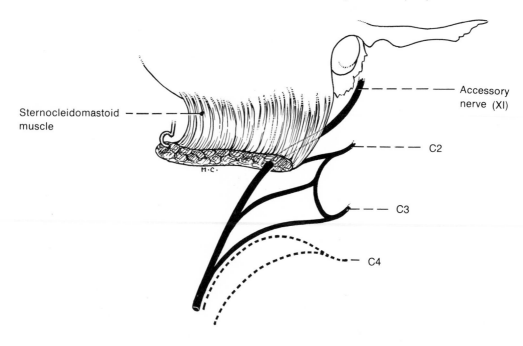

Sternocleidomastoid
muscle

Accessory
nerve (XI)

C2

C3

C4

Ansa Cervicalis

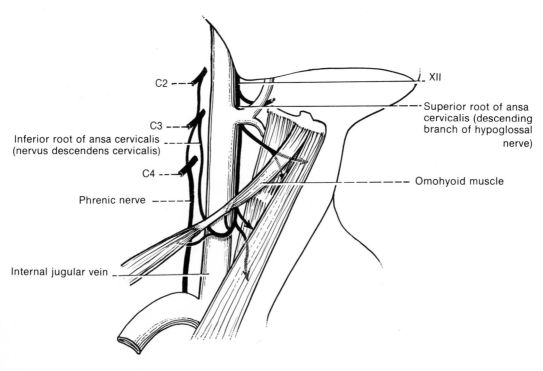

C2

C3

Inferior root of ansa cervicalis
(nervus descendens cervicalis)

C4

Phrenic nerve

Internal jugular vein

XII

Superior root of ansa
cervicalis (descending
branch of hypoglossal
nerve)

Omohyoid muscle

Interconnections with the Autonomic Nervous System

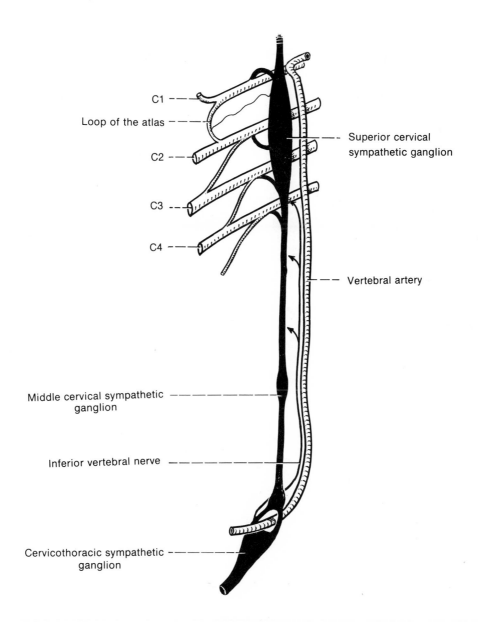

C1

Loop of the atlas

C2

C3

C4

Superior cervical
sympathetic ganglion

Vertebral artery

Middle cervical sympathetic
ganglion

Inferior vertebral nerve

Cervicothoracic sympathetic
ganglion

DIAGRAM OF THE CERVICAL PLEXUS

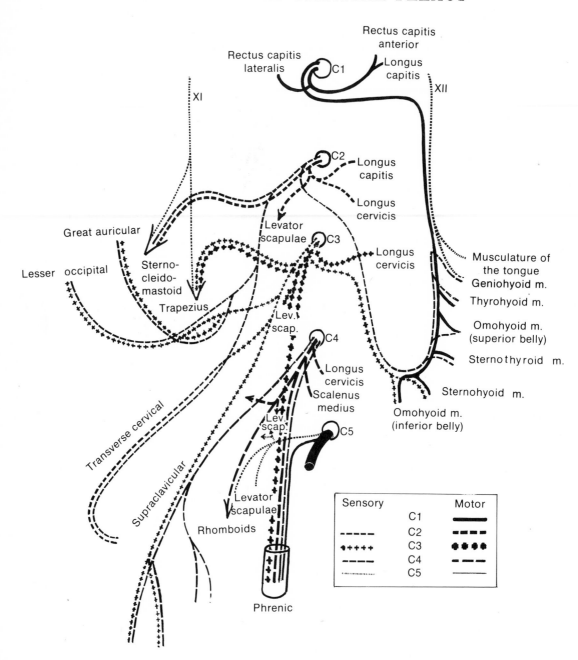

Brachial Plexus

General Diagram

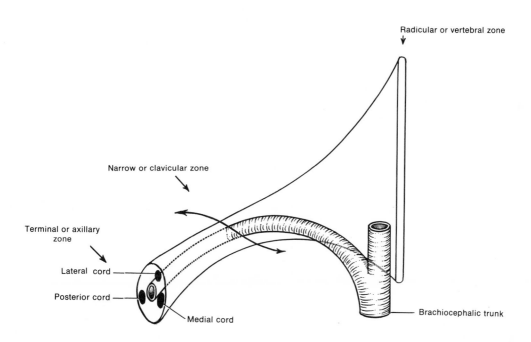

Radicular or vertebral zone

Narrow or clavicular zone

Terminal or axillary zone

Lateral cord

Posterior cord

Medial cord

Brachiocephalic trunk

Arrangement of the Brachial Plexus

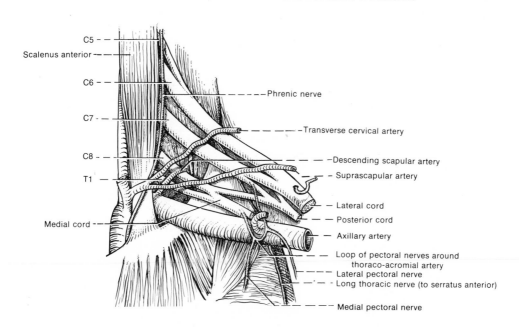

C5

Scalenus anterior

C6

C7

C8

T1

Medial cord

Phrenic nerve

Transverse cervical artery

Descending scapular artery

Suprascapular artery

Lateral cord

Posterior cord

Axillary artery

Loop of pectoral nerves around thoraco-acromial artery

Lateral pectoral nerve

Long thoracic nerve (to serratus anterior)

Medial pectoral nerve

TOPOGRAPHY OF THE BRACHIAL PLEXUS

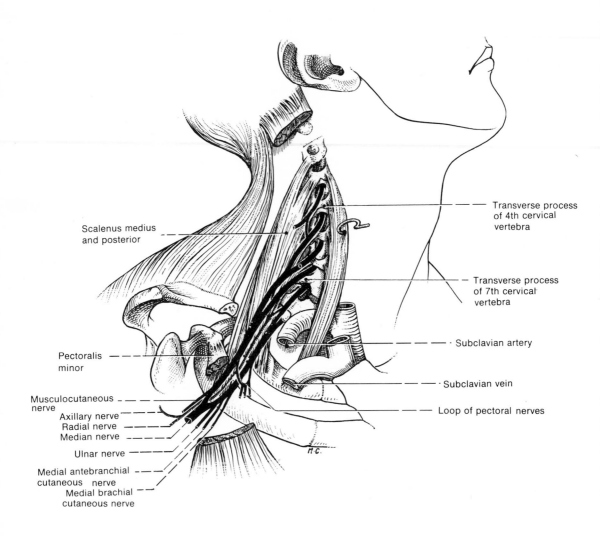

Scalenus medius
and posterior

Pectoralis
minor

Musculocutaneous
nerve

Axillary nerve
Radial nerve
Median nerve

Ulnar nerve

Medial antebranchial
cutaneous nerve
Medial brachial
cutaneous nerve

Transverse process
of 4th cervical
vertebra

Transverse process
of 7th cervical
vertebra

Subclavian artery

Subclavian vein

Loop of pectoral nerves

COLLATERAL BRANCHES OF THE BRACHIAL PLEXUS

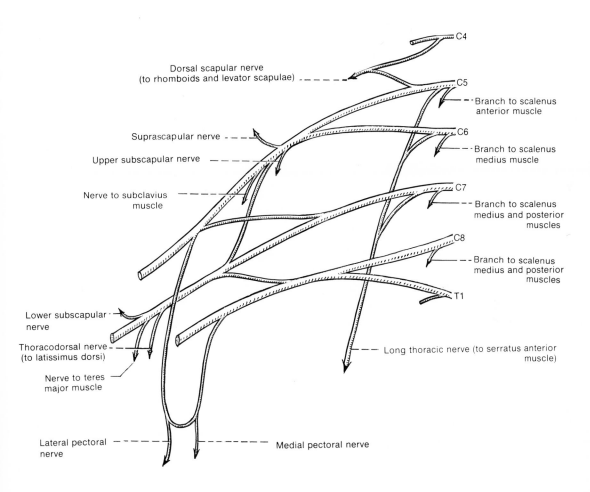

Dorsal scapular nerve
(to rhomboids and levator scapulae) - - - - - - -

C4

C5

Branch to scalenus
anterior muscle

Suprascapular nerve - - - -

C6

Upper subscapular nerve - - - - -

Branch to scalenus
medius muscle

Nerve to subclavius
muscle

C7

Branch to scalenus
medius and posterior
muscles

C8

Branch to scalenus
medius and posterior
muscles

Lower subscapular
nerve

T1

Thoracodorsal nerve
(to latissimus dorsi)

Long thoracic nerve (to serratus anterior
muscle)

Nerve to teres
major muscle

Lateral pectoral - - - - - - - - - - - - - Medial pectoral nerve
nerve

MUSCULOCUTANEOUS NERVE

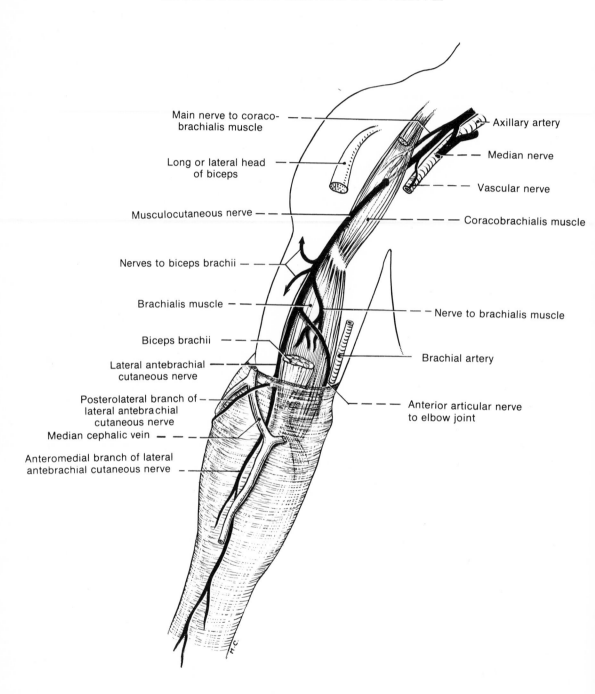

Main nerve to coraco-brachialis muscle

Long or lateral head of biceps

Musculocutaneous nerve

Nerves to biceps brachii

Brachialis muscle

Biceps brachii

Lateral antebrachial cutaneous nerve

Posterolateral branch of lateral antebrachial cutaneous nerve

Median cephalic vein

Anteromedial branch of lateral antebrachial cutaneous nerve

Axillary artery

Median nerve

Vascular nerve

Coracobrachialis muscle

Nerve to brachialis muscle

Brachial artery

Anterior articular nerve to elbow joint

Page 50

DIAGRAM OF THE MUSCULOCUTANEOUS NERVE

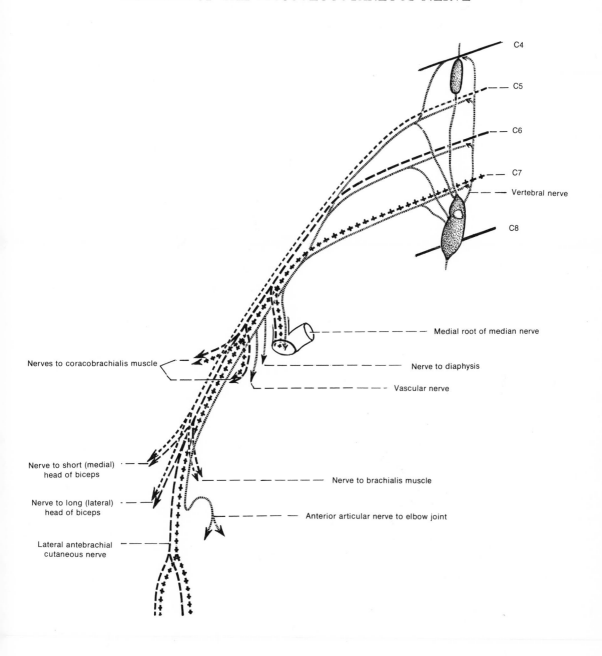

C4

C5

C6

C7

Vertebral nerve

C8

Medial root of median nerve

Nerves to coracobrachialis muscle

Nerve to diaphysis

Vascular nerve

Nerve to short (medial) head of biceps

Nerve to brachialis muscle

Nerve to long (lateral) head of biceps

Anterior articular nerve to elbow joint

Lateral antebrachial cutaneous nerve

MEDIAN NERVE

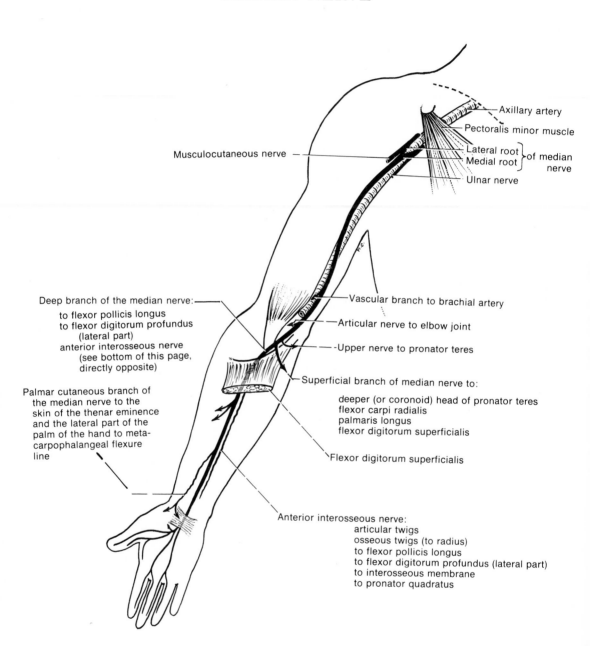

Axillary artery

Pectoralis minor muscle

Lateral root } of median
Medial root } nerve

Musculocutaneous nerve

Ulnar nerve

Deep branch of the median nerve:

　to flexor pollicis longus
　to flexor digitorum profundus
　　(lateral part)
　anterior interosseous nerve
　　(see bottom of this page,
　　directly opposite)

Vascular branch to brachial artery

Articular nerve to elbow joint

Upper nerve to pronator teres

Superficial branch of median nerve to:

　deeper (or coronoid) head of pronator teres
　flexor carpi radialis
　palmaris longus
　flexor digitorum superficialis

Palmar cutaneous branch of
the median nerve to the
skin of the thenar eminence
and the lateral part of the
palm of the hand to meta-
carpophalangeal flexure
line

Flexor digitorum superficialis

Anterior interosseous nerve:
　articular twigs
　osseous twigs (to radius)
　to flexor pollicis longus
　to flexor digitorum profundus (lateral part)
　to interosseous membrane
　to pronator quadratus

Branches of the Median Nerve in the Palmar Aspect of the Hand and Fingers

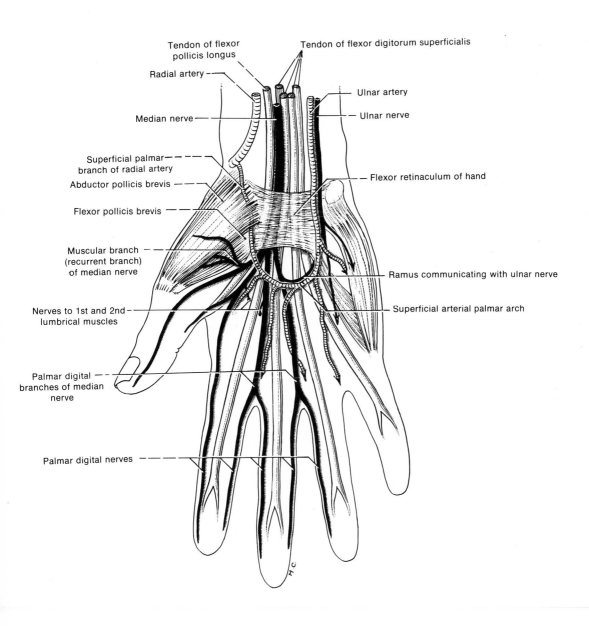

Tendon of flexor pollicis longus

Tendon of flexor digitorum superficialis

Radial artery

Median nerve

Ulnar artery

Ulnar nerve

Superficial palmar branch of radial artery

Abductor pollicis brevis

Flexor pollicis brevis

Flexor retinaculum of hand

Muscular branch (recurrent branch) of median nerve

Ramus communicating with ulnar nerve

Nerves to 1st and 2nd lumbrical muscles

Superficial arterial palmar arch

Palmar digital branches of median nerve

Palmar digital nerves

Diagram of the Median Nerve

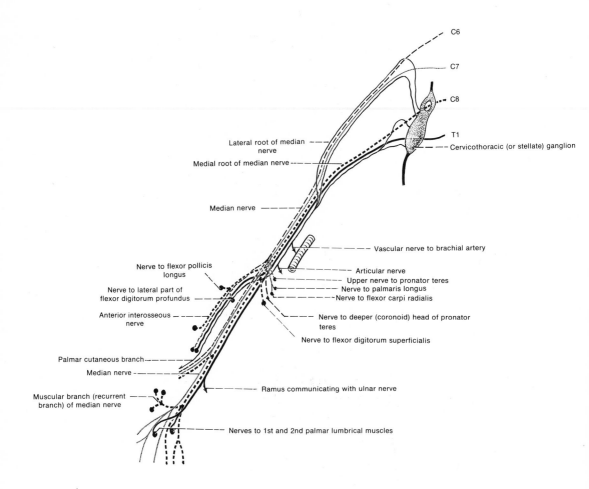

C6

C7

C8

T1

Cervicothoracic (or stellate) ganglion

Lateral root of median nerve

Medial root of median nerve

Median nerve

Vascular nerve to brachial artery

Nerve to flexor pollicis longus

Nerve to lateral part of flexor digitorum profundus

Anterior interosseous nerve

Articular nerve

Upper nerve to pronator teres

Nerve to palmaris longus

Nerve to flexor carpi radialis

Nerve to deeper (coronoid) head of pronator teres

Nerve to flexor digitorum superficialis

Palmar cutaneous branch

Median nerve

Ramus communicating with ulnar nerve

Muscular branch (recurrent branch) of median nerve

Nerves to 1st and 2nd palmar lumbrical muscles

ULNAR NERVE

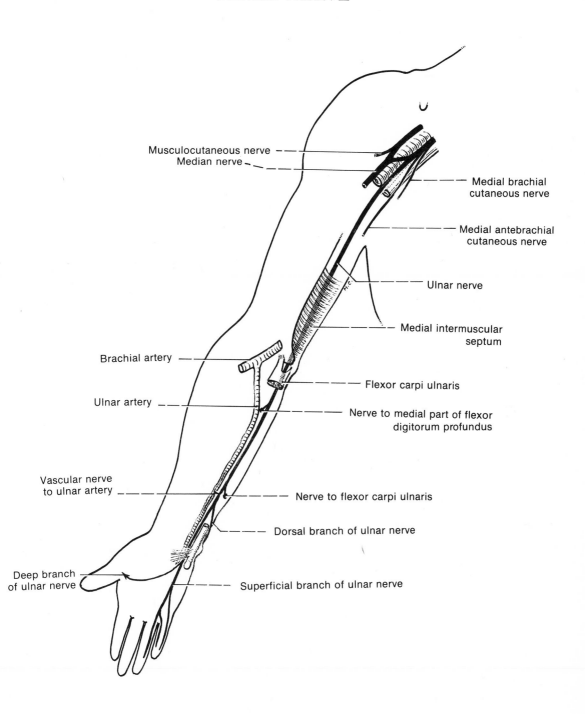

Musculocutaneous nerve
Median nerve
Medial brachial cutaneous nerve
Medial antebrachial cutaneous nerve
Ulnar nerve
Medial intermuscular septum
Brachial artery
Flexor carpi ulnaris
Ulnar artery
Nerve to medial part of flexor digitorum profundus
Vascular nerve to ulnar artery
Nerve to flexor carpi ulnaris
Dorsal branch of ulnar nerve
Deep branch of ulnar nerve
Superficial branch of ulnar nerve

DORSAL ASPECT OF THE HAND

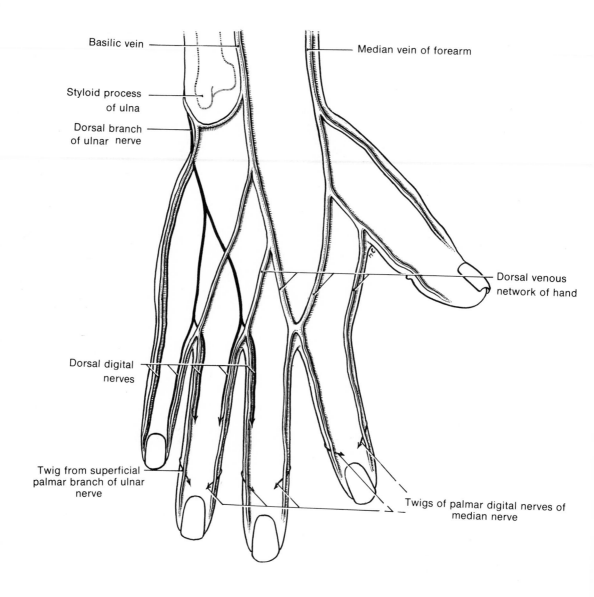

Basilic vein

Median vein of forearm

Styloid process
of ulna

Dorsal branch
of ulnar nerve

Dorsal venous
network of hand

Dorsal digital
nerves

Twig from superficial
palmar branch of ulnar
nerve

Twigs of palmar digital nerves of
median nerve

Palmar (Ventral) Aspect of the Hand

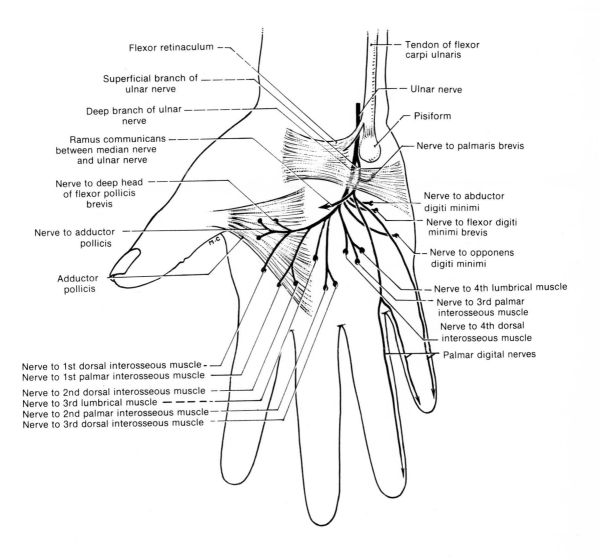

Flexor retinaculum

Superficial branch of ulnar nerve

Deep branch of ulnar nerve

Ramus communicans between median nerve and ulnar nerve

Nerve to deep head of flexor pollicis brevis

Nerve to adductor pollicis

Adductor pollicis

Tendon of flexor carpi ulnaris

Ulnar nerve

Pisiform

Nerve to palmaris brevis

Nerve to abductor digiti minimi

Nerve to flexor digiti minimi brevis

Nerve to opponens digiti minimi

Nerve to 4th lumbrical muscle

Nerve to 3rd palmar interosseous muscle

Nerve to 4th dorsal interosseous muscle

Palmar digital nerves

Nerve to 1st dorsal interosseous muscle
Nerve to 1st palmar interosseous muscle
Nerve to 2nd dorsal interosseous muscle
Nerve to 3rd lumbrical muscle
Nerve to 2nd palmar interosseous muscle
Nerve to 3rd dorsal interosseous muscle

Page 57

DIAGRAM OF THE ULNAR NERVE

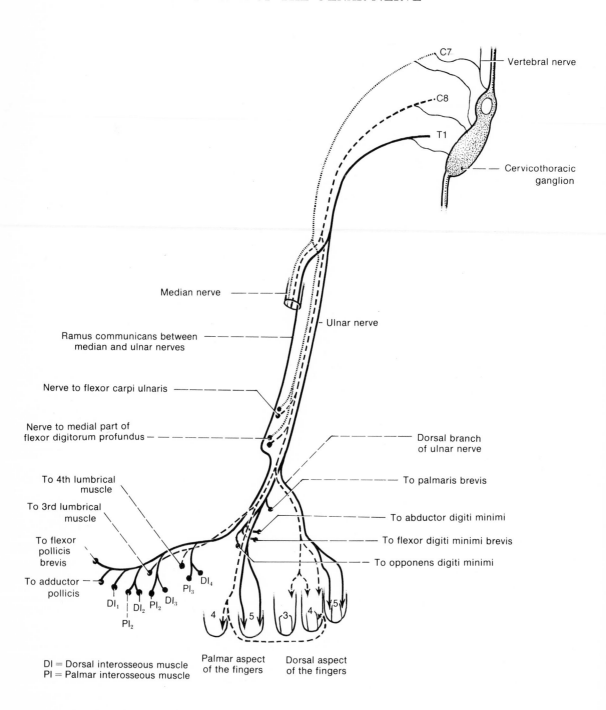

C7

Vertebral nerve

C8

T1

Cervicothoracic ganglion

Median nerve

Ulnar nerve

Ramus communicans between median and ulnar nerves

Nerve to flexor carpi ulnaris

Nerve to medial part of flexor digitorum profundus

Dorsal branch of ulnar nerve

To 4th lumbrical muscle

To 3rd lumbrical muscle

To palmaris brevis

To abductor digiti minimi

To flexor pollicis brevis

To flexor digiti minimi brevis

To opponens digiti minimi

To adductor pollicis

DI_4

PI_3

DI_1 DI_2 PI_2 DI_3

PI_2

4   5   3   4   5

DI = Dorsal interosseous muscle
PI = Palmar interosseous muscle

Palmar aspect of the fingers

Dorsal aspect of the fingers

MEDIAL BRACHIAL AND MEDIAL ANTEBRACHIAL CUTANEOUS NERVES

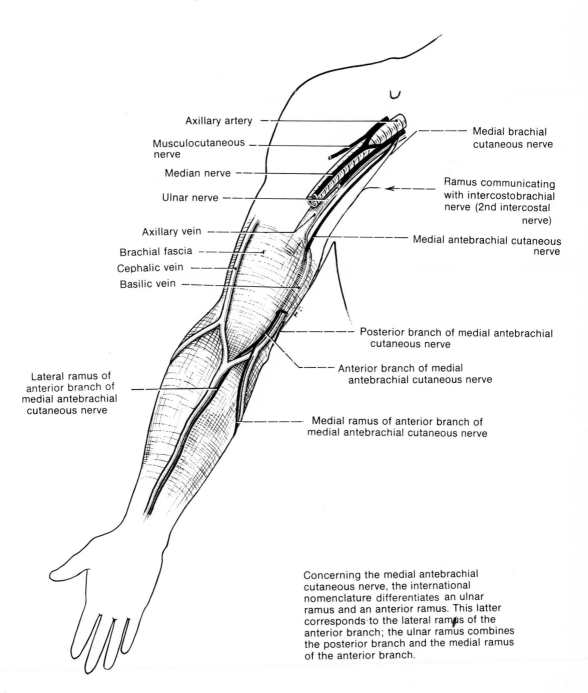

Axillary artery

Musculocutaneous nerve

Median nerve

Ulnar nerve

Axillary vein

Brachial fascia

Cephalic vein

Basilic vein

Medial brachial cutaneous nerve

Ramus communicating with intercostobrachial nerve (2nd intercostal nerve)

Medial antebrachial cutaneous nerve

Posterior branch of medial antebrachial cutaneous nerve

Anterior branch of medial antebrachial cutaneous nerve

Lateral ramus of anterior branch of medial antebrachial cutaneous nerve

Medial ramus of anterior branch of medial antebrachial cutaneous nerve

Concerning the medial antebrachial cutaneous nerve, the international nomenclature differentiates an ulnar ramus and an anterior ramus. This latter corresponds to the lateral ramus of the anterior branch; the ulnar ramus combines the posterior branch and the medial ramus of the anterior branch.

Posterolateral Aspect of the Elbow Joint

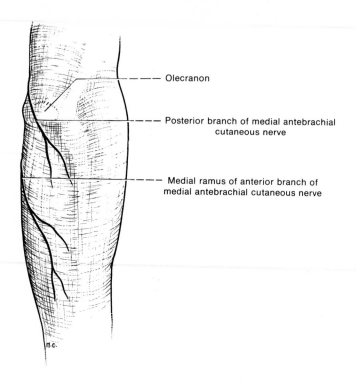

— Olecranon

— Posterior branch of medial antebrachial
cutaneous nerve

— Medial ramus of anterior branch of
medial antebrachial cutaneous nerve

Diagram of the Medial Brachial and Medial Antebrachial Cutaneous Nerves

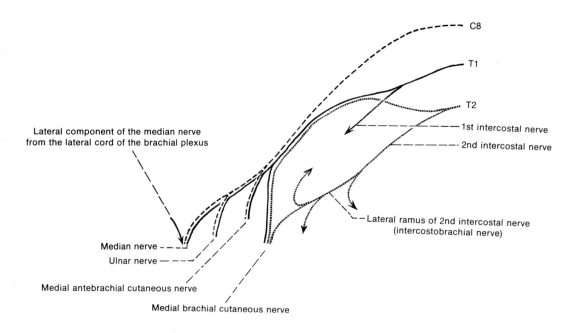

C8

T1

T2

Lateral component of the median nerve
from the lateral cord of the brachial plexus

1st intercostal nerve

2nd intercostal nerve

Lateral ramus of 2nd intercostal nerve
(intercostobrachial nerve)

Median nerve

Ulnar nerve

Medial antebrachial cutaneous nerve

Medial brachial cutaneous nerve

AXILLARY (CIRCUMFLEX) NERVE

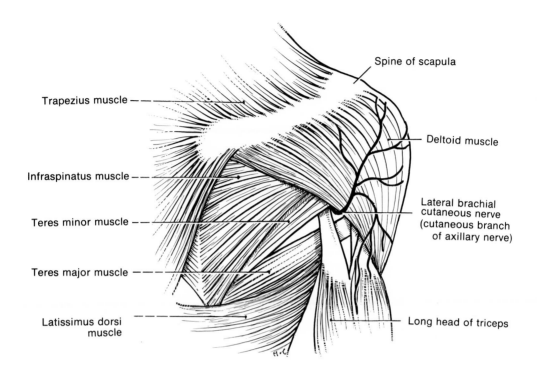

Spine of scapula

Trapezius muscle

Deltoid muscle

Infraspinatus muscle

Teres minor muscle

Lateral brachial cutaneous nerve (cutaneous branch of axillary nerve)

Teres major muscle

Latissimus dorsi muscle

Long head of triceps

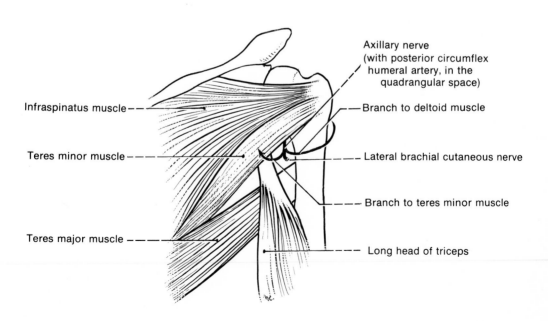

Axillary nerve (with posterior circumflex humeral artery, in the quadrangular space)

Infraspinatus muscle

Branch to deltoid muscle

Teres minor muscle

Lateral brachial cutaneous nerve

Branch to teres minor muscle

Teres major muscle

Long head of triceps

DIAGRAM OF THE AXILLARY NERVE

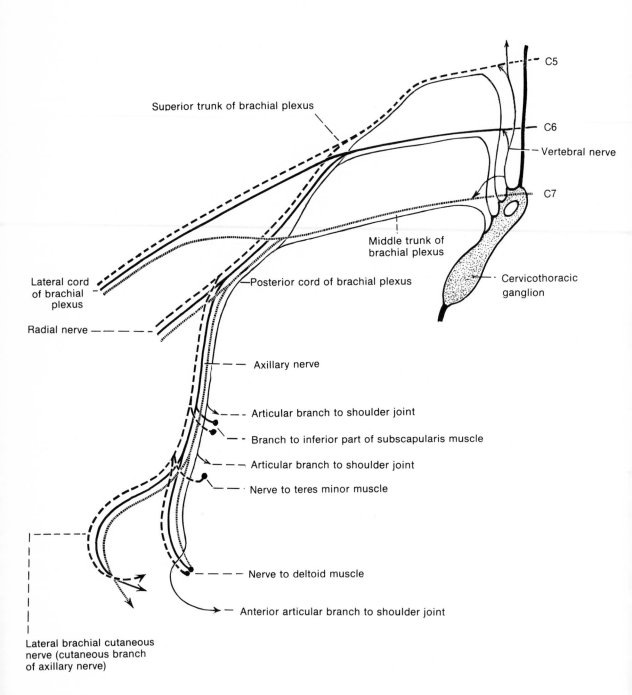

Superior trunk of brachial plexus

C5

C6

Vertebral nerve

C7

Middle trunk of brachial plexus

Cervicothoracic ganglion

Lateral cord of brachial plexus

Posterior cord of brachial plexus

Radial nerve ———————

—— Axillary nerve

—— Articular branch to shoulder joint

—— Branch to inferior part of subscapularis muscle

—— Articular branch to shoulder joint

—— Nerve to teres minor muscle

—— Nerve to deltoid muscle

—— Anterior articular branch to shoulder joint

Lateral brachial cutaneous nerve (cutaneous branch of axillary nerve)

Page 62

RADIAL (OR MUSCULOSPIRAL) NERVE

DIAGRAM OF THE COURSE OF THE RADIAL NERVE
(RIGHT LATERAL ASPECT)

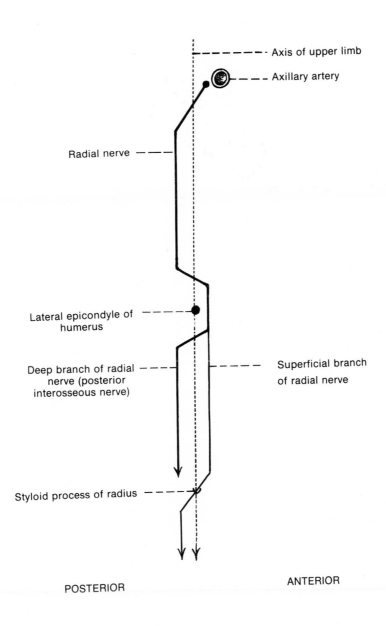

POSTERIOR   ANTERIOR

COURSE OF THE RADIAL NERVE IN THE ARM

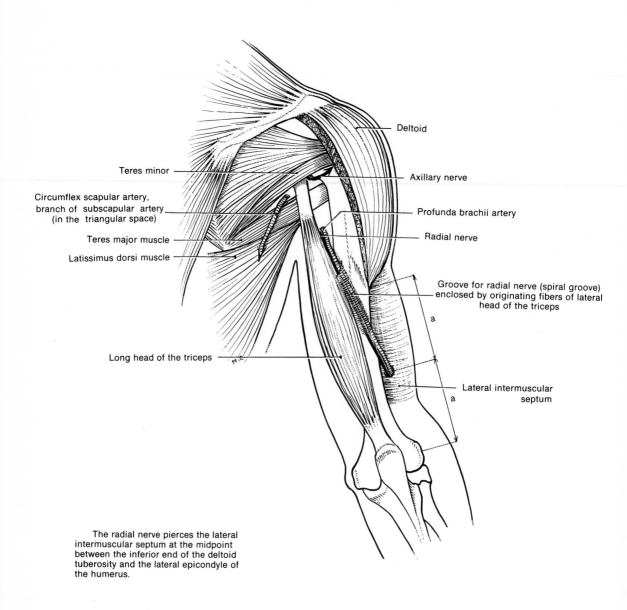

Teres minor

Circumflex scapular artery,
branch of subscapular artery
(in the triangular space)

Teres major muscle

Latissimus dorsi muscle

Long head of the triceps

Deltoid

Axillary nerve

Profunda brachii artery

Radial nerve

Groove for radial nerve (spiral groove)
enclosed by originating fibers of lateral
head of the triceps

Lateral intermuscular
septum

The radial nerve pierces the lateral
intermuscular septum at the midpoint
between the inferior end of the deltoid
tuberosity and the lateral epicondyle of
the humerus.

Cutaneous Nerves of the Lateral Surface of the Upper Limb

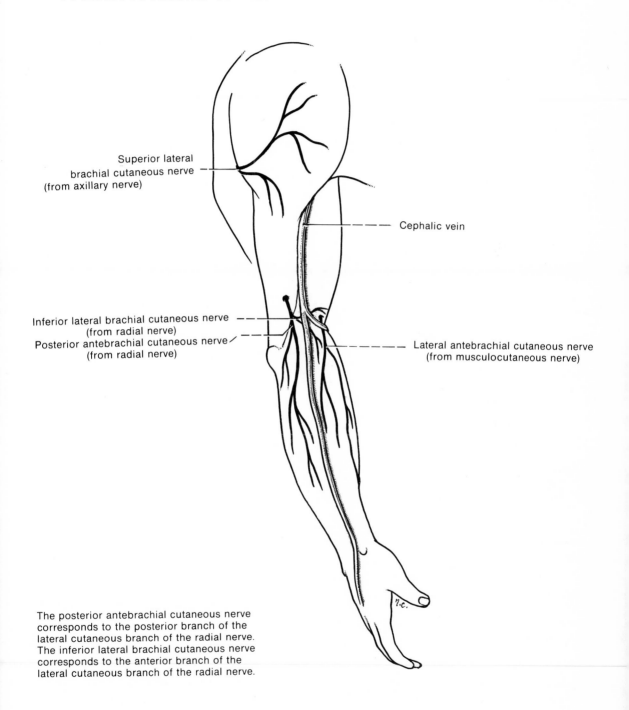

Superior lateral brachial cutaneous nerve (from axillary nerve)

Cephalic vein

Inferior lateral brachial cutaneous nerve (from radial nerve)
Posterior antebrachial cutaneous nerve (from radial nerve)

Lateral antebrachial cutaneous nerve (from musculocutaneous nerve)

The posterior antebrachial cutaneous nerve corresponds to the posterior branch of the lateral cutaneous branch of the radial nerve. The inferior lateral brachial cutaneous nerve corresponds to the anterior branch of the lateral cutaneous branch of the radial nerve.

Branches of the Radial Nerve

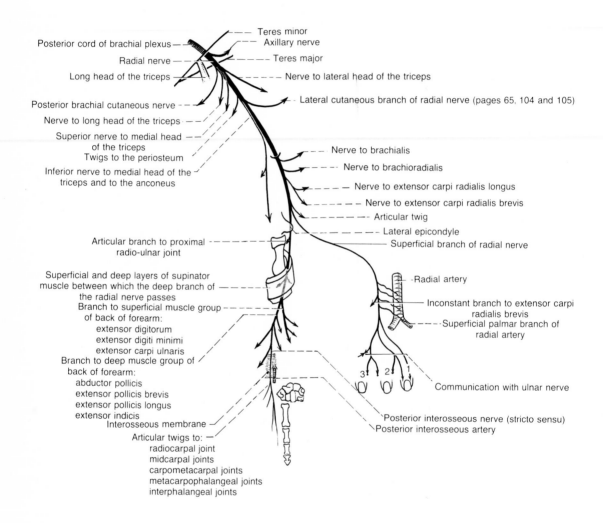

Posterior cord of brachial plexus —
Radial nerve —
Long head of the triceps —
Teres minor
Axillary nerve
Teres major
Nerve to lateral head of the triceps

Posterior brachial cutaneous nerve —
Nerve to long head of the triceps —
Superior nerve to medial head of the triceps
Twigs to the periosteum
Inferior nerve to medial head of the triceps and to the anconeus

Lateral cutaneous branch of radial nerve (pages 65, 104 and 105)

Nerve to brachialis
Nerve to brachioradialis
Nerve to extensor carpi radialis longus
Nerve to extensor carpi radialis brevis
Articular twig
Lateral epicondyle
Superficial branch of radial nerve

Articular branch to proximal radio-ulnar joint

Superficial and deep layers of supinator muscle between which the deep branch of the radial nerve passes
Branch to superficial muscle group of back of forearm:
    extensor digitorum
    extensor digiti minimi
    extensor carpi ulnaris
Branch to deep muscle group of back of forearm:
    abductor pollicis
    extensor pollicis brevis
    extensor pollicis longus
    extensor indicis
    Interosseous membrane
Articular twigs to:
    radiocarpal joint
    midcarpal joints
    carpometacarpal joints
    metacarpophalangeal joints
    interphalangeal joints

Radial artery
Inconstant branch to extensor carpi radialis brevis
Superficial palmar branch of radial artery

3 2 1

Communication with ulnar nerve

Posterior interosseous nerve (stricto sensu)
Posterior interosseous artery

DIAGRAM OF THE RADIAL NERVE

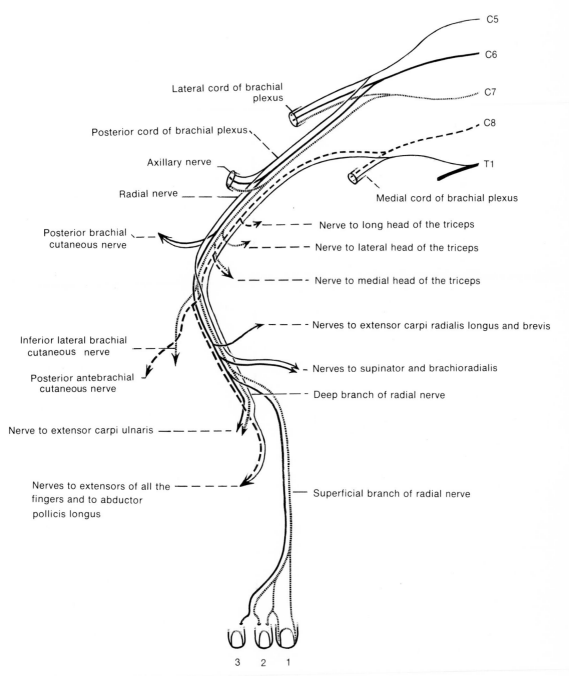

Lateral cord of brachial plexus

Posterior cord of brachial plexus

Axillary nerve

Radial nerve

Posterior brachial cutaneous nerve

Inferior lateral brachial cutaneous nerve

Posterior antebrachial cutaneous nerve

Nerve to extensor carpi ulnaris

Nerves to extensors of all the fingers and to abductor pollicis longus

C5

C6

C7

C8

T1

Medial cord of brachial plexus

Nerve to long head of the triceps

Nerve to lateral head of the triceps

Nerve to medial head of the triceps

Nerves to extensor carpi radialis longus and brevis

Nerves to supinator and brachioradialis

Deep branch of radial nerve

Superficial branch of radial nerve

3   2   1

Dorsal aspect of the fingers

GENERAL DIAGRAM OF THE BRACHIAL PLEXUS AND ITS AUTONOMIC COMMUNICATING RAMI

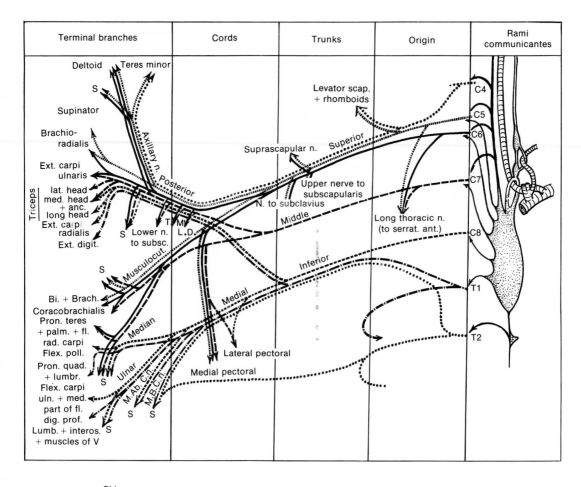

Terminal branches	Cords	Trunks	Origin	Rami communicantes

S = Skin
T.M. = Teres major muscle
L.D. = Latissimus dorsi muscle
M. B. C. n. = Medial brachial cutaneous nerve
M. Ab. C. n. = Medial antibrachial cutaneous nerve

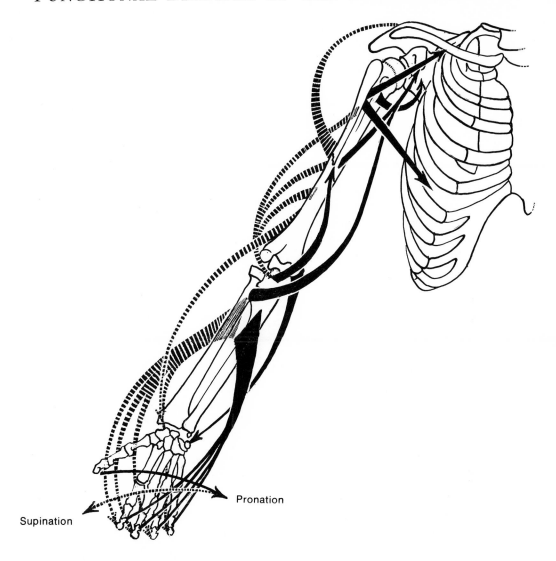

Supination

Pronation

Analysis of the Actions Which the Various Segments of the Upper Limb Undergo

————: Actions dependent on the anterior branches of the brachial plexus

|||||||||||||||: Actions dependent on the posterior branches of the brachial plexus

A diagram of the actions of the main groups of muscles of the upper limb. The muscles innervated by the anterior branches of the brachial plexus act as adductors, flexors and pronators; the muscles innervated by the posterior branches ensure abduction, extension and supination. Only the brachioradialis muscle, innervated by the radial nerve, is a flexor of the forearm.

THORACIC NERVES

After giving off a meningeal branch a short distance beyond the intervertebral foramen, each thoracic nerve divides into a dorsal ramus (see pages 16 and 37) and a ventral ramus (intercostal nerve). This latter goes along the intercostal space, supplying motor and sensory branches. During its course it gives rise to a lateral cutaneous branch. It ends close to the lateral border of the sternum as the anterior cutaneous branch (see page 72).

SECTIONS OF AN INTERCOSTAL SPACE

At the Level of the
Neck of the Rib

At the Middle of the
Intercostal Space

At the Anterior Part of
the Intercostal Space

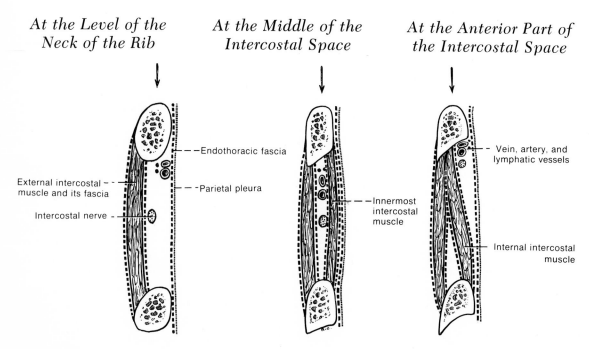

Endothoracic fascia

External intercostal
muscle and its fascia

Parietal pleura

Intercostal nerve

Innermost
intercostal
muscle

Vein, artery, and
lymphatic vessels

Internal intercostal
muscle

VISCERAL ASPECT OF AN INTERCOSTAL SPACE

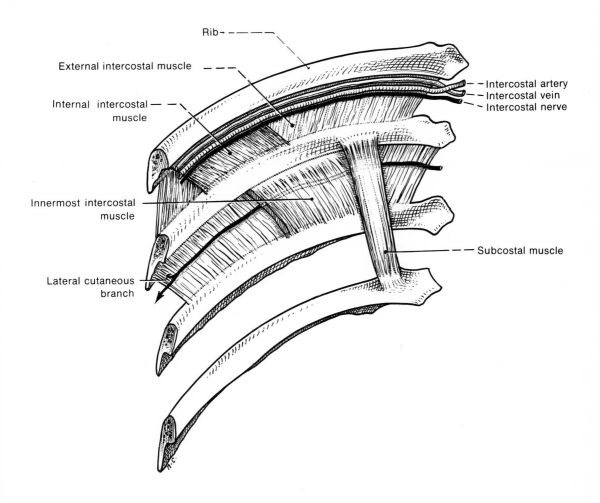

Rib

External intercostal muscle

Internal intercostal muscle

Innermost intercostal muscle

Lateral cutaneous branch

Intercostal artery
Intercostal vein
Intercostal nerve

Subcostal muscle

The external intercostal muscles have all been removed except those in the first three intercostal spaces. The oblique muscles of the abdominal wall have been removed in order to show the course of the thoraco-abdominal nerves.

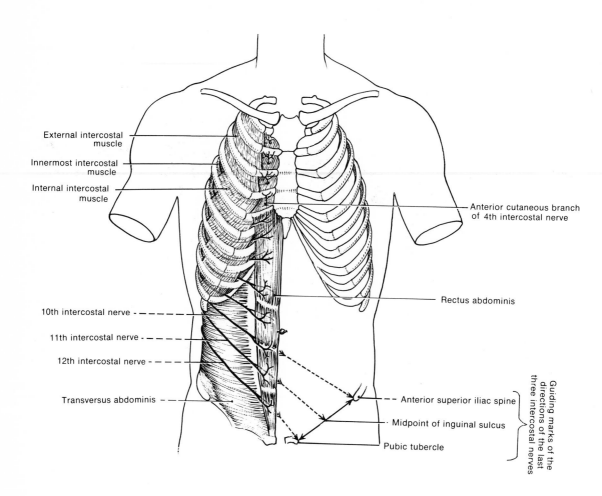

External intercostal muscle

Innermost intercostal muscle

Internal intercostal muscle

Anterior cutaneous branch of 4th intercostal nerve

Rectus abdominis

10th intercostal nerve

11th intercostal nerve

12th intercostal nerve

Transversus abdominis

Anterior superior iliac spine

Midpoint of inguinal sulcus

Pubic tubercle

Guiding marks of the directions of the last three intercostal nerves

Anterior End of the Thoracic Nerves

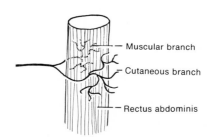

Muscular branch

Cutaneous branch

Rectus abdominis

The *thoracic nerves* do not form plexuses. After their emergence from the vertebral canal, they divide into a dorsal ramus and a ventral ramus like the other spinal nerves.

Their ventral rami spread like a fan; they do not meet each other and never fuse at their origin.

The part of these nerves which continues through an intercostal space is called an *intercostal nerve.* Similarly, the 12th thoracic nerve which passes under the 12th rib is called the *subcostal nerve.*

In addition, the last six thoracic nerves follow a thoracic and abdominal course and are distributed in the thoracic and abdominal regions; they are called *thoraco-abdominal nerves.*

The first two thoracic nerves which are connected with the brachial plexus are considered as *intercostobrachial nerves*; in fact, the 1st thoracic nerve participates directly in the formation of the brachial plexus, connecting with the 8th cervical nerve. The 2nd thoracic nerve may send fibers to the 1st thoracic nerve, which conducts them to the vertebral part of the brachial plexus, or it may send a communicating branch to the medial brachial cutaneous nerve by way of its lateral branch.

The thoracic nerves supply almost all the muscles of the thorax and abdominal walls; the diaphragm is partially innervated by the last four or five intercostal nerves; the iliohypogastric nerve contributes to the nerve supply of the inferior part of the muscles of the anterolateral wall of the abdomen.

The description of a thoracic type nerve has been studied in the general considerations of the spinal nervous system, page 16.

Lumbar Plexus

FORMATION

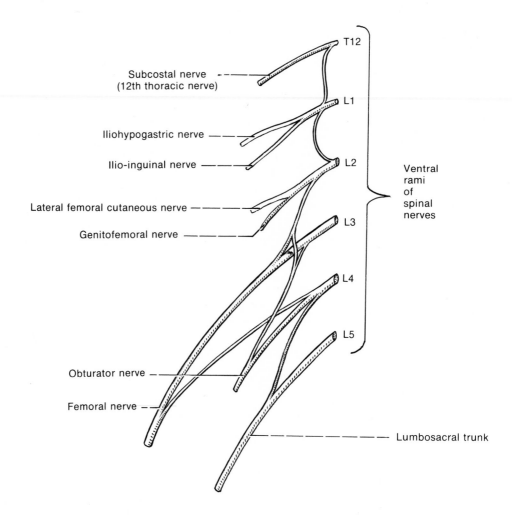

Subcostal nerve
(12th thoracic nerve)

T12

L1

Iliohypogastric nerve

Ilio-inguinal nerve

L2

Lateral femoral cutaneous nerve

Genitofemoral nerve

L3

Ventral
rami
of
spinal
nerves

L4

L5

Obturator nerve

Femoral nerve

Lumbosacral trunk

TOPOGRAPHY AND BRANCHES OF
THE LUMBAR PLEXUS

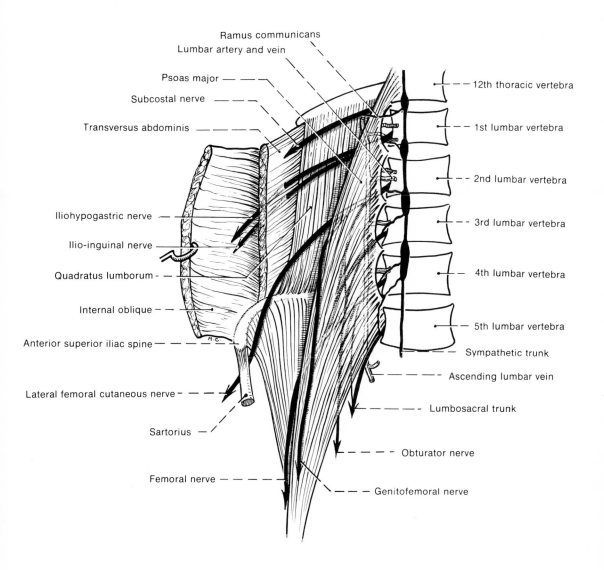

Ramus communicans

Lumbar artery and vein

Psoas major

Subcostal nerve

Transversus abdominis

12th thoracic vertebra

1st lumbar vertebra

2nd lumbar vertebra

Iliohypogastric nerve

3rd lumbar vertebra

Ilio-inguinal nerve

Quadratus lumborum

4th lumbar vertebra

Internal oblique

5th lumbar vertebra

Anterior superior iliac spine

Sympathetic trunk

Ascending lumbar vein

Lateral femoral cutaneous nerve

Lumbosacral trunk

Sartorius

Obturator nerve

Femoral nerve

Genitofemoral nerve

ILIOHYPOGASTRIC AND ILIO-INGUINAL NERVES

According to Hovelacque, the iliohypogastric and ilio-inguinal nerves follow a similar course; the ilio-inguinal nerve is not always distinct. There is often an intermixing of the branches of these two nerves which share a common termination.

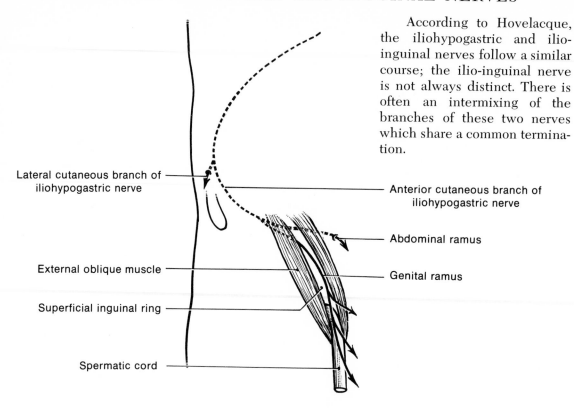

Lateral cutaneous branch of iliohypogastric nerve

Anterior cutaneous branch of iliohypogastric nerve

Abdominal ramus

External oblique muscle

Genital ramus

Superficial inguinal ring

Spermatic cord

Cutaneous Nerves of the Lateral Surface of Buttock (Gluteal Region)

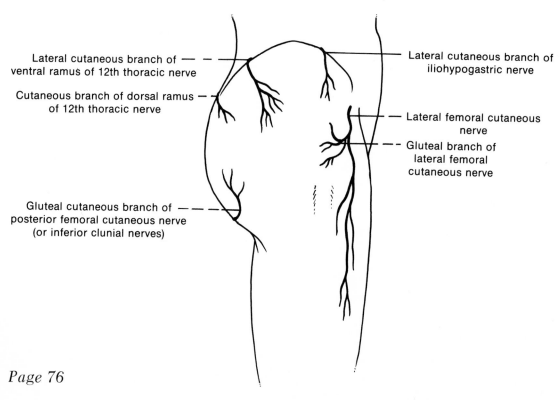

Lateral cutaneous branch of ventral ramus of 12th thoracic nerve

Cutaneous branch of dorsal ramus of 12th thoracic nerve

Lateral cutaneous branch of iliohypogastric nerve

Lateral femoral cutaneous nerve

Gluteal branch of lateral femoral cutaneous nerve

Gluteal cutaneous branch of posterior femoral cutaneous nerve (or inferior clunial nerves)

GENITOFEMORAL NERVE

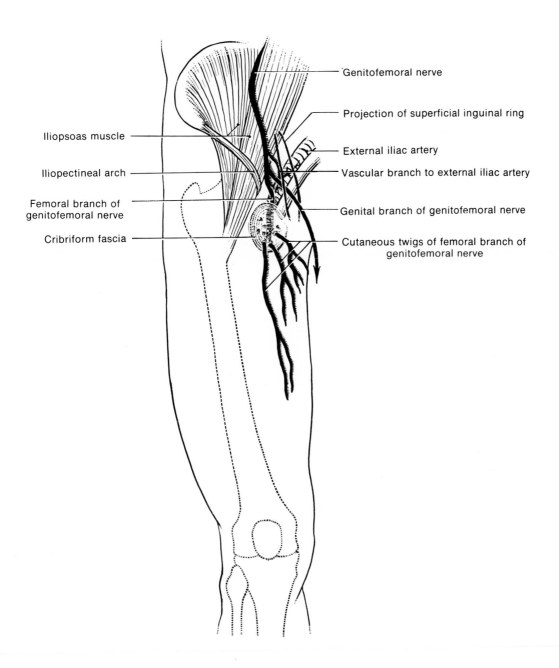

Iliopsoas muscle

Iliopectineal arch

Femoral branch of
genitofemoral nerve

Cribriform fascia

Genitofemoral nerve

Projection of superficial inguinal ring

External iliac artery

Vascular branch to external iliac artery

Genital branch of genitofemoral nerve

Cutaneous twigs of femoral branch of
genitofemoral nerve

LATERAL FEMORAL CUTANEOUS NERVE

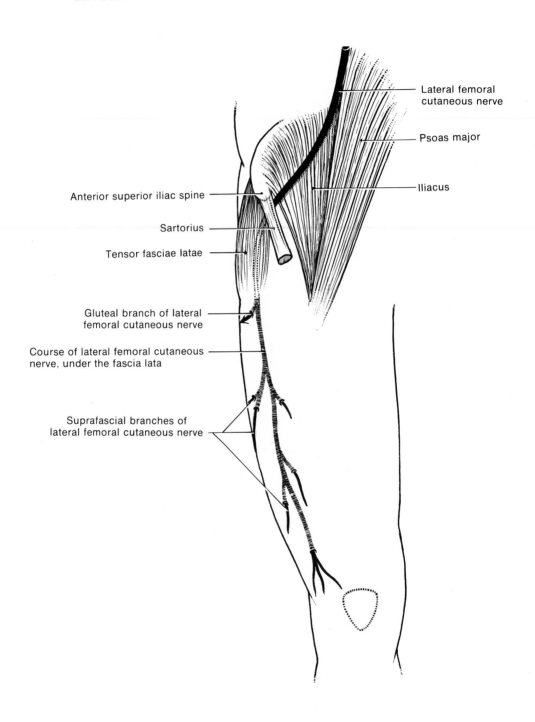

Lateral femoral
cutaneous nerve

Psoas major

Iliacus

Anterior superior iliac spine

Sartorius

Tensor fasciae latae

Gluteal branch of lateral
femoral cutaneous nerve

Course of lateral femoral cutaneous
nerve, under the fascia lata

Suprafascial branches of
lateral femoral cutaneous nerve

FEMORAL NERVE

The intermediate and medial musculocutaneous branches of the femoral nerve have no corresponding names in the Nomina Anatomica. In fact, the international nomenclature covers only medial and anterior cutaneous branches of the femoral nerve.

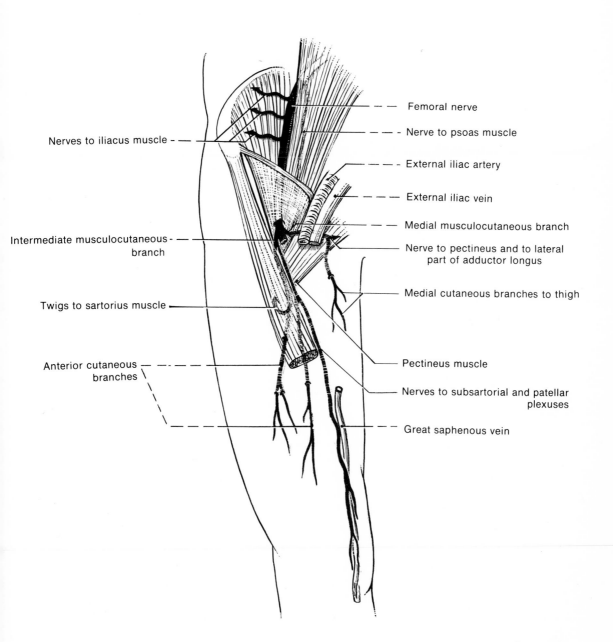

Nerves to iliacus muscle

Intermediate musculocutaneous branch

Twigs to sartorius muscle

Anterior cutaneous branches

Femoral nerve

Nerve to psoas muscle

External iliac artery

External iliac vein

Medial musculocutaneous branch

Nerve to pectineus and to lateral part of adductor longus

Medial cutaneous branches to thigh

Pectineus muscle

Nerves to subsartorial and patellar plexuses

Great saphenous vein

NERVE OF THE QUADRICEPS FEMORIS

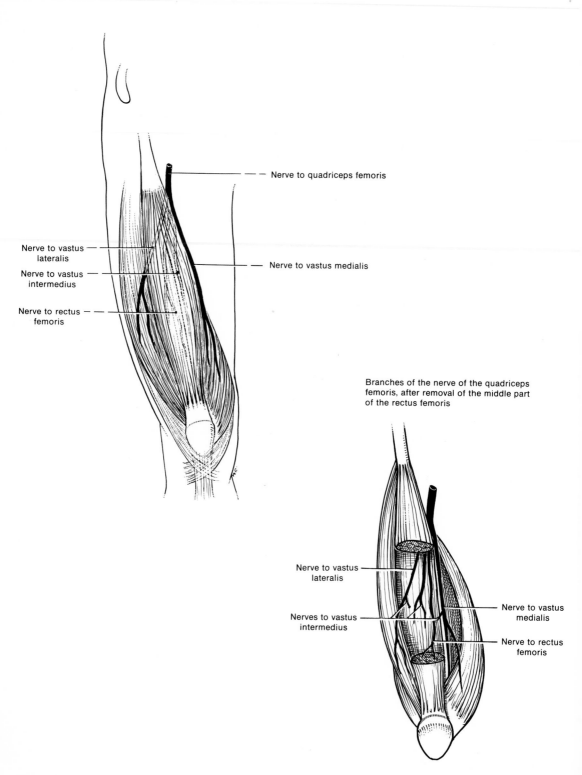

Nerve to quadriceps femoris

Nerve to vastus
lateralis

Nerve to vastus
intermedius

Nerve to rectus
femoris

Nerve to vastus medialis

Branches of the nerve of the quadriceps
femoris, after removal of the middle part
of the rectus femoris

Nerve to vastus
lateralis

Nerves to vastus
intermedius

Nerve to vastus
medialis

Nerve to rectus
femoris

SAPHENOUS NERVE

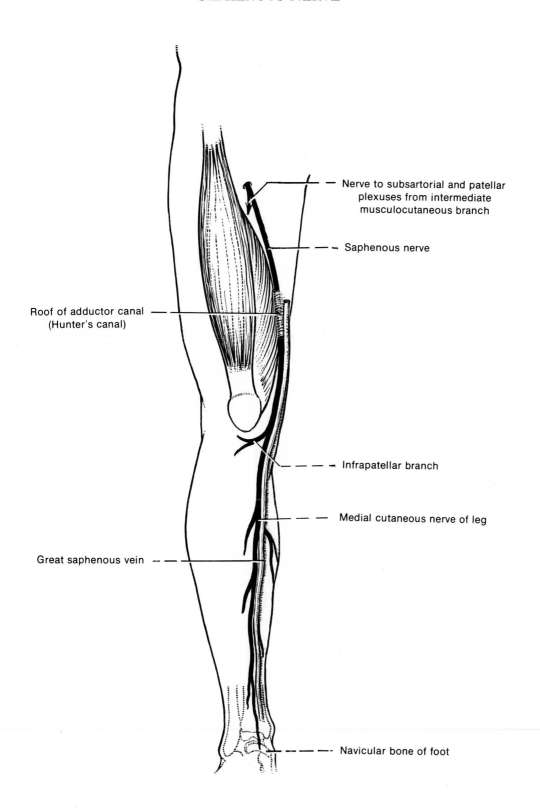

Nerve to subsartorial and patellar plexuses from intermediate musculocutaneous branch

Saphenous nerve

Roof of adductor canal (Hunter's canal)

Infrapatellar branch

Medial cutaneous nerve of leg

Great saphenous vein

Navicular bone of foot

OBTURATOR NERVE

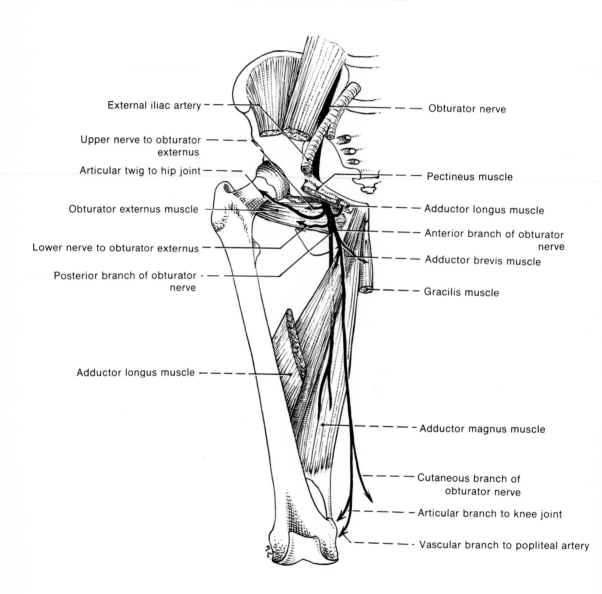

External iliac artery

Upper nerve to obturator externus

Articular twig to hip joint

Obturator externus muscle

Lower nerve to obturator externus

Posterior branch of obturator nerve

Adductor longus muscle

Obturator nerve

Pectineus muscle

Adductor longus muscle

Anterior branch of obturator nerve

Adductor brevis muscle

Gracilis muscle

Adductor magnus muscle

Cutaneous branch of obturator nerve

Articular branch to knee joint

Vascular branch to popliteal artery

DIAGRAM OF THE LUMBAR PLEXUS

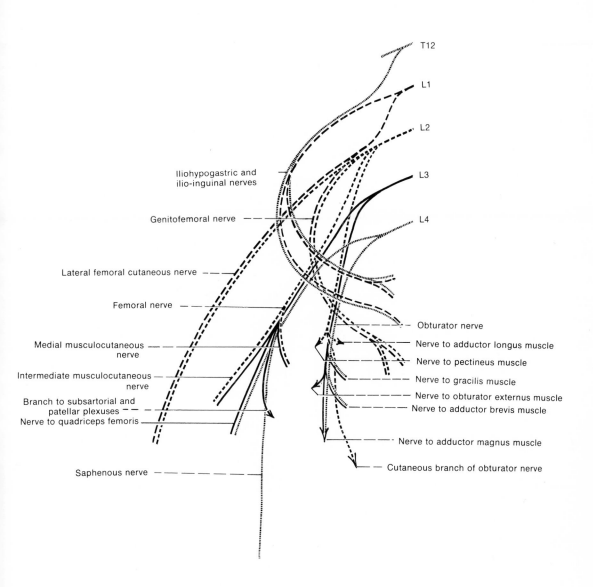

ORIGIN AND FORMATION

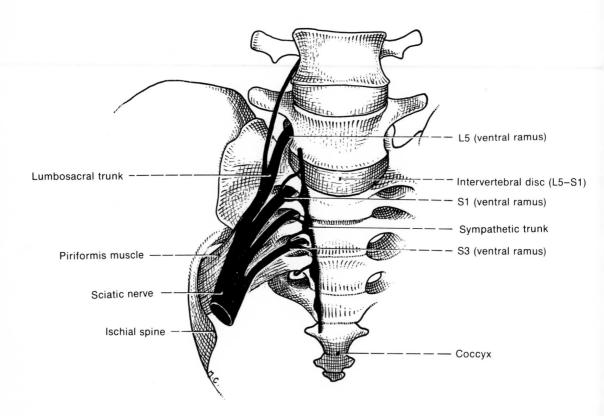

Lumbosacral trunk

Piriformis muscle

Sciatic nerve

Ischial spine

L5 (ventral ramus)

Intervertebral disc (L5–S1)

S1 (ventral ramus)

Sympathetic trunk

S3 (ventral ramus)

Coccyx

COLLATERAL BRANCHES OF THE SACRAL PLEXUS

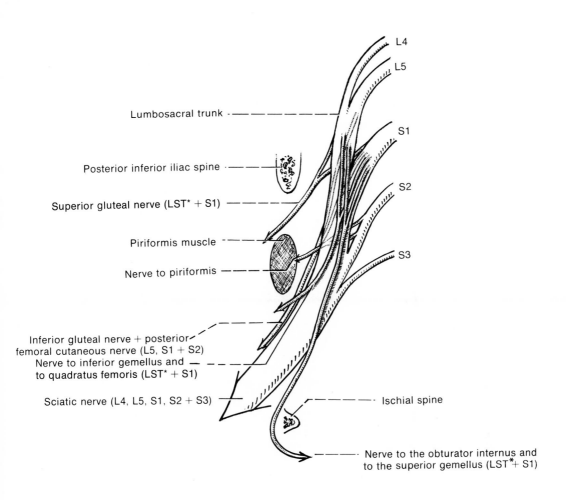

The ventral (or anterior) collateral branches of the sacral plexus consist of:
the nerve to the inferior gemellus and to the quadratus femoris
the nerve to the obturator internus and to the superior gemellus

The dorsal (or posterior) collateral branches of the sacral plexus consist of:
the superior gluteal nerve
the nerve to the piriformis
the inferior gluteal nerve
the posterior femoral cutaneous nerve

°LST = lumbosacral trunk.

COLLATERAL BRANCHES AND RELATIONSHIPS OF THE SACRAL PLEXUS

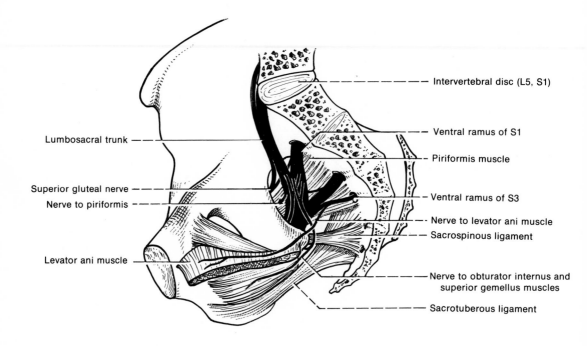

Lumbosacral trunk

Superior gluteal nerve

Nerve to piriformis

Levator ani muscle

Intervertebral disc (L5, S1)

Ventral ramus of S1

Piriformis muscle

Ventral ramus of S3

Nerve to levator ani muscle

Sacrospinous ligament

Nerve to obturator internus and superior gemellus muscles

Sacrotuberous ligament

NERVES OF THE GLUTEAL REGION

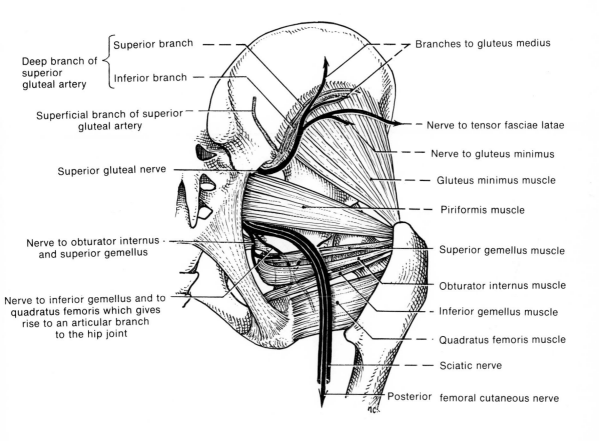

Deep branch of superior gluteal artery
— Superior branch
— Inferior branch

Branches to gluteus medius

Superficial branch of superior gluteal artery

Nerve to tensor fasciae latae

Nerve to gluteus minimus

Superior gluteal nerve

Gluteus minimus muscle

Piriformis muscle

Nerve to obturator internus and superior gemellus

Superior gemellus muscle

Obturator internus muscle

Nerve to inferior gemellus and to quadratus femoris which gives rise to an articular branch to the hip joint

Inferior gemellus muscle

Quadratus femoris muscle

Sciatic nerve

Posterior femoral cutaneous nerve

THE POSTERIOR FEMORAL CUTANEOUS NERVE
AND THE INFERIOR GLUTEAL NERVE

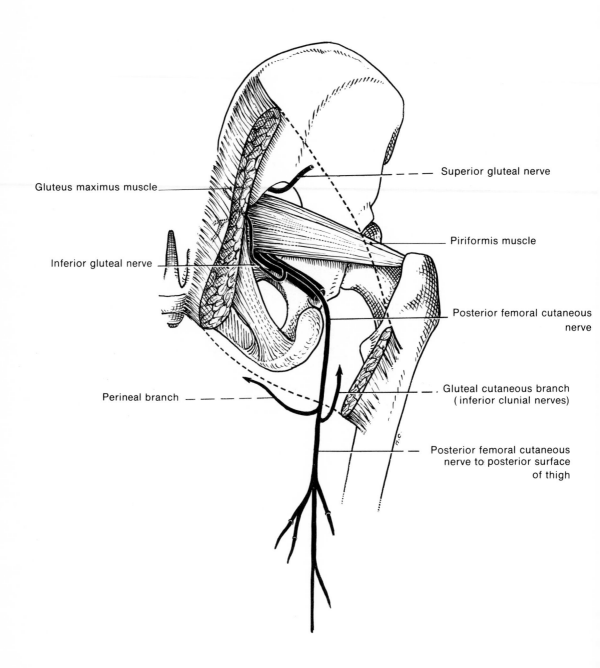

Gluteus maximus muscle

Inferior gluteal nerve

Perineal branch

Superior gluteal nerve

Piriformis muscle

Posterior femoral cutaneous nerve

Gluteal cutaneous branch (inferior clunial nerves)

Posterior femoral cutaneous nerve to posterior surface of thigh

THE SCIATIC NERVE

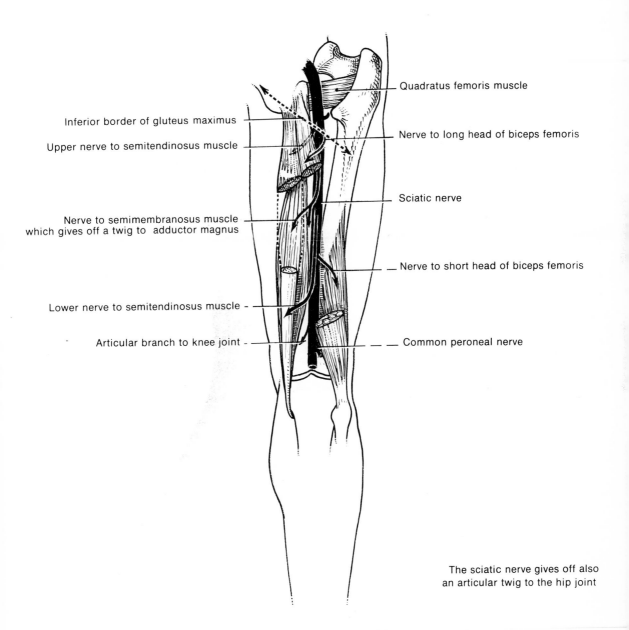

Quadratus femoris muscle

Inferior border of gluteus maximus

Nerve to long head of biceps femoris

Upper nerve to semitendinosus muscle

Sciatic nerve

Nerve to semimembranosus muscle
which gives off a twig to adductor magnus

Nerve to short head of biceps femoris

Lower nerve to semitendinosus muscle -

Articular branch to knee joint -

Common peroneal nerve

The sciatic nerve gives off also
an articular twig to the hip joint

COMMON PERONEAL (OR LATERAL POPLITEAL) NERVE

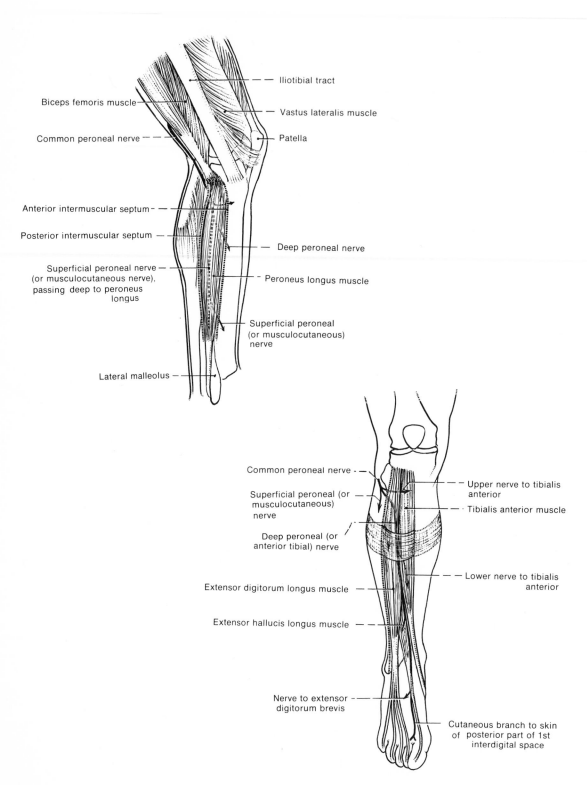

Iliotibial tract

Biceps femoris muscle

Vastus lateralis muscle

Common peroneal nerve

Patella

Anterior intermuscular septum

Posterior intermuscular septum

Deep peroneal nerve

Superficial peroneal nerve
(or musculocutaneous nerve),
passing deep to peroneus
longus

Peroneus longus muscle

Superficial peroneal
(or musculocutaneous)
nerve

Lateral malleolus

Common peroneal nerve

Upper nerve to tibialis
anterior

Superficial peroneal (or
musculocutaneous)
nerve

Tibialis anterior muscle

Deep peroneal (or
anterior tibial) nerve

Lower nerve to tibialis
anterior

Extensor digitorum longus muscle

Extensor hallucis longus muscle

Nerve to extensor
digitorum brevis

Cutaneous branch to skin
of posterior part of 1st
interdigital space

SUPERFICIAL PERONEAL NERVE

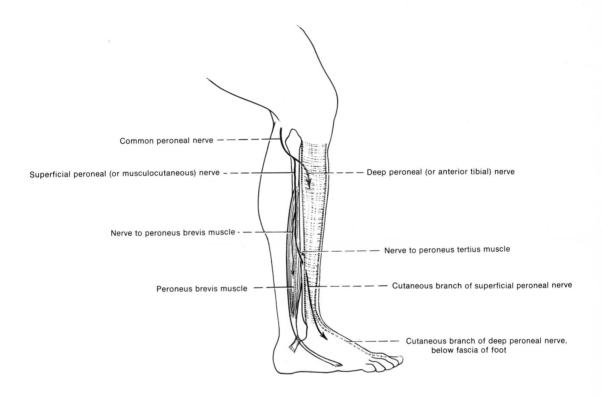

Common peroneal nerve

Superficial peroneal (or musculocutaneous) nerve

Deep peroneal (or anterior tibial) nerve

Nerve to peroneus brevis muscle

Nerve to peroneus tertius muscle

Peroneus brevis muscle

Cutaneous branch of superficial peroneal nerve

Cutaneous branch of deep peroneal nerve, below fascia of foot

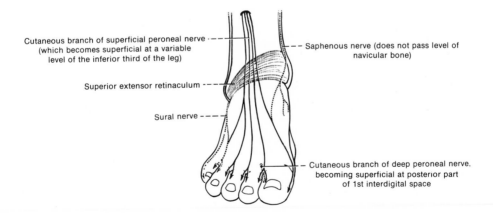

Cutaneous branch of superficial peroneal nerve (which becomes superficial at a variable level of the inferior third of the leg)

Saphenous nerve (does not pass level of navicular bone)

Superior extensor retinaculum

Sural nerve

Cutaneous branch of deep peroneal nerve, becoming superficial at posterior part of 1st interdigital space

TIBIAL (OR MEDIAL POPLITEAL) NERVE

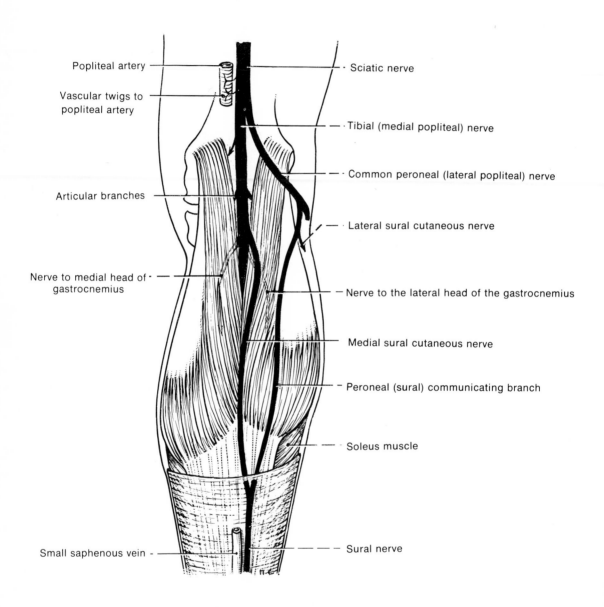

Popliteal artery

Vascular twigs to popliteal artery

Articular branches

Nerve to medial head of gastrocnemius

Small saphenous vein

Sciatic nerve

Tibial (medial popliteal) nerve

Common peroneal (lateral popliteal) nerve

Lateral sural cutaneous nerve

Nerve to the lateral head of the gastrocnemius

Medial sural cutaneous nerve

Peroneal (sural) communicating branch

Soleus muscle

Sural nerve

MUSCULAR BRANCHES OF THE UPPER PART OF THE TIBIAL NERVE

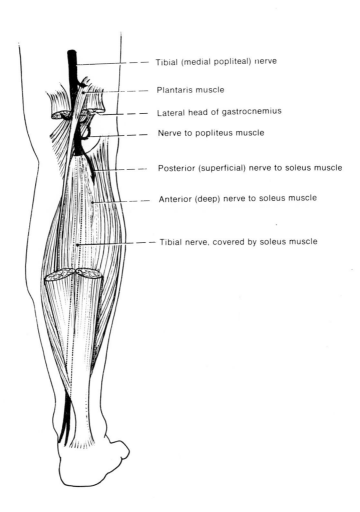

— Tibial (medial popliteal) nerve

— Plantaris muscle

— Lateral head of gastrocnemius

— Nerve to popliteus muscle

— Posterior (superficial) nerve to soleus muscle

— Anterior (deep) nerve to soleus muscle

— Tibial nerve, covered by soleus muscle

MUSCULAR BRANCHES OF THE LOWER PART
OF THE TIBIAL NERVE

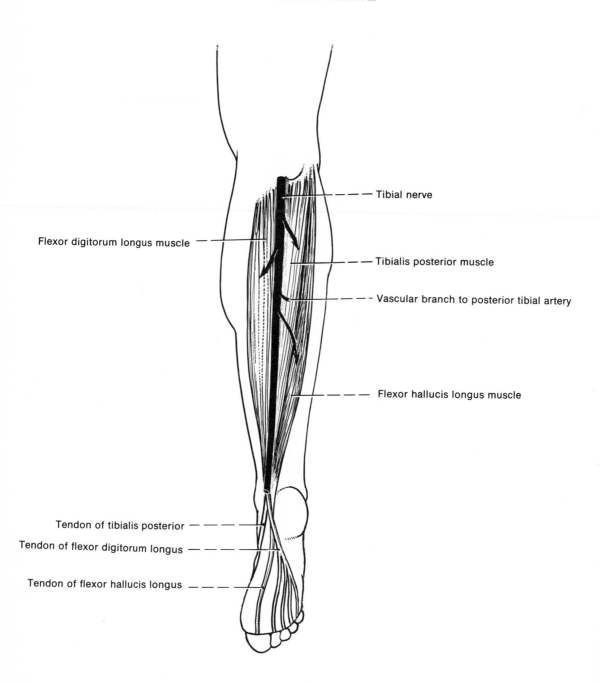

Flexor digitorum longus muscle

Tibial nerve

Tibialis posterior muscle

Vascular branch to posterior tibial artery

Flexor hallucis longus muscle

Tendon of tibialis posterior

Tendon of flexor digitorum longus

Tendon of flexor hallucis longus

LATERAL AND MEDIAL PLANTAR NERVES

ORIGIN

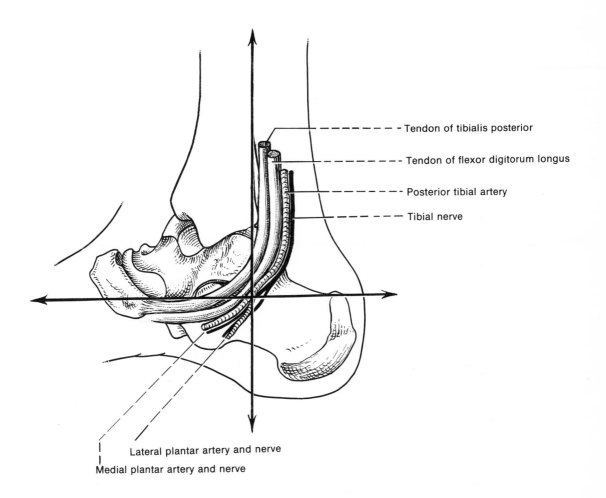

Tendon of tibialis posterior

Tendon of flexor digitorum longus

Posterior tibial artery

Tibial nerve

Lateral plantar artery and nerve

Medial plantar artery and nerve

The vertical line is the retromalleolar tangent. The horizontal line passes through the tuberosity of the navicular bone and the sustentaculum tali.

The intersection of these two lines serves as a landmark for the arterial bifurcation. The division of the tibial nerve usually overlies that of the tibial artery.

Course and Distribution of the Plantar Nerves

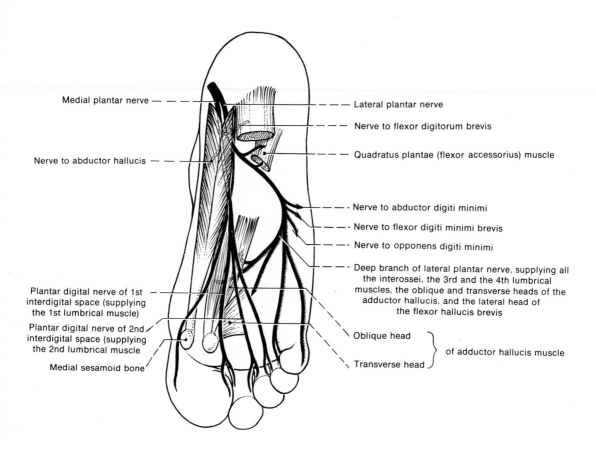

Medial plantar nerve

Nerve to abductor hallucis

Lateral plantar nerve

Nerve to flexor digitorum brevis

Quadratus plantae (flexor accessorius) muscle

Nerve to abductor digiti minimi

Nerve to flexor digiti minimi brevis

Nerve to opponens digiti minimi

Deep branch of lateral plantar nerve, supplying all the interossei, the 3rd and the 4th lumbrical muscles, the oblique and transverse heads of the adductor hallucis, and the lateral head of the flexor hallucis brevis

Plantar digital nerve of 1st interdigital space (supplying the 1st lumbrical muscle)

Plantar digital nerve of 2nd interdigital space (supplying the 2nd lumbrical muscle

Medial sesamoid bone

Oblique head

Transverse head

of adductor hallucis muscle

DIAGRAM OF THE SACRAL PLEXUS

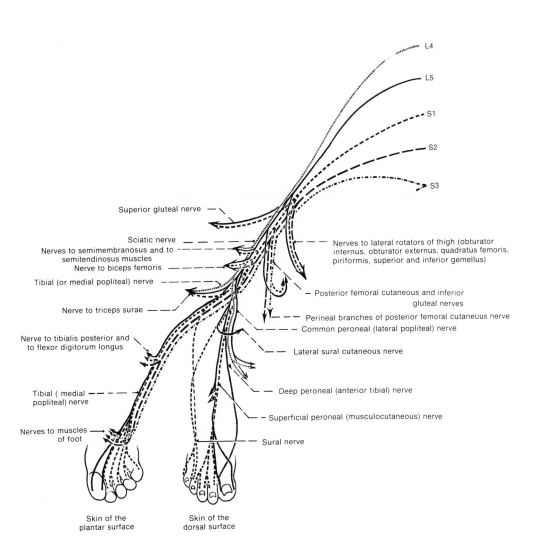

L4

L5

S1

S2

S3

Superior gluteal nerve —

Sciatic nerve —

Nerves to semimembranosus and to
semitendinosus muscles

Nerve to biceps femoris —

Tibial (or medial popliteal) nerve —

Nerve to triceps surae —

Nerve to tibialis posterior and
to flexor digitorum longus

Tibial (medial
popliteal) nerve

Nerves to muscles
of foot

Nerves to lateral rotators of thigh (obturator
internus, obturator externus, quadratus femoris,
piriformis, superior and inferior gemellus)

Posterior femoral cutaneous and inferior
gluteal nerves

Perineal branches of posterior femoral cutaneous nerve

Common peroneal (lateral popliteal) nerve

Lateral sural cutaneous nerve

Deep peroneal (anterior tibial) nerve

Superficial peroneal (musculocutaneous) nerve

Sural nerve

Skin of the
plantar surface

Skin of the
dorsal surface

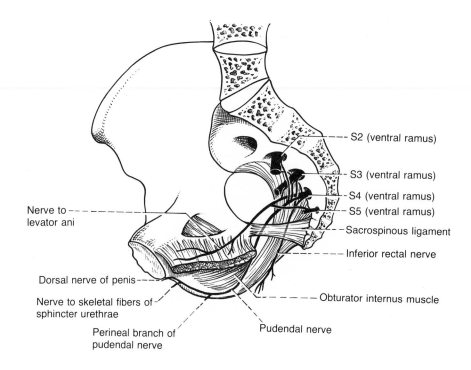

Nerve to
levator ani

S2 (ventral ramus)

S3 (ventral ramus)

S4 (ventral ramus)

S5 (ventral ramus)

Sacrospinous ligament

Inferior rectal nerve

Dorsal nerve of penis

Nerve to skeletal fibers of
sphincter urethrae

Obturator internus muscle

Perineal branch of
pudendal nerve

Pudendal nerve

INFERIOR RECTAL BRANCHES

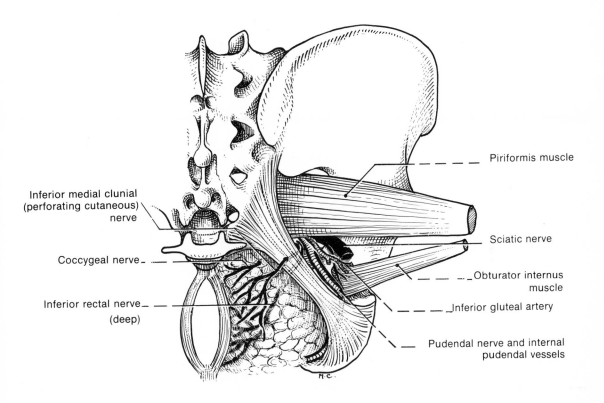

Piriformis muscle

Inferior medial clunial
(perforating cutaneous)
nerve

Sciatic nerve

Coccygeal nerve

Obturator internus
muscle

Inferior rectal nerve
(deep)

Inferior gluteal artery

Pudendal nerve and internal
pudendal vessels

PERINEAL BRANCHES

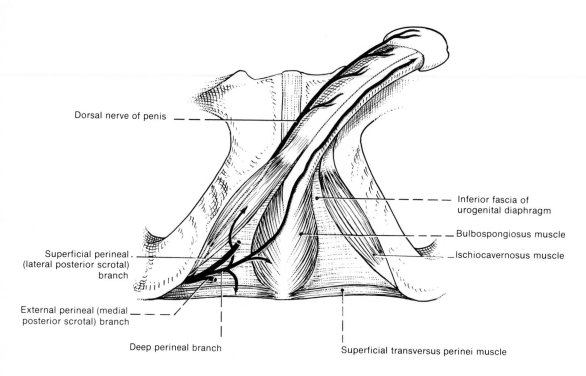

Dorsal nerve of penis

Inferior fascia of urogenital diaphragm

Bulbospongiosus muscle

Ischiocavernosus muscle

Superficial perineal (lateral posterior scrotal) branch

External perineal (medial posterior scrotal) branch

Deep perineal branch

Superficial transversus perinei muscle

The ischiobulbar triangle is narrower, almost cleftlike.

DIAGRAM OF THE PUDENDAL NERVE

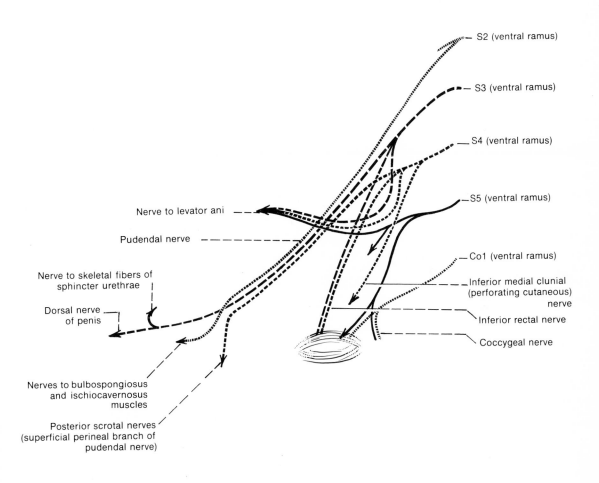

S2 (ventral ramus)

S3 (ventral ramus)

S4 (ventral ramus)

S5 (ventral ramus)

Nerve to levator ani

Pudendal nerve

Co1 (ventral ramus)

Inferior medial clunial (perforating cutaneous) nerve

Nerve to skeletal fibers of sphincter urethrae

Inferior rectal nerve

Dorsal nerve of penis

Coccygeal nerve

Nerves to bulbospongiosus and ischiocavernosus muscles

Posterior scrotal nerves (superficial perineal branch of pudendal nerve)

Coccygeal Nerve

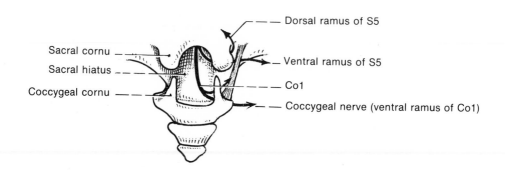

Dorsal ramus of S5

Sacral cornu

Sacral hiatus

Coccygeal cornu

Ventral ramus of S5

Co1

Coccygeal nerve (ventral ramus of Co1)

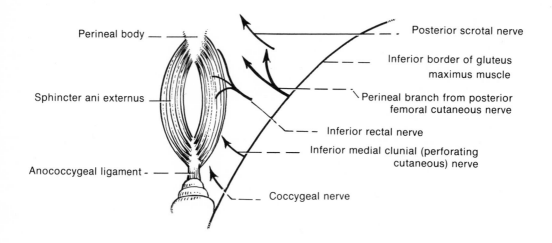

Perineal body

Sphincter ani externus

Anococcygeal ligament

Posterior scrotal nerve

Inferior border of gluteus maximus muscle

Perineal branch from posterior femoral cutaneous nerve

Inferior rectal nerve

Inferior medial clunial (perforating cutaneous) nerve

Coccygeal nerve

Segmental Motor Innervation

(Ventral Rami)

Column headings: AXIS of BODY | GIRDLES | LIMBS

Row labels (left side): C1, C2, C3, C4, C5, C6, C7, C8, T1, T2, T3, T4, T5, T6, T7, T8, T9, T10, T11, T12, L1, L2, L3, L4, L5, S1, S2, S3, S4, S5, Co1

AXIS of BODY
- Longus capitis
- Longus colli
- Infrahyoid mm.
- Diaphragm
- Serratus post. sup.
- Intercostales, subcostales, levatores costarum
- Sternalis
- Transversus thoracis
- Serratus post. inf.
- Diaphragm
- Ext. oblique
- Int. oblique
- Transversus abdom.
- Pyramidalis
- Rectus abdominis
- Quadratus lumborum
- Cremaster
- Sph. urethrae
- Sphincter ani
- Levator ani + ischiococcygeus mm.
- Mm. of anterior perineum

GIRDLES
- S.C.M. & trapezius
- Levator scap.
- Rhomb.
- Pect. major
- Subscapularis
- Serratus ant.
- Deltoid
- Teres min.
- Teres maj.
- Latissimus dorsi
- Supra & infraspinatus
- Pect. minor
- Iliopsoas
- Pelvitrochanteric mm.
- Gluteus max., med., min.
- Obturator ext.

LIMBS
- Coracobrachialis
- Biceps brachii
- Brachioradialis
- Supinator
- Ext. carp. uln.
- Lateral head
- Medial head
- Long head
- Pron. teres, palm. long. & flex. carp. radial.
- Flexor digitorum
- Flex. carp. uln.
- Short mm. of the thumb
- Triceps
- Pron. quadrat.
- Ext. digitorum
- Interossei
- Lumbricales
- Short mm. of the digit. V
- Sartorius
- Gracilis, add. brev. & magn.
- Semimemb., semitend., & bi. fem.
- Pectineus
- Add. long.
- Peroneus
- Quadriceps
- Triceps surae
- Deep post. mm.
- Ant. mm. of the leg
- Mm. of the foot
- Ext. digit. brevis

Peripheral and Segmental Sensory Innervation

ANTERIOR VIEW

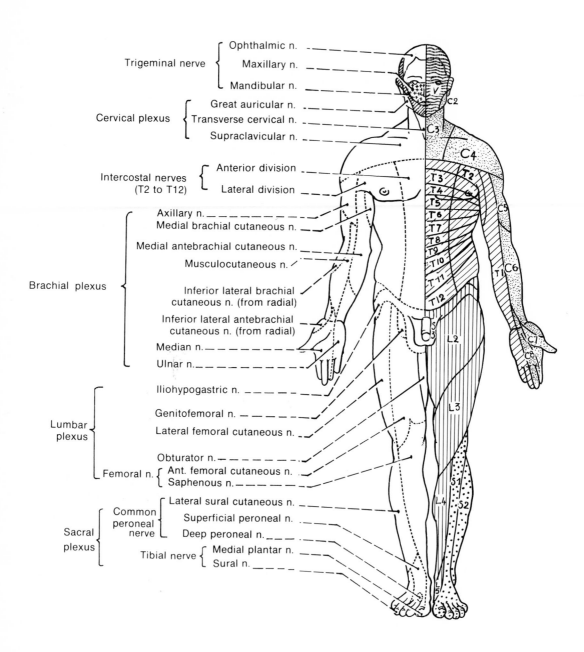

Trigeminal nerve
- Ophthalmic n.
- Maxillary n.
- Mandibular n.

Cervical plexus
- Great auricular n.
- Transverse cervical n.
- Supraclavicular n.

Intercostal nerves (T2 to T12)
- Anterior division
- Lateral division

Brachial plexus
- Axillary n.
- Medial brachial cutaneous n.
- Medial antebrachial cutaneous n.
- Musculocutaneous n.
- Inferior lateral brachial cutaneous n. (from radial)
- Inferior lateral antebrachial cutaneous n. (from radial)
- Median n.
- Ulnar n.

Lumbar plexus
- Iliohypogastric n.
- Genitofemoral n.
- Lateral femoral cutaneous n.
- Obturator n.
- Femoral n.
  - Ant. femoral cutaneous n.
  - Saphenous n.

Sacral plexus
- Common peroneal nerve
  - Lateral sural cutaneous n.
  - Superficial peroneal n.
  - Deep peroneal n.
- Tibial nerve
  - Medial plantar n.
  - Sural n.

Posterior View

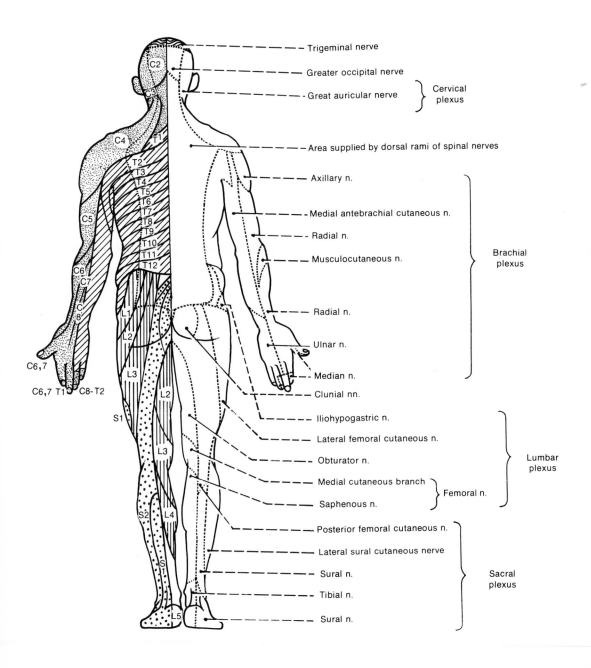

Trigeminal nerve

Greater occipital nerve

Great auricular nerve

Cervical plexus

Area supplied by dorsal rami of spinal nerves

Axillary n.

Medial antebrachial cutaneous n.

Radial n.

Musculocutaneous n.

Brachial plexus

Radial n.

Ulnar n.

Median n.

Clunial nn.

Iliohypogastric n.

Lateral femoral cutaneous n.

Obturator n.

Medial cutaneous branch

Saphenous n.

Femoral n.

Lumbar plexus

Posterior femoral cutaneous n.

Lateral sural cutaneous nerve

Sural n.

Tibial n.

Sural n.

Sacral plexus

C6,7

C6,7 T1 C8-T2

Page 105

Part Three

Central Nervous System

Spinal Cord

EXTERNAL AND GENERAL FEATURES

THE PORTIONS OF THE SPINAL CORD AND RELATIONS WITH VERTEBRAE (ANTERIOR VIEW)

SCHEMATIC DIAGRAM OF THE SPINAL GRAY MATTER ISOLATED IN SPACE

MACROSCOPIC ASPECT OF A CROSS SECTION OF THE SPINAL CORD

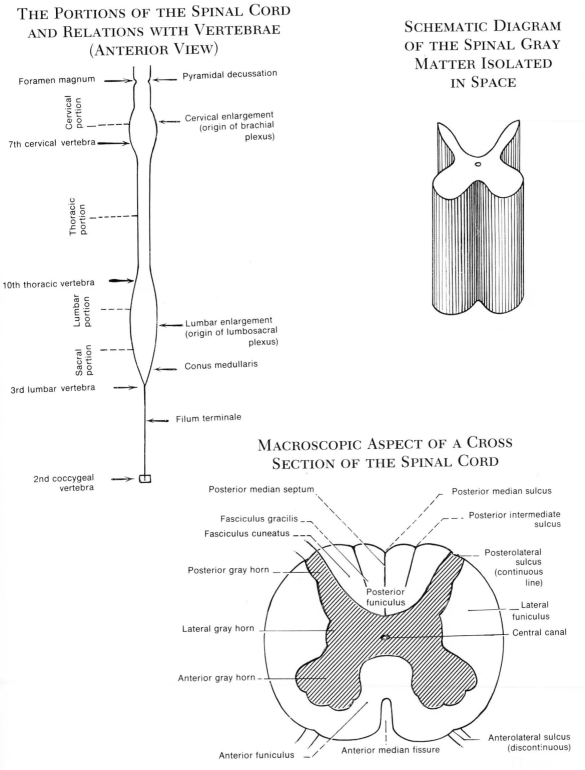

Foramen magnum → ← Pyramidal decussation

Cervical portion

Cervical enlargement (origin of brachial plexus)

7th cervical vertebra →

Thoracic portion

10th thoracic vertebra →

Lumbar portion

Lumbar enlargement (origin of lumbosacral plexus)

Sacral portion

Conus medullaris

3rd lumbar vertebra →

Filum terminale

2nd coccygeal vertebra →

Posterior median septum — Posterior median sulcus

Fasciculus gracilis — Posterior intermediate sulcus

Fasciculus cuneatus —

Posterior gray horn — Posterolateral sulcus (continuous line)

Posterior funiculus — Lateral funiculus

Lateral gray horn — Central canal

Anterior gray horn —

Anterolateral sulcus (discontinuous)

Anterior funiculus — Anterior median fissure

SCHEMATIC DIAGRAM OF THE GRAY MATTER AND THE CELL COLUMNS

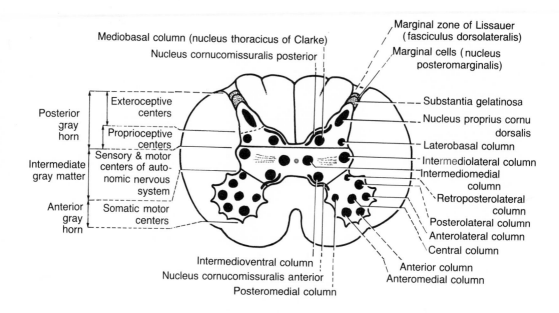

Mediobasal column (nucleus thoracicus of Clarke)
Nucleus cornucomissuralis posterior

Marginal zone of Lissauer (fasciculus dorsolateralis)
Marginal cells (nucleus posteromarginalis)

Posterior gray horn
Intermediate gray matter
Anterior gray horn

Exteroceptive centers
Proprioceptive centers
Sensory & motor centers of autonomic nervous system
Somatic motor centers

Substantia gelatinosa
Nucleus proprius cornu dorsalis
Laterobasal column
Intermediolateral column
Intermediomedial column
Retroposterolateral column
Posterolateral column
Anterolateral column
Central column
Anterior column
Anteromedial column

Intermedioventral column
Nucleus cornucomissuralis anterior
Posteromedial column

MOTOR CENTERS

Functional Localizations of
the Anterior Horns

(From the works of Foerster, Kappers, and Delmas)

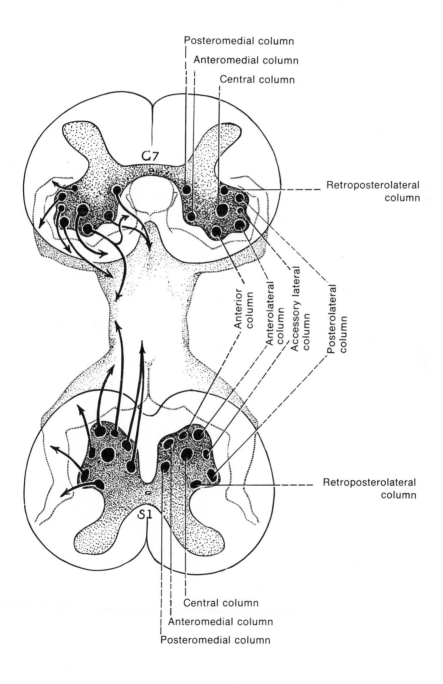

Posteromedial column

Anteromedial column

Central column

C7

Retroposterolateral column

Anterior column

Anterolateral column

Accessory lateral column

Posterolateral column

Retroposterolateral column

S1

Central column

Anteromedial column

Posteromedial column

SEGMENTAL SENSORY CENTERS

SEGMENTAL MOTOR CENTERS

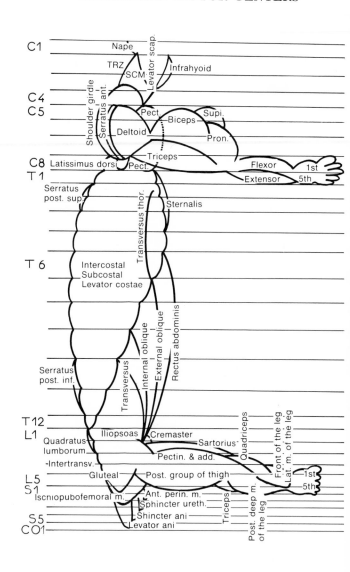

SPINAL AUTONOMIC CENTERS

AUTONOMIC COLUMNS OF THE SPINAL CORD

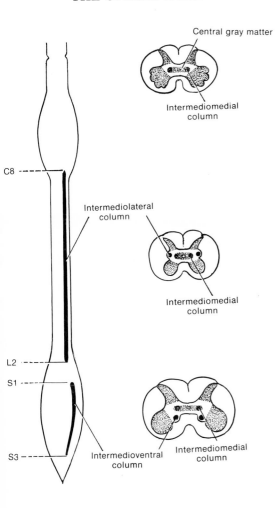

Central gray matter

Intermediomedial column

Intermediolateral column

Intermediomedial column

Intermedioventral column

Intermediomedial column

C8

L2

S1

S3

TOPOGRAPHY OF THE SEGMENTAL CENTERS OF VISCERA AND DIAPHRAGM

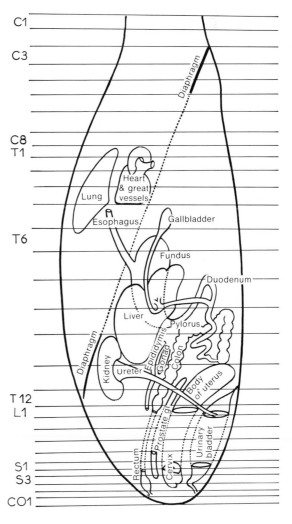

WHITE MATTER: ASCENDING TRACTS

PATHWAYS AND SYNAPTIC JUNCTIONS OF THE ASCENDING TRACTS OF EXTEROCEPTIVE SENSIBILITY

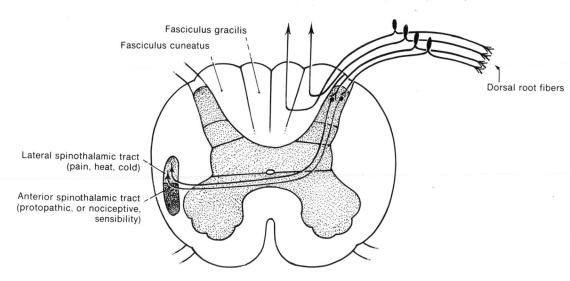

Epicritic sensibility (touch, pressure)

Fasciculus gracilis

Fasciculus cuneatus

Dorsal root fibers

Lateral spinothalamic tract
(pain, heat, cold)

Anterior spinothalamic tract
(protopathic, or nociceptive,
sensibility)

PATHWAYS AND SYNAPTIC JUNCTIONS OF THE ASCENDING TRACTS OF PROPRIOCEPTIVE SENSIBILITY

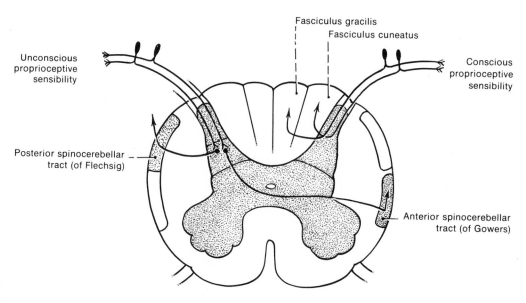

Fasciculus gracilis

Fasciculus cuneatus

Unconscious
proprioceptive
sensibility

Conscious
proprioceptive
sensibility

Posterior spinocerebellar
tract (of Flechsig)

Anterior spinocerebellar
tract (of Gowers)

WHITE MATTER: DESCENDING TRACTS

Pathways and Synaptic Junctions of the Pyrimidal System

The anterolateral pyramidal tract of Barnes, not represented on this drawing, is formed by uncrossed and fine corticospinal fibers.

The majority of pyramidal fibers are projected upon the anterior horn cells through internuncial cells.

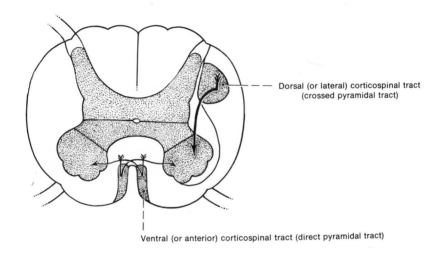

Dorsal (or lateral) corticospinal tract
(crossed pyramidal tract)

Ventral (or anterior) corticospinal tract (direct pyramidal tract)

Pathways and Synaptic Junctions of the Extrapyramidal System

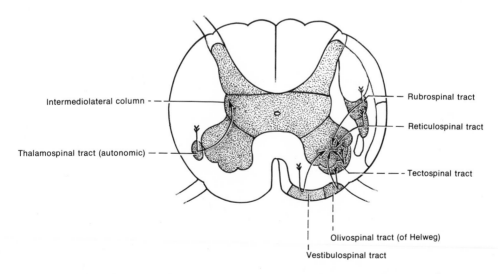

Intermediolateral column

Thalamospinal tract (autonomic)

Rubrospinal tract

Reticulospinal tract

Tectospinal tract

Olivospinal tract (of Helweg)

Vestibulospinal tract

The *final common pathway* is formed by the axons of the α-motor neurons, located in the ventral horn and receiving all the impulses of the descending tracts.

WHITE MATTER: SPINAL ASSOCIATION FIBERS

FASCICULI PROPRII (SPINOSPINAL FIBERS, INTERSEGMENTAL FIBERS)

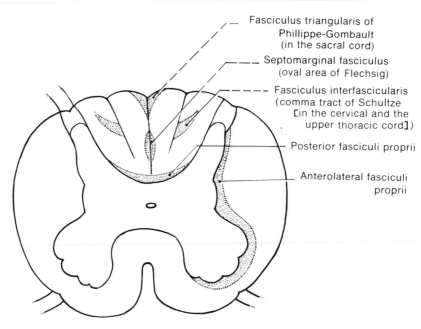

Fasciculus triangularis of
Phillippe-Gombault
(in the sacral cord)

Septomarginal fasciculus
(oval area of Flechsig)

Fasciculus interfascicularis
(comma tract of Schultze
[in the cervical and the
upper thoracic cord])

Posterior fasciculi proprii

Anterolateral fasciculi
proprii

SYNTHETIC DIAGRAM OF THE SPINAL WHITE MATTER

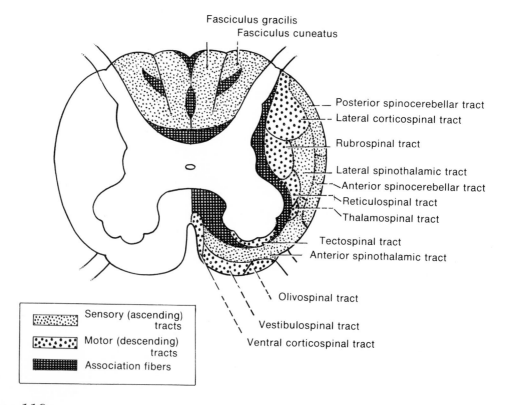

Fasciculus gracilis
Fasciculus cuneatus

Posterior spinocerebellar tract
Lateral corticospinal tract

Rubrospinal tract

Lateral spinothalamic tract
Anterior spinocerebellar tract
Reticulospinal tract
Thalamospinal tract

Tectospinal tract
Anterior spinothalamic tract

Olivospinal tract

Vestibulospinal tract

Ventral corticospinal tract

Sensory (ascending)
tracts
Motor (descending)
tracts
Association fibers

Page 116

NEUROGLIA OF THE SPINAL CORD

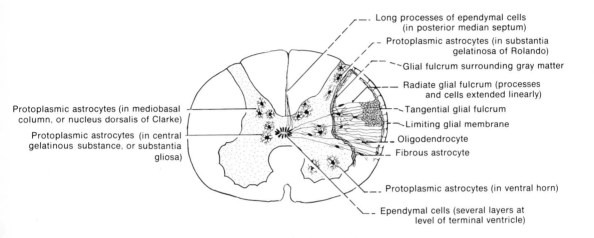

Long processes of ependymal cells
(in posterior median septum)

Protoplasmic astrocytes (in substantia
gelatinosa of Rolando)

Glial fulcrum surrounding gray matter

Radiate glial fulcrum (processes
and cells extended linearly)

Tangential glial fulcrum

Limiting glial membrane

Oligodendrocyte

Fibrous astrocyte

Protoplasmic astrocytes (in ventral horn)

Ependymal cells (several layers at
level of terminal ventricle)

Protoplasmic astrocytes (in mediobasal
column, or nucleus dorsalis of Clarke)

Protoplasmic astrocytes (in central
gelatinous substance, or substantia
gliosa)

NERVE CELLS OF THE SPINAL CORD

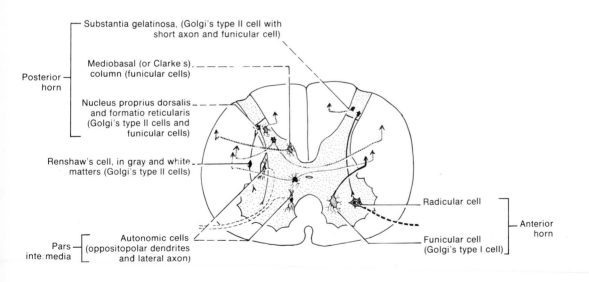

Substantia gelatinosa, (Golgi's type II cell with
short axon and funicular cell)

Mediobasal (or Clarke's)
column (funicular cells)

Nucleus proprius dorsalis
and formatio reticularis
(Golgi's type II cells and
funicular cells)

Renshaw's cell, in gray and white
matters (Golgi's type II cells)

Posterior
horn

Radicular cell

Anterior
horn

Autonomic cells
(oppositopolar dendrites
and lateral axon)

Funicular cell
(Golgi's type I cell)

Pars
inte media

Page 117

Brain Stem

EXTERNAL FEATURES

Ventral Aspect

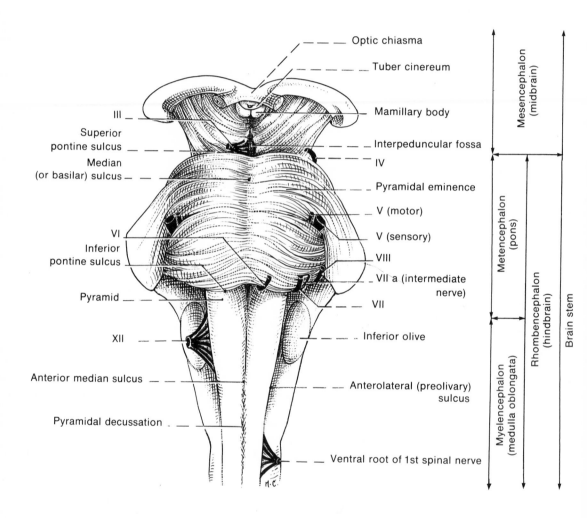

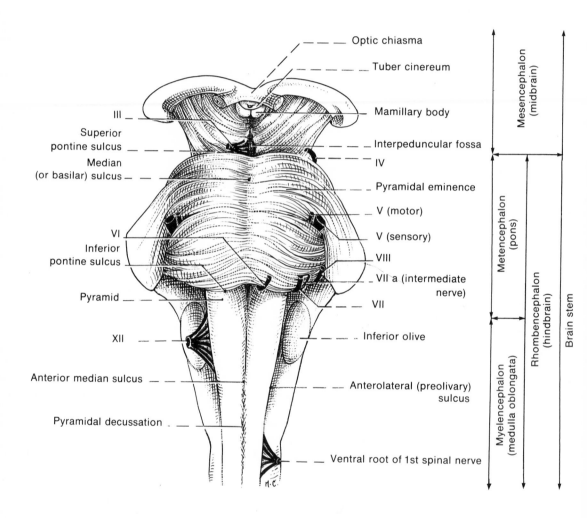

Optic chiasma

Tuber cinereum

Mamillary body

III

Superior pontine sulcus

Interpeduncular fossa

Median (or basilar) sulcus

IV

Pyramidal eminence

V (motor)

VI

V (sensory)

Inferior pontine sulcus

VIII

VII a (intermediate nerve)

Pyramid

VII

XII

Inferior olive

Anterior median sulcus

Anterolateral (preolivary) sulcus

Pyramidal decussation

Ventral root of 1st spinal nerve

Mesencephalon (midbrain)

Metencephalon (pons)

Rhombencephalon (hindbrain)

Myelencephalon (medulla oblongata)

Brain stem

LATERAL ASPECT

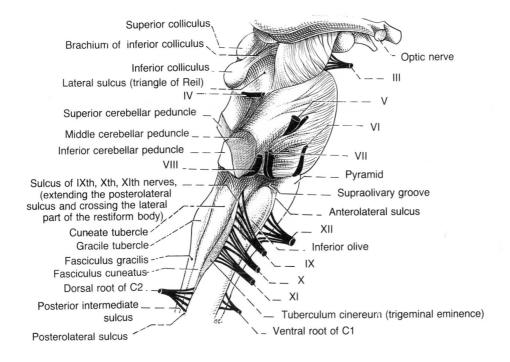

Superior colliculus

Brachium of inferior colliculus

Inferior colliculus

Lateral sulcus (triangle of Reil)

IV

Superior cerebellar peduncle

Middle cerebellar peduncle

Inferior cerebellar peduncle

VIII

Sulcus of IXth, Xth, XIth nerves,
(extending the posterolateral
sulcus and crossing the lateral
part of the restiform body)

Cuneate tubercle

Gracile tubercle

Fasciculus gracilis

Fasciculus cuneatus

Dorsal root of C2

Posterior intermediate
sulcus

Posterolateral sulcus

Optic nerve

III

V

VI

VII

Pyramid

Supraolivary groove

Anterolateral sulcus

XII

Inferior olive

IX

X

XI

Tuberculum cinereum (trigeminal eminence)

Ventral root of C1

Dorsal Aspect

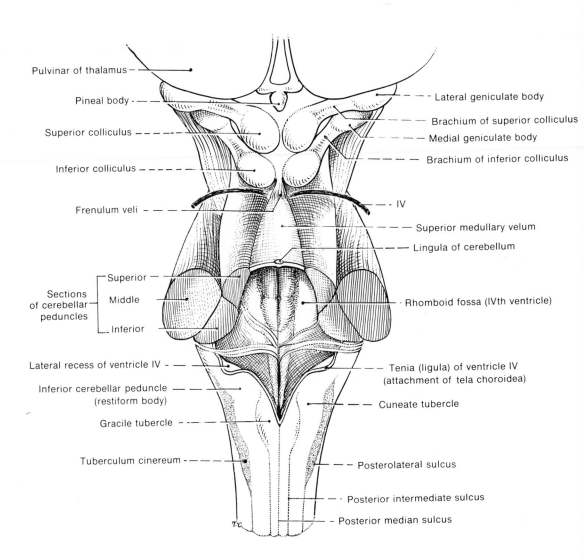

Pulvinar of thalamus

Pineal body

Superior colliculus

Inferior colliculus

Frenulum veli

Sections of cerebellar peduncles
- Superior
- Middle
- Inferior

Lateral recess of ventricle IV

Inferior cerebellar peduncle (restiform body)

Gracile tubercle

Tuberculum cinereum

Lateral geniculate body

Brachium of superior colliculus

Medial geniculate body

Brachium of inferior colliculus

IV

Superior medullary velum

Lingula of cerebellum

Rhomboid fossa (IVth ventricle)

Tenia (ligula) of ventricle IV (attachment of tela choroidea)

Cuneate tubercle

Posterolateral sulcus

Posterior intermediate sulcus

Posterior median sulcus

FLOOR OF THE FOURTH VENTRICLE

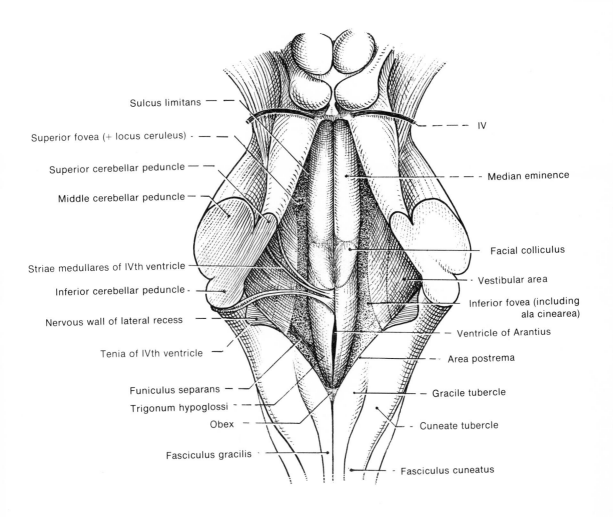

Sulcus limitans

Superior fovea (+ locus ceruleus)

Superior cerebellar peduncle

Middle cerebellar peduncle

Striae medullares of IVth ventricle

Inferior cerebellar peduncle

Nervous wall of lateral recess

Tenia of IVth ventricle

Funiculus separans

Trigonum hypoglossi

Obex

Fasciculus gracilis

IV

Median eminence

Facial colliculus

Vestibular area

Inferior fovea (including ala cinearea)

Ventricle of Arantius

Area postrema

Gracile tubercle

Cuneate tubercle

Fasciculus cuneatus

ROOF OF THE FOURTH VENTRICLE

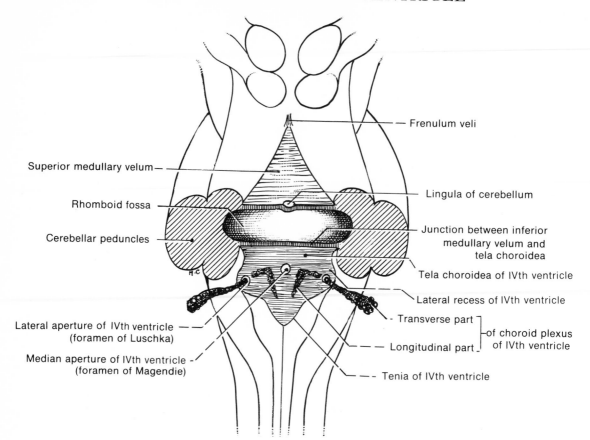

Frenulum veli

Superior medullary velum—

Lingula of cerebellum

Rhomboid fossa

Junction between inferior
medullary velum and
tela choroidea

Cerebellar peduncles

Tela choroidea of IVth ventricle

Lateral recess of IVth ventricle

Transverse part ⌉
of choroid plexus
of IVth ventricle

Lateral aperture of IVth ventricle — —
(foramen of Luschka)

Longitudinal part ⌋

Median aperture of IVth ventricle -
(foramen of Magendie)

Tenia of IVth ventricle

SAGITTAL SECTION OF
THE BRAIN STEM

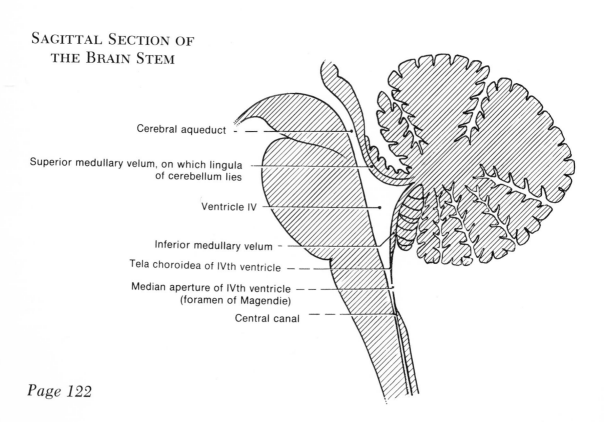

Cerebral aqueduct - —

Superior medullary velum, on which lingula
of cerebellum lies

Ventricle IV

Inferior medullary velum -

Tela choroidea of IVth ventricle — —

Median aperture of IVth ventricle — —
(foramen of Magendie)

Central canal

GRAY MATTER OF THE BRAIN STEM
SEGMENTAL FORMATIONS, NUCLEI OF THE CRANIAL NERVES

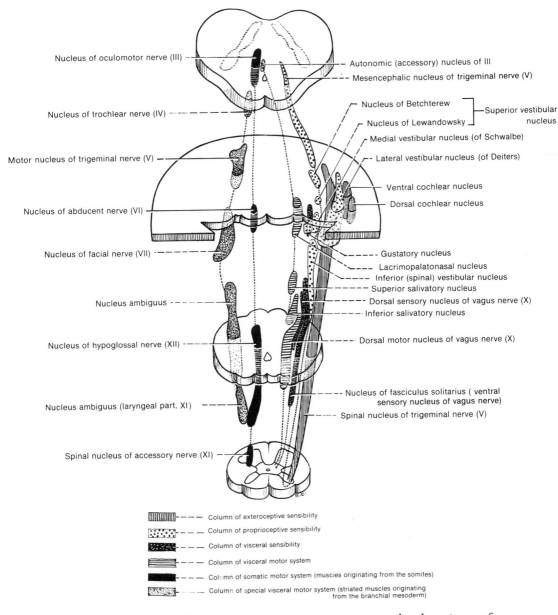

Nucleus of oculomotor nerve (III)

Autonomic (accessory) nucleus of III

Mesencephalic nucleus of trigeminal nerve (V)

Nucleus of Betchterew

Nucleus of Lewandowsky

Superior vestibular nucleus

Nucleus of trochlear nerve (IV)

Medial vestibular nucleus (of Schwalbe)

Lateral vestibular nucleus (of Deiters)

Motor nucleus of trigeminal nerve (V)

Ventral cochlear nucleus

Dorsal cochlear nucleus

Nucleus of abducent nerve (VI)

Gustatory nucleus

Lacrimopalatonasal nucleus

Inferior (spinal) vestibular nucleus

Superior salivatory nucleus

Dorsal sensory nucleus of vagus nerve (X)

Inferior salivatory nucleus

Nucleus of facial nerve (VII)

Nucleus ambiguus

Dorsal motor nucleus of vagus nerve (X)

Nucleus of hypoglossal nerve (XII)

Nucleus of fasciculus solitarius (ventral sensory nucleus of vagus nerve)

Spinal nucleus of trigeminal nerve (V)

Nucleus ambiguus (laryngeal part, XI)

Spinal nucleus of accessory nerve (XI)

Column of exteroceptive sensibility

Column of proprioceptive sensibility

Column of visceral sensibility

Column of visceral motor system

Column of somatic motor system (muscles originating from the somites)

Column of special visceral motor system (striated muscles originating from the branchial mesoderm)

There are differences of opinion concerning the locations of some nuclei in this diagram:

Kappers situates the nucleus of the trochlear nerve in the special visceral motor column, as in the above figure; Braus and Delmas place it in the somatic motor column with other motor ocular nuclei.

The spinal nucleus of the accessory nerve (XI) is located in the special visceral motor column by Straus and Howell, Clara, Goerttler.

Delmas divides the sensory columns into:

column of special visceral sensibility (nucleus of the fasciculus solitarius, gustatory nucleus, sensory nuclei of V)

column of somatic sensibility (auditory and vestibular)

Unsegmented Formations of the Brain Stem

Schematic lateral aspect*

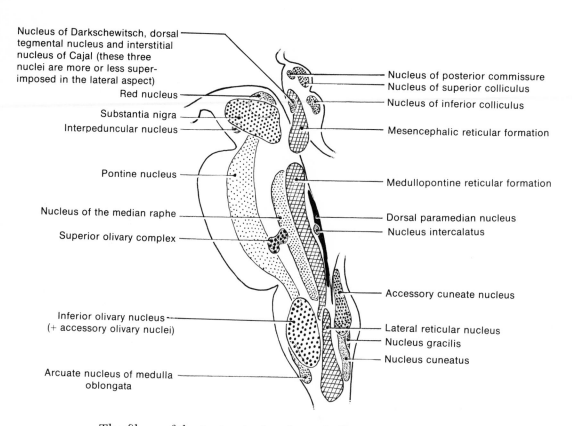

Nucleus of Darkschewitsch, dorsal tegmental nucleus and interstitial nucleus of Cajal (these three nuclei are more or less super-imposed in the lateral aspect)

Red nucleus

Substantia nigra

Interpeduncular nucleus

Pontine nucleus

Nucleus of the median raphe

Superior olivary complex

Inferior olivary nucleus (+ accessory olivary nuclei)

Arcuate nucleus of medulla oblongata

Nucleus of posterior commissure
Nucleus of superior colliculus
Nucleus of inferior colliculus

Mesencephalic reticular formation

Medullopontine reticular formation

Dorsal paramedian nucleus
Nucleus intercalatus

Accessory cuneate nucleus

Lateral reticular nucleus
Nucleus gracilis
Nucleus cuneatus

The fibers of the tectospinal and tectobulbar tracts originate from the motor neurons of the deep layer of the superior colliculus. Sometimes this group of motor neurons is called the tectal nucleus.

*In part from Cuba, J. M.: Les formations non segmentaires du tronc cérébral de l'homme. In Mémoires du Laboratoire de la Faculté de Médecine de Paris, No. 1, 1962.

CHOROID PLEXUSES AND TELA CHOROIDEA OF THE FOURTH VENTRICLE

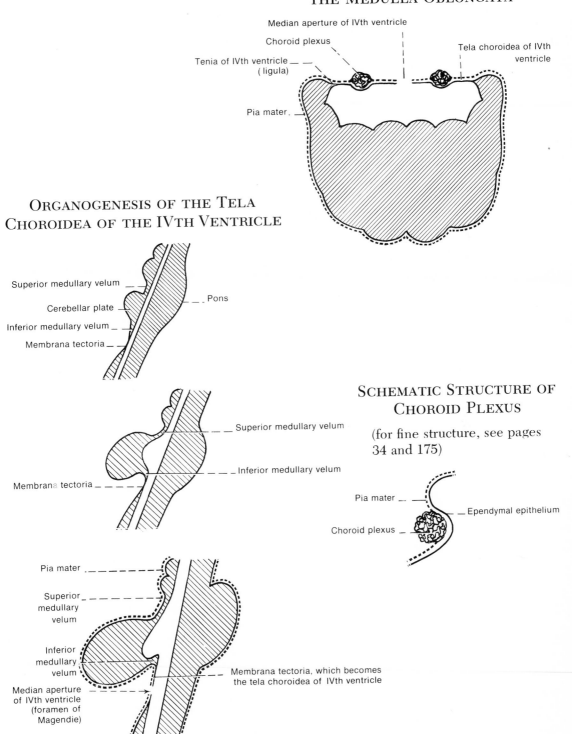

SCHEMATIC TRANSVERSE SECTION OF THE MEDULLA OBLONGATA

Median aperture of IVth ventricle

Choroid plexus

Tela choroidea of IVth ventricle

Tenia of IVth ventricle (ligula)

Pia mater

ORGANOGENESIS OF THE TELA CHOROIDEA OF THE IVTH VENTRICLE

Superior medullary velum

Cerebellar plate

Inferior medullary velum

Membrana tectoria

Pons

Superior medullary velum

Inferior medullary velum

Membrana tectoria

SCHEMATIC STRUCTURE OF CHOROID PLEXUS

(for fine structure, see pages 34 and 175)

Pia mater

Ependymal epithelium

Choroid plexus

Pia mater

Superior medullary velum

Inferior medullary velum

Median aperture of IVth ventricle (foramen of Magendie)

Membrana tectoria, which becomes the tela choroidea of IVth ventricle

LATERAL ASPECT OF THE BRAIN STEM

The lines indicate the levels and the directions of the sections that follow.

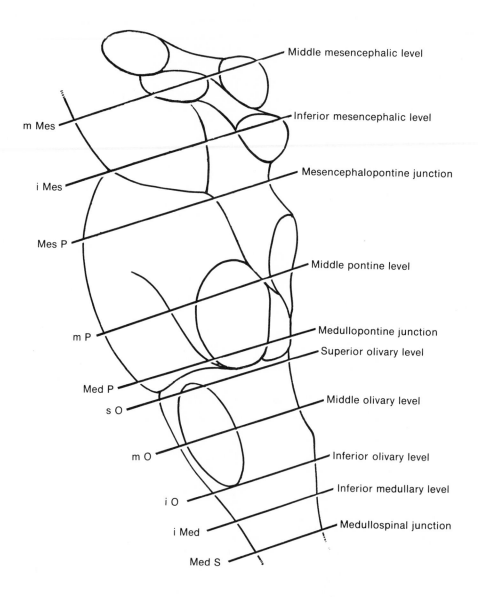

Middle mesencephalic level

Inferior mesencephalic level

m Mes

Mesencephalopontine junction

i Mes

Mes P

Middle pontine level

Medullopontine junction

m P

Superior olivary level

Med P

Middle olivary level

s O

m O

Inferior olivary level

Inferior medullary level

i O

Medullospinal junction

i Med

Med S

"Med S" Level

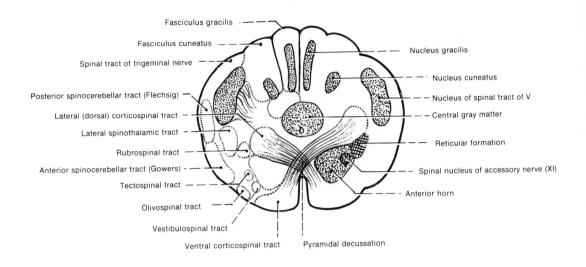

Fasciculus gracilis
Fasciculus cuneatus
Spinal tract of trigeminal nerve
Posterior spinocerebellar tract (Flechsig)
Lateral (dorsal) corticospinal tract
Lateral spinothalamic tract
Rubrospinal tract
Anterior spinocerebellar tract (Gowers)
Tectospinal tract
Olivospinal tract
Vestibulospinal tract
Ventral corticospinal tract

Nucleus gracilis
Nucleus cuneatus
Nucleus of spinal tract of V
Central gray matter
Reticular formation
Spinal nucleus of accessory nerve (XI)
Anterior horn
Pyramidal decussation

"I Med" Level

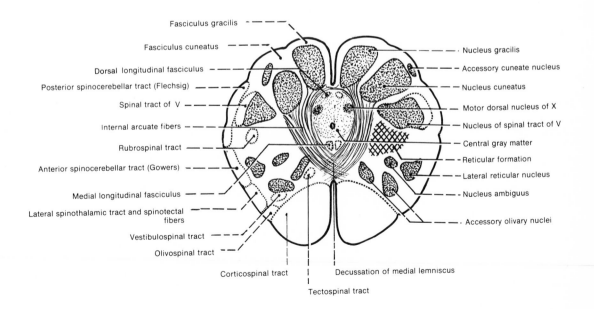

Fasciculus gracilis
Fasciculus cuneatus
Dorsal longitudinal fasciculus
Posterior spinocerebellar tract (Flechsig)
Spinal tract of V
Internal arcuate fibers
Rubrospinal tract
Anterior spinocerebellar tract (Gowers)
Medial longitudinal fasciculus
Lateral spinothalamic tract and spinotectal fibers
Vestibulospinal tract
Olivospinal tract

Nucleus gracilis
Accessory cuneate nucleus
Nucleus cuneatus
Motor dorsal nucleus of X
Nucleus of spinal tract of V
Central gray matter
Reticular formation
Lateral reticular nucleus
Nucleus ambiguus
Accessory olivary nuclei

Corticospinal tract
Tectospinal tract
Decussation of medial lemniscus

Page 127

"I O" Level

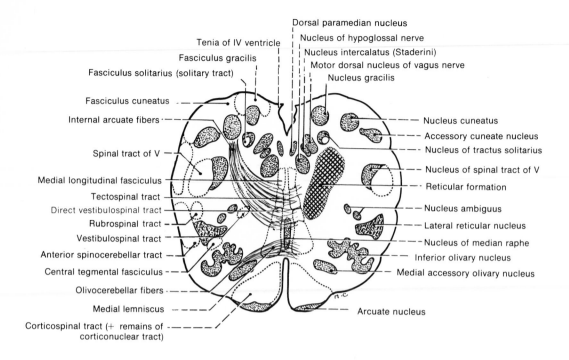

Dorsal paramedian nucleus
Nucleus of hypoglossal nerve
Nucleus intercalatus (Staderini)
Motor dorsal nucleus of vagus nerve
Nucleus gracilis

Tenia of IV ventricle
Fasciculus gracilis
Fasciculus solitarius (solitary tract)
Fasciculus cuneatus
Internal arcuate fibers
Spinal tract of V
Medial longitudinal fasciculus
Tectospinal tract
Direct vestibulospinal tract
Rubrospinal tract
Vestibulospinal tract
Anterior spinocerebellar tract
Central tegmental fasciculus
Olivocerebellar fibers
Medial lemniscus
Corticospinal tract (+ remains of corticonuclear tract)

Nucleus cuneatus
Accessory cuneate nucleus
Nucleus of tractus solitarius
Nucleus of spinal tract of V
Reticular formation
Nucleus ambiguus
Lateral reticular nucleus
Nucleus of median raphe
Inferior olivary nucleus
Medial accessory olivary nucleus
Arcuate nucleus

"M O" Level

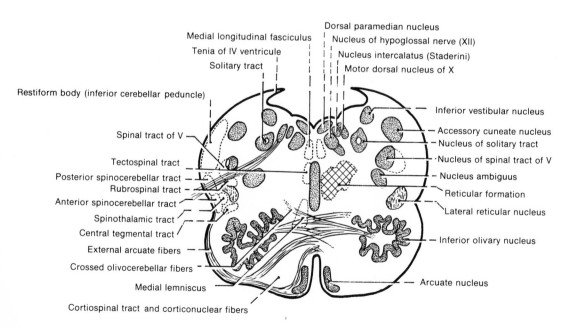

Dorsal paramedian nucleus
Nucleus of hypoglossal nerve (XII)
Nucleus intercalatus (Staderini)
Motor dorsal nucleus of X

Medial longitudinal fasciculus
Tenia of IV ventricule
Solitary tract
Restiform body (inferior cerebellar peduncle)
Spinal tract of V
Tectospinal tract
Posterior spinocerebellar tract
Rubrospinal tract
Anterior spinocerebellar tract
Spinothalamic tract
Central tegmental tract
External arcuate fibers
Crossed olivocerebellar fibers
Medial lemniscus
Cortiospinal tract and corticonuclear fibers

Inferior vestibular nucleus
Accessory cuneate nucleus
Nucleus of solitary tract
Nucleus of spinal tract of V
Nucleus ambiguus
Reticular formation
Lateral reticular nucleus
Inferior olivary nucleus
Arcuate nucleus

"s O" Level

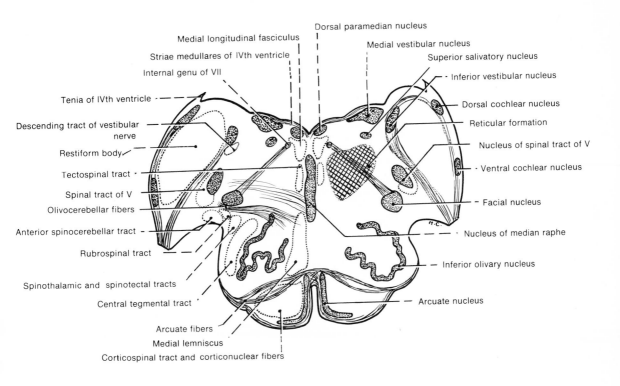

Medial longitudinal fasciculus
Striae medullares of IVth ventricle
Internal genu of VII
Tenia of IVth ventricle
Descending tract of vestibular nerve
Restiform body
Tectospinal tract
Spinal tract of V
Olivocerebellar fibers
Anterior spinocerebellar tract
Rubrospinal tract
Spinothalamic and spinotectal tracts
Central tegmental tract
Arcuate fibers
Medial lemniscus
Corticospinal tract and corticonuclear fibers

Dorsal paramedian nucleus
Medial vestibular nucleus
Superior salivatory nucleus
Inferior vestibular nucleus
Dorsal cochlear nucleus
Reticular formation
Nucleus of spinal tract of V
Ventral cochlear nucleus
Facial nucleus
Nucleus of median raphe
Inferior olivary nucleus
Arcuate nucleus

"Med P" Level

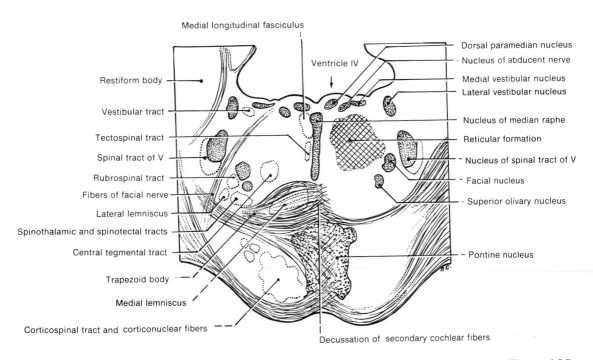

Medial longitudinal fasciculus
Ventricle IV
Restiform body
Vestibular tract
Tectospinal tract
Spinal tract of V
Rubrospinal tract
Fibers of facial nerve
Lateral lemniscus
Spinothalamic and spinotectal tracts
Central tegmental tract
Trapezoid body
Medial lemniscus
Corticospinal tract and corticonuclear fibers

Dorsal paramedian nucleus
Nucleus of abducent nerve
Medial vestibular nucleus
Lateral vestibular nucleus
Nucleus of median raphe
Reticular formation
Nucleus of spinal tract of V
Facial nucleus
Superior olivary nucleus
Pontine nucleus

Decussation of secondary cochlear fibers

"M P" Level

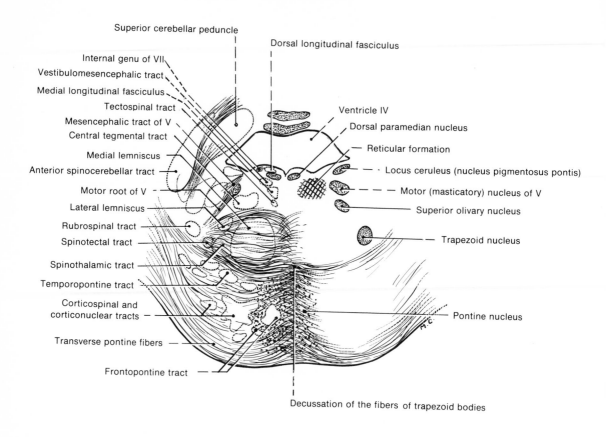

Superior cerebellar peduncle

Internal genu of VII

Vestibulomesencephalic tract

Medial longitudinal fasciculus

Tectospinal tract

Mesencephalic tract of V

Central tegmental tract

Medial lemniscus

Anterior spinocerebellar tract

Motor root of V

Lateral lemniscus

Rubrospinal tract

Spinotectal tract

Spinothalamic tract

Temporopontine tract

Corticospinal and corticonuclear tracts

Transverse pontine fibers

Frontopontine tract

Dorsal longitudinal fasciculus

Ventricle IV

Dorsal paramedian nucleus

Reticular formation

Locus ceruleus (nucleus pigmentosus pontis)

Motor (masticatory) nucleus of V

Superior olivary nucleus

Trapezoid nucleus

Pontine nucleus

Decussation of the fibers of trapezoid bodies

"Mes P" Level

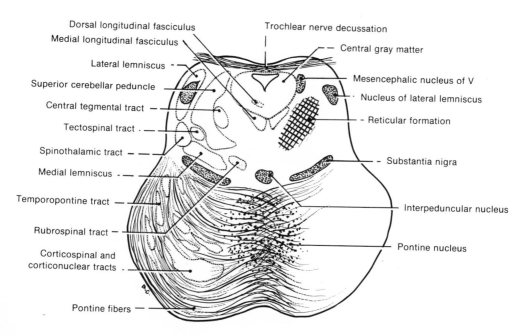

Dorsal longitudinal fasciculus

Medial longitudinal fasciculus

Lateral lemniscus

Superior cerebellar peduncle

Central tegmental tract

Tectospinal tract

Spinothalamic tract

Medial lemniscus

Temporopontine tract

Rubrospinal tract

Corticospinal and corticonuclear tracts

Pontine fibers

Trochlear nerve decussation

Central gray matter

Mesencephalic nucleus of V

Nucleus of lateral lemniscus

Reticular formation

Substantia nigra

Interpeduncular nucleus

Pontine nucleus

"I Mes" Level

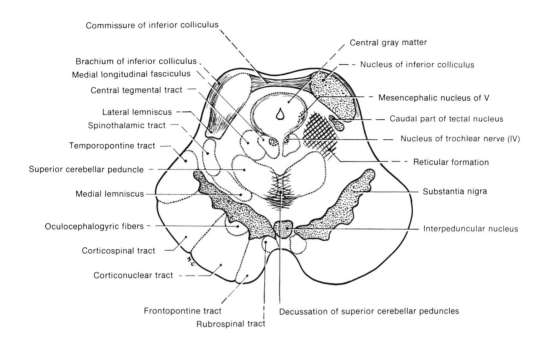

Commissure of inferior colliculus

Brachium of inferior colliculus
Medial longitudinal fasciculus
Central tegmental tract

Lateral lemniscus
Spinothalamic tract

Temporopontine tract

Superior cerebellar peduncle

Medial lemniscus

Oculocephalogyric fibers

Corticospinal tract

Corticonuclear tract

Central gray matter
Nucleus of inferior colliculus

Mesencephalic nucleus of V
Caudal part of tectal nucleus
Nucleus of trochlear nerve (IV)
Reticular formation

Substantia nigra

Interpeduncular nucleus

Frontopontine tract
Rubrospinal tract

Decussation of superior cerebellar peduncles

"M Mes" Level

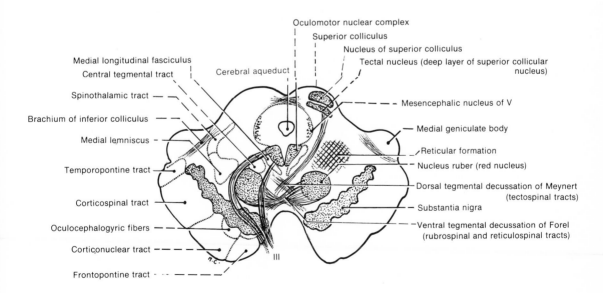

Oculomotor nuclear complex
Superior colliculus
Nucleus of superior colliculus
Tectal nucleus (deep layer of superior collicular nucleus)

Medial longitudinal fasciculus
Central tegmental tract
Cerebral aqueduct

Spinothalamic tract

Brachium of inferior colliculus

Medial lemniscus

Temporopontine tract

Corticospinal tract

Oculocephalogyric fibers

Corticonuclear tract

Frontopontine tract

Mesencephalic nucleus of V

Medial geniculate body

Reticular formation
Nucleus ruber (red nucleus)
Dorsal tegmental decussation of Meynert (tectospinal tracts)
Substantia nigra
Ventral tegmental decussation of Forel (rubrospinal and reticulospinal tracts)

III

LATERAL ASPECT OF THE GREAT PATHWAYS
LOCATED IN THE BRAIN STEM

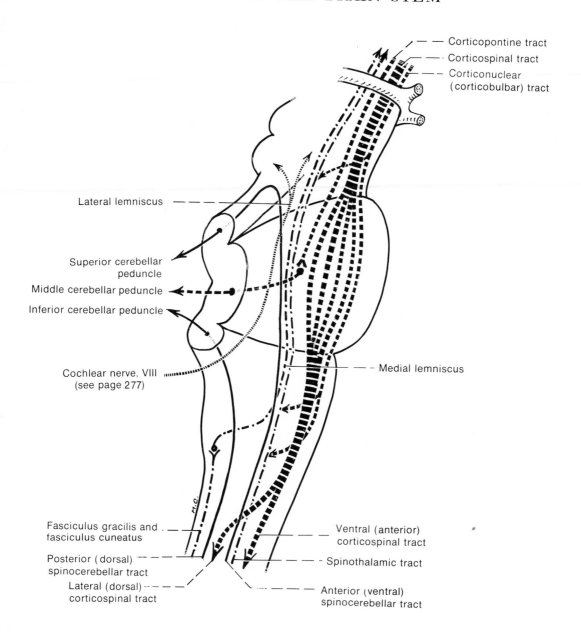

Corticopontine tract

Corticospinal tract

Corticonuclear (corticobulbar) tract

Lateral lemniscus

Superior cerebellar peduncle

Middle cerebellar peduncle

Inferior cerebellar peduncle

Cochlear nerve, VIII (see page 277)

Medial lemniscus

Fasciculus gracilis and fasciculus cuneatus

Ventral (anterior) corticospinal tract

Posterior (dorsal) spinocerebellar tract

Spinothalamic tract

Lateral (dorsal) corticospinal tract

Anterior (ventral) spinocerebellar tract

Cerebellum

Median Section of the Vermis

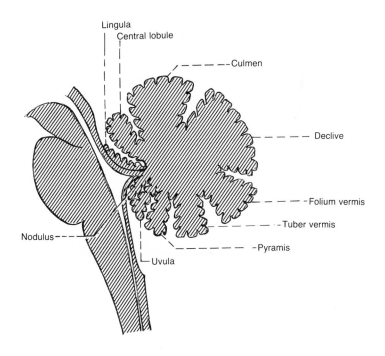

Lingula
Central lobule
Culmen
Declive
Folium vermis
Tuber vermis
Pyramis
Nodulus
Uvula

Superior View of the Cerebellum, Showing the Surface Applied Against the Tentorium Cerebelli

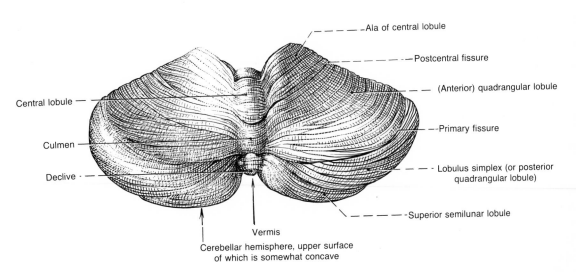

Ala of central lobule
Postcentral fissure
(Anterior) quadrangular lobule
Central lobule
Primary fissure
Culmen
Lobulus simplex (or posterior quadrangular lobule)
Declive
Superior semilunar lobule
Vermis
Cerebellar hemisphere, upper surface of which is somewhat concave

INFERIOR ASPECT OF THE CEREBELLUM

The surface is convex and rests on the cerebellar fossae of the occipital bone

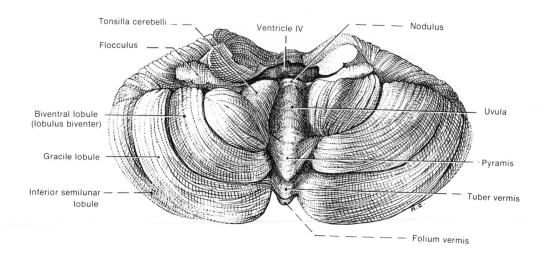

Tonsilla cerebelli — Ventricle IV — Nodulus
Flocculus —
Biventral lobule (lobulus biventer) — Uvula
Gracile lobule — Pyramis
Inferior semilunar lobule — Tuber vermis
Folium vermis

ANTERIOR ASPECT OF THE CEREBELLUM

The cerebellar peduncles have been cut in order to remove the brain stem which hides its middle portion

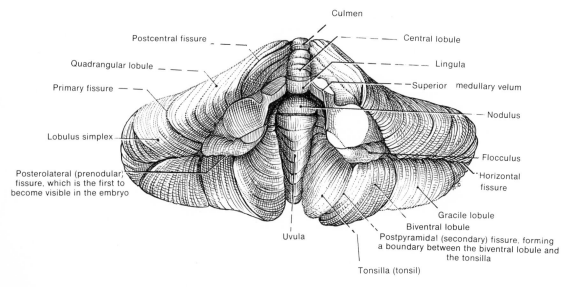

Culmen
Postcentral fissure — Central lobule
Quadrangular lobule — Lingula
Primary fissure — Superior medullary velum
Nodulus
Lobulus simplex — Flocculus
Posterolateral (prenodular) fissure, which is the first to become visible in the embryo — Horizontal fissure
Gracile lobule
Biventral lobule
Uvula — Postpyramidal (secondary) fissure, forming a boundary between the biventral lobule and the tonsilla
Tonsilla (tonsil)

GRAY MATTER OF THE CEREBELLUM

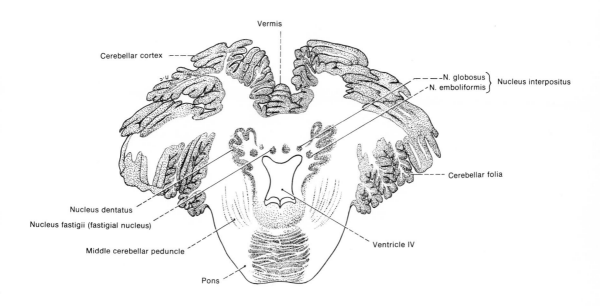

Vermis

Cerebellar cortex

N. globosus
N. emboliformis
Nucleus interpositus

Cerebellar folia

Nucleus dentatus

Nucleus fastigii (fastigial nucleus)

Middle cerebellar peduncle

Ventricle IV

Pons

SCHEMATIC DIAGRAM ACCORDING TO JANSEN AND BRODAL

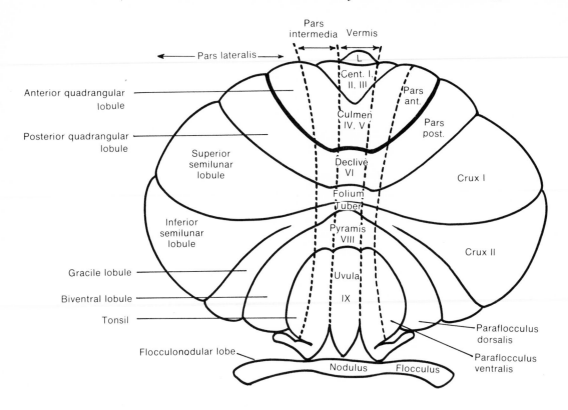

Pars intermedia

Vermis

Pars lateralis

L

Cent. I, II, III

Pars ant.

Pars post.

Anterior quadrangular lobule

Posterior quadrangular lobule

Culmen IV, V

Superior semilunar lobule

Declive VI

Crux I

Folium

Tuber

Inferior semilunar lobule

Pyramis VIII

Crux II

Gracile lobule

Uvula

IX

Biventral lobule

Tonsil

Paraflocculus dorsalis

Paraflocculus ventralis

Flocculonodular lobe

Nodulus   Flocculus

SCHEMATIC DIAGRAM ACCORDING TO LARSELL

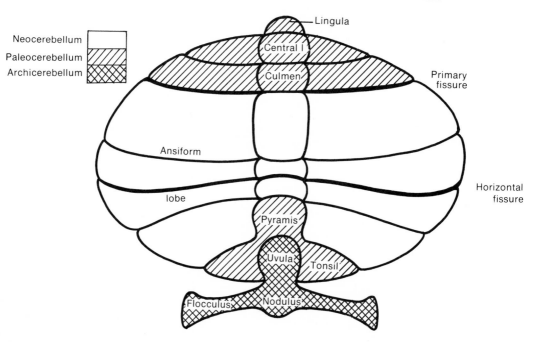

Lingula

Neocerebellum

Paleocerebellum

Archicerebellum

Central I

Culmen

Primary fissure

Ansiform

lobe

Horizontal fissure

Pyramis

Uvula   Tonsil

Flocculus   Nodulus

Page 136

STRUCTURE OF THE CEREBELLAR CORTEX

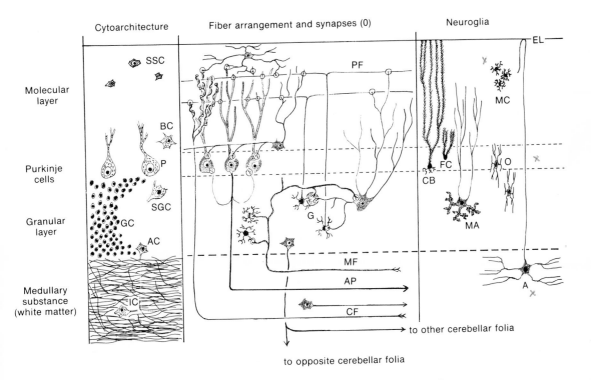

Cytoarchitecture | Fiber arrangement and synapses (0) | Neuroglia

Molecular layer

Purkinje cells

Granular layer

Medullary substance (white matter)

to other cerebellar folia

to opposite cerebellar folia

  A: astrocyte
 AC: association cell (Golgi type I)
 AP: axon of Purkinje cell
 BC: basket cell
 CB: cell of Bergmann
 CF: climbing fiber
 EL: external limiting membrane
 FC: Fañanas' cell
  G: glomerulus
 GC: granule cell
 IC: internuncial cell
 MA: mixed astrocyte (both protoplasmic and fibrous type)
 MC: microglial cell
 MF: mossy fiber
  P: Purkinje cell
 PF: parallel fiber
SSC: superficial stellate cell
SGC: large stellate cell (Golgi type II)

DIVISION OF THE THALAMIC REGION ON A SAGITTAL SECTION OF THE BRAIN

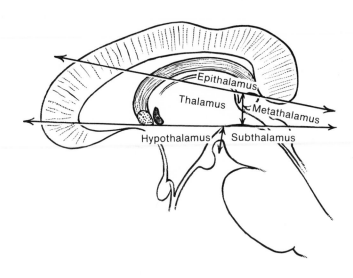

DIVISION OF THE THALAMIC REGION ON A FRONTAL SECTION OF THE BRAIN

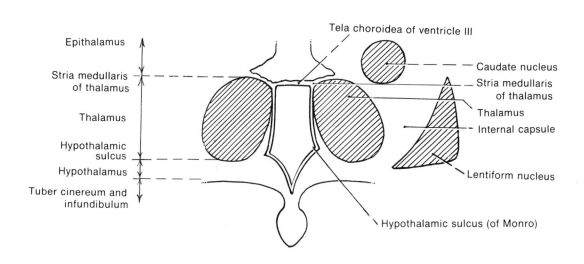

SOME ORGANOGENETIC DATA

SCHEMATIC FRONTAL SECTION OF AN 8 WEEK OLD FETUS (BEFORE FORMATION OF THE FOSSA OF THE LATERAL SULCUS)

SCHEMATIC FRONTAL SECTION OF A 12 WEEK OLD FETUS (WHEN THE FOSSA OF THE LATERAL SULCUS APPEARS)

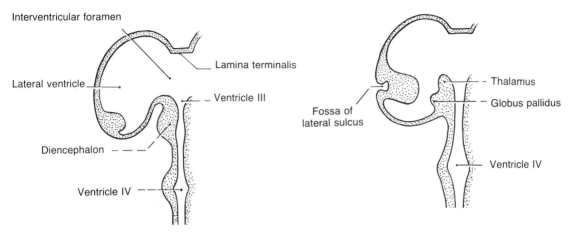

Interventricular foramen

Lamina terminalis

Lateral ventricle

Ventricle III

Diencephalon

Ventricle IV

Fossa of lateral sulcus

Thalamus

Globus pallidus

Ventricle IV

DEVELOPMENT OF THE COMMISSURAL FIBERS

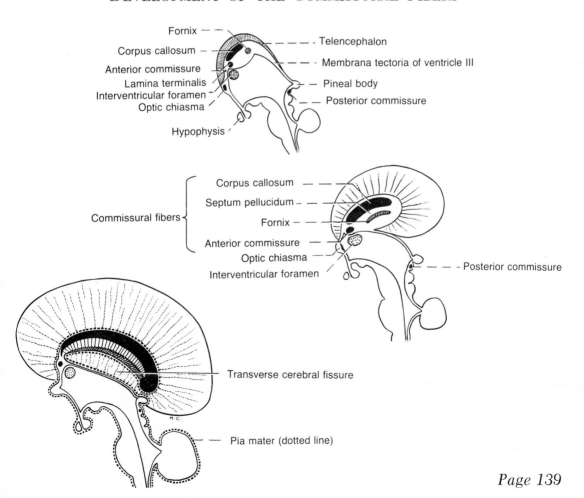

Fornix

Corpus callosum

Anterior commissure

Lamina terminalis

Interventricular foramen

Optic chiasma

Hypophysis

Telencephalon

Membrana tectoria of ventricle III

Pineal body

Posterior commissure

Commissural fibers

Corpus callosum

Septum pellucidum

Fornix

Anterior commissure

Optic chiasma

Interventricular foramen

Posterior commissure

Transverse cerebral fissure

Pia mater (dotted line)

THIRD VENTRICLE

MEDIAN SECTION OF THE THIRD VENTRICLE

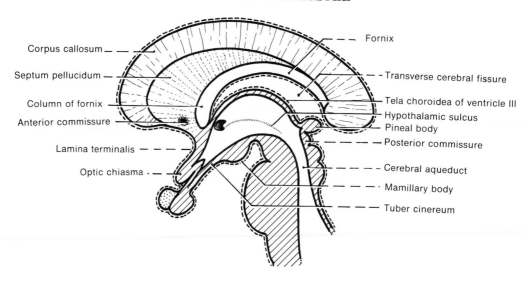

- Corpus callosum
- Septum pellucidum
- Column of fornix
- Anterior commissure
- Lamina terminalis
- Optic chiasma
- Fornix
- Transverse cerebral fissure
- Tela choroidea of ventricle III
- Hypothalamic sulcus
- Pineal body
- Posterior commissure
- Cerebral aqueduct
- Mamillary body
- Tuber cinereum

FRONTAL SECTION OF THE THIRD VENTRICLE

(On the right side, the arrow indicates the boundary between hypothalamus medially and subthalamus laterally)

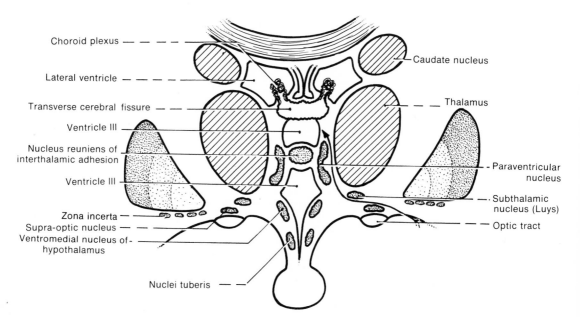

- Choroid plexus
- Lateral ventricle
- Transverse cerebral fissure
- Ventricle III
- Nucleus reuniens of interthalamic adhesion
- Ventricle III
- Zona incerta
- Supra-optic nucleus
- Ventromedial nucleus of hypothalamus
- Nuclei tuberis
- Caudate nucleus
- Thalamus
- Paraventricular nucleus
- Subthalamic nucleus (Luys)
- Optic tract

Hypothalamic nuclei: see page 329.

Page 140

BASAL GANGLIA ISOLATED IN SPACE

SUPERIOR VIEW

LEFT LATERAL VIEW

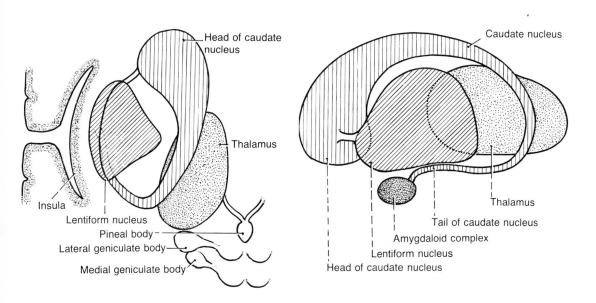

Head of caudate nucleus

Thalamus

Insula

Lentiform nucleus

Pineal body

Lateral geniculate body

Medial geniculate body

Caudate nucleus

Thalamus

Tail of caudate nucleus

Amygdaloid complex

Lentiform nucleus

Head of caudate nucleus

DRAWING OF A SPECIMEN
(LEFT ANTEROSUPERIOR ASPECT)

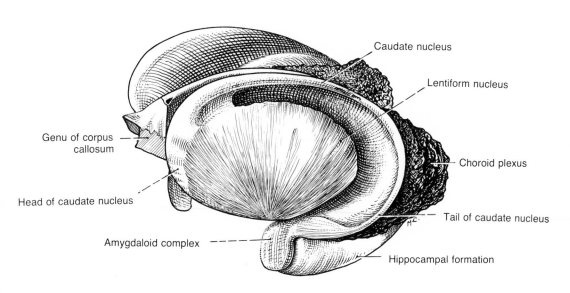

Caudate nucleus

Lentiform nucleus

Genu of corpus callosum

Choroid plexus

Head of caudate nucleus

Tail of caudate nucleus

Amygdaloid complex

Hippocampal formation

Page 141

GENERAL DIAGRAM OF THE THALAMUS

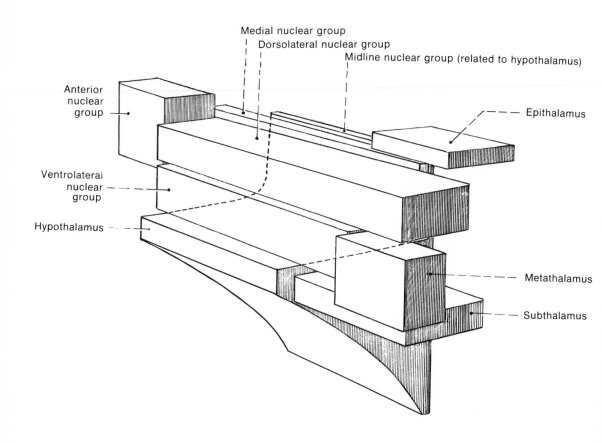

Medial nuclear group
Dorsolateral nuclear group
Midline nuclear group (related to hypothalamus)

Anterior nuclear group

Epithalamus

Ventrolateral nuclear group

Hypothalamus

Metathalamus

Subthalamus

Superior Aspect of the Thalamus

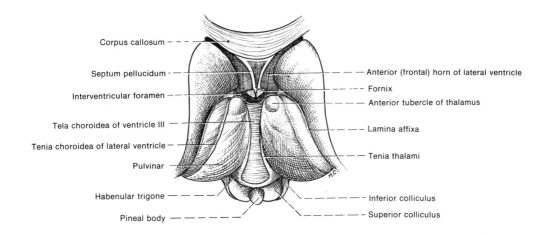

Corpus callosum

Septum pellucidum

Interventricular foramen

Tela choroidea of ventricle III

Tenia choroidea of lateral ventricle

Pulvinar

Habenular trigone

Pineal body

Anterior (frontal) horn of lateral ventricle

Fornix

Anterior tubercle of thalamus

Lamina affixa

Tenia thalami

Inferior colliculus

Superior colliculus

Thalamocaudate Groove*

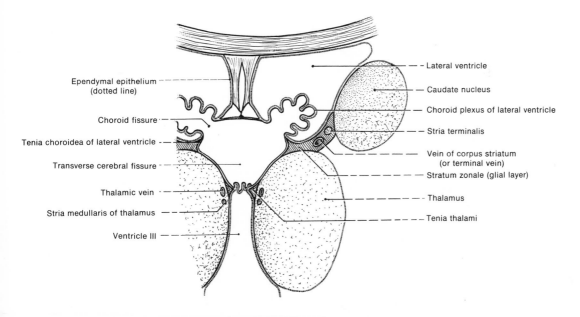

Ependymal epithelium (dotted line)

Choroid fissure

Tenia choroidea of lateral ventricle

Transverse cerebral fissure

Thalamic vein

Stria medullaris of thalamus

Ventricle III

Lateral ventricle

Caudate nucleus

Choroid plexus of lateral ventricle

Stria terminalis

Vein of corpus striatum (or terminal vein)

Stratum zonale (glial layer)

Thalamus

Tenia thalami

The obliquely hatched area corresponds to the lamina affixa.

*From Beau, A.: La lame cornée. Acta Anat., 30:37-43, 1957.

THALAMUS

Group	Nuclei	Nomina Anatomica	Internuclear connections	Thalamopetal fibers	Thalamofugal fibers	Functional considerations
Anterior nuclear group	Anteroventral n. (anterior n.) Anterodorsal n. (accessory anterior nucleus)	Nucleus anterior Nucleus anterodorsalis	Lateral & medial nuclei of thalamus Contralateral ant. nucleus by commissural fibers	Mamilothalamic tract	To gyrus cingularis To mamillary body	Interrelations between olfactory and visceral impulses and somatic impulses Thalamic level relay of the olfactory pathways
Medial nuclear group	Medial (dorsomedial) nucleus	Nucleus medialis	All the thalamic nuclei	Midline nuclear group Superior cerebellar peduncle Lemniscus of V	To hypothalamus To frontal cortex (areas 6, 32, 46) To mesencephalon	Integration of some somatic and visceral impulses
	Centromedian (central)° nucleus	Nucleus centrum medianum	All the thalamic nuclei	Brain stem reticular formation Proprioceptive spinal fibers (Petit et Mallart) Protopathic fibers of V (Kappers)	To putamen To mesencephalon To frontal cortex (area 46)?	Association and regulating mechanism Subcortical connections
Lateral nuclear group (pars ventralis)	Ventral anterior nucleus	Nucleus ventralis anterior	Medial nucleus Centromedian nucleus Subthalamic nucleus	Globus pallidus (through ansa lenticularis and thalamic fasciculus) Dentate nuclei	To area 6 and insular cortex To globus pallidus	Role upon extrapyramidal system
	Ventral intermediate nucleus	Nucleus ventralis intermedius	Centromedian nucleus	Dentate nuclei (contralateral) Red nucleus	To area 4 and 6	Specific relay and influence upon motor functions
	Ventral posterior nucleus — • ventral posteromedial (arcuate, or semilunar) n.	Nucleus ventralis posterior	Centromedian nucleus Pulvinar	Trigeminothalamic tract	To facial somesthetic area (areas 3, 1, 2)	Facial sensibility Proprioceptive sensibility of the muscles of the head
	• accessory semilunar n.			Secondary gustatory pathways	To area 43	Gustatory sense
	• Ventral posterolateral nucleus		Centromedian nucleus Pulvinar Subthalamic nucleus	Medial lemniscus Spinothalamic tracts	To postcentral gyrus areas 3, 1, 2 To subthalamus To striatum	Sensibility of trunk and limbs
Lateral nuclear group (pars dorsalis)	Lateral nucleus (including laterodorsal and lateral posterior nuclei)	Nucleus lateralis	Ventral and medial nuclei of thalamus	Fibers from medial lemniscus	To postcentral gyrus (areas 3, 1, 2) To areas 5 and 7 To precentral gyrus	Association
	Pulvinar	Pulvinar	Geniculate bodies Colliculi Medial and ventral posterolateral n.		To areas 18 and 19 (para and peristriate areas) To areas 22 and 42	Integration of visual and auditory impulses

THE THALAMIC NUCLEI

| | METATHALAMUS | EPITHALAMUS | SUBTHALAMUS |

Nucleus	Nucleus (Latin)	Afferent connections	Related nuclei	Efferent / projection	Functional significance
Midline intralaminar and reticular nuclear groups: Reticular nuclei; Nucleus parafascicularis; Nuclei of the internal medullary lamina; Midline nuclei (paleothalamus)		Cerebellar and tectothalamic fibers; Related to reticular nucleus and formations		projection of the brain stem; Diffuse cortical projection; Related to hypothalamus	Subcortical association; Visceral activities
Nucleus of the lateral geniculate body	Nucleus corporis geniculati lateralis	80% of crossed & uncrossed fibers of optic tract super. colliculus	Ventral and lateral thalamic nuclei; Pulvinar	To area 17; To sup. colliculus; To pretectal area; To zona incerta	Vision
Nucleus of the medial geniculate body	Nucleus corporis geniculati medialis	Cochlear nuclei; Trapezoid nuclei; Superior olivary nuclei; Nuclei of the lateral lemniscus; Inferior colliculus	Contralateral medial geniculate body	To geniculotemporal (auditory) radiations; To area 41; To subthalamus; To homo- and contra-lateral inferior colliculi	Audition
Habenular nucleus	Nucleus habenulae	Stria medullaris (fibers from septal nuclei, hippocampal formation, olfactory tubercle)		Fasciculus retroreflexus (habenulopeduncular tract) to interpeduncular nucleus	Correlation of the olfactory and the somatic impulses
Subthalamic nucleus	Nucleus subthalamicus	Globus pallidus, through the subthalamic fasciculus	Thalamic nuclei	Fibers from lenticular fasciculus, ansa lenticularis and thalamic fasciculus to: globus pallidus, red nucleus, substantia nigra and tegmentum	Somatic coordinating motor center related to extrapyramidal system; Inhibitory and regulating influence upon the globus pallidus
Interpeduncular nucleus	Nucleus interpeduncularis	Habenular nucleus; Suprasegmental visceral centers		To dorsal tegmental n. and reticular nuclei of the brain stem tegmentum	Extrapyramidal system; Olfactosomatic and olfactovisceral reflexes
Nucleus of the tegmental field of Forel (n. of prerubral field, field H)		Lenticular fasciculus; Pallidum; Dentate nucleus		To red nucleus; To pallidum	In relationship with the extrapyramidal system; resembles reticular formation in its morphology and function
Zona incerta (continuation of the mesencephalic reticular formation)	Intralaminar nuclei	Globus pallidus; Precentral cortex; Medial and lateral thalamic nuclei; Lateral geniculate body; Red nucleus; Midbrain		To red nucleus; To midbrain tegmentum	In relationship with the extrapyramidal system

*The centromedian nucleus should be related to the intralaminar group, functionally and morphologically.

WHITE MATTER OF THE THALAMIC REGION

Horizontal Section of a Cerebral Hemisphere Through the Anterior Commissure and the Splenium of the Corpus Callosum

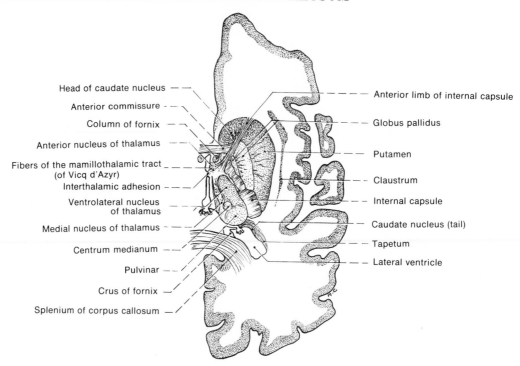

Head of caudate nucleus
Anterior commissure
Column of fornix
Anterior nucleus of thalamus
Fibers of the mamillothalamic tract (of Vicq d'Azyr)
Interthalamic adhesion
Ventrolateral nucleus of thalamus
Medial nucleus of thalamus
Centrum medianum
Pulvinar
Crus of fornix
Splenium of corpus callosum

Anterior limb of internal capsule
Globus pallidus
Putamen
Claustrum
Internal capsule
Caudate nucleus (tail)
Tapetum
Lateral ventricle

Diagram of the White Matter of the Thalamic Region (Frontal Section)

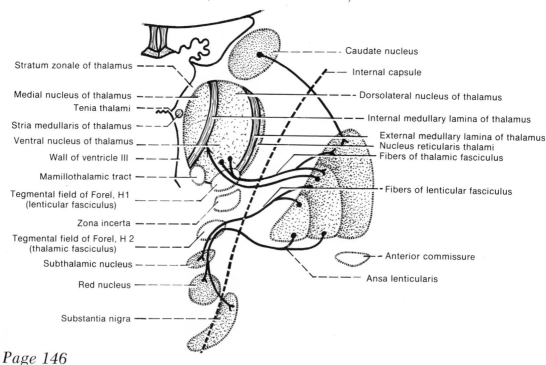

Stratum zonale of thalamus
Medial nucleus of thalamus
Tenia thalami
Stria medullaris of thalamus
Ventral nucleus of thalamus
Wall of ventricle III
Mamillothalamic tract
Tegmental field of Forel, H1 (lenticular fasciculus)
Zona incerta
Tegmental field of Forel, H 2 (thalamic fasciculus)
Subthalamic nucleus
Red nucleus
Substantia nigra

Caudate nucleus
Internal capsule
Dorsolateral nucleus of thalamus
Internal medullary lamina of thalamus
External medullary lamina of thalamus
Nucleus reticularis thalami
Fibers of thalamic fasciculus
Fibers of lenticular fasciculus
Anterior commissure
Ansa lenticularis

DIAGRAM OF THE THALAMOPETAL
AND THE THALAMOFUGAL
PATHWAYS

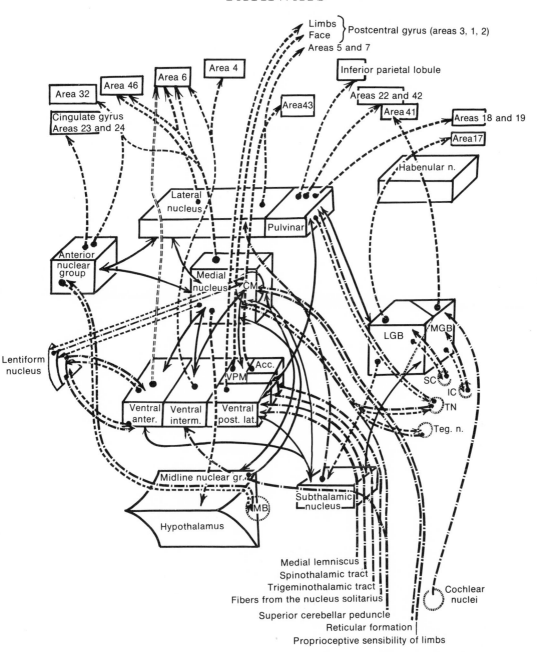

Limbs
Face } Postcentral gyrus (areas 3, 1, 2)
Areas 5 and 7

Area 4

Inferior parietal lobule

Area 6

Areas 22 and 42

Area 46

Area43

Area 41

Areas 18 and 19

Area 32

Area17

Cingulate gyrus
Areas 23 and 24

Habenular n.

Lateral
nucleus

Pulvinar

Anterior
nuclear
group

Medial
nucleus   CM

LGB   MGB

Lentiform
nucleus

Acc.

VPM

SC

IC

Ventral
anter.

Ventral
interm.

Ventral
post. lat.

TN

Teg. n.

Midline nuclear gr.

MB

Subthalamic
nucleus

Hypothalamus

Medial lemniscus
Spinothalamic tract
Trigeminothalamic tract
Fibers from the nucleus solitarius

Cochlear
nuclei

Superior cerebellar peduncle
Reticular formation
Proprioceptive sensibility of limbs

—·—·—·— Afferent, thalamopetal fibers
- - - - - - - Efferent, thalamofugal fibers
—————— Connections between the thalamic nuclei

CM: centromedian nucleus
VPM: ventral posteromedial nucleus
Acc: accessory semilunar nucleus
MGB: medial geniculate body
LGB: lateral geniculate body
SC: superior colliculus
IC: inferior colliculus
TN: tectal nucleus
Teg: tegmentum
MB: mamillary body

Page 147

Cerebral Hemispheres

A *fissure* is a deep furrow on the surface of an organ (brain). A *sulcus* is less deep and gives rise to the lobes and gyri. The gyri are most often designated by a capital letter followed by a number (T1, T2, . . .); the sulci by a small letter with a number (t1, t2, . . .). Sulci are also found on the surface of the spinal cord and the brain stem.

EXTERNAL FEATURES

MEDIAN SECTION OF THE BRAIN

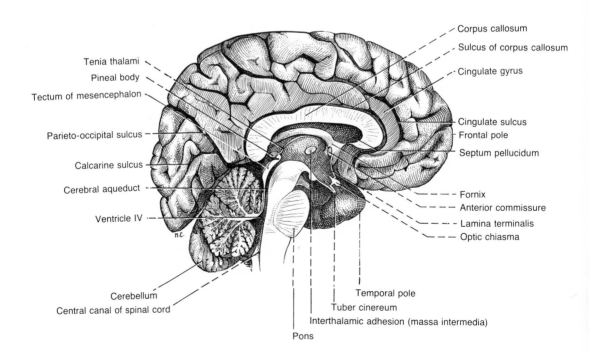

Tenia thalami

Pineal body

Tectum of mesencephalon

Parieto-occipital sulcus

Calcarine sulcus

Cerebral aqueduct

Ventricle IV

n.c.

Cerebellum

Central canal of spinal cord

Pons

Temporal pole

Tuber cinereum

Interthalamic adhesion (massa intermedia)

Corpus callosum

Sulcus of corpus callosum

Cingulate gyrus

Cingulate sulcus

Frontal pole

Septum pellucidum

Fornix

Anterior commissure

Lamina terminalis

Optic chiasma

LATERAL ASPECT OF LEFT CEREBRAL HEMISPHERE

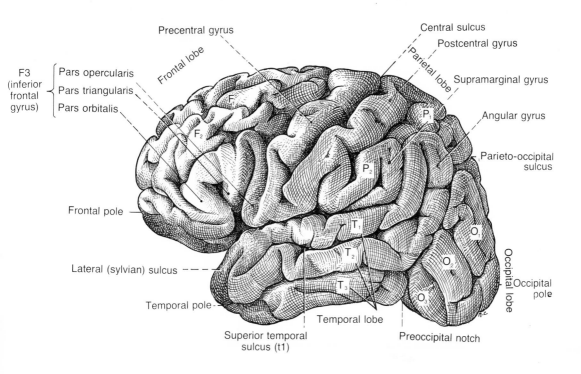

Precentral gyrus

Central sulcus

Postcentral gyrus

Parietal lobe

Frontal lobe

Supramarginal gyrus

F3 (inferior frontal gyrus)
- Pars opercularis
- Pars triangularis
- Pars orbitalis

Angular gyrus

Parieto-occipital sulcus

Frontal pole

Lateral (sylvian) sulcus

Temporal pole

Superior temporal sulcus (t1)

Temporal lobe

Preoccipital notch

Occipital lobe

Occipital pole

MEDIAL ASPECT OF RIGHT CEREBRAL HEMISPHERE

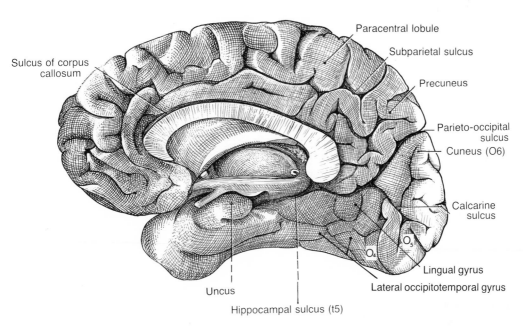

Paracentral lobule

Subparietal sulcus

Sulcus of corpus callosum

Precuneus

Parieto-occipital sulcus

Cuneus (O6)

Calcarine sulcus

Lingual gyrus

Lateral occipitotemporal gyrus

Uncus

Hippocampal sulcus (t5)

Page 149

INFERIOR ASPECT OF THE HEMISPHERES

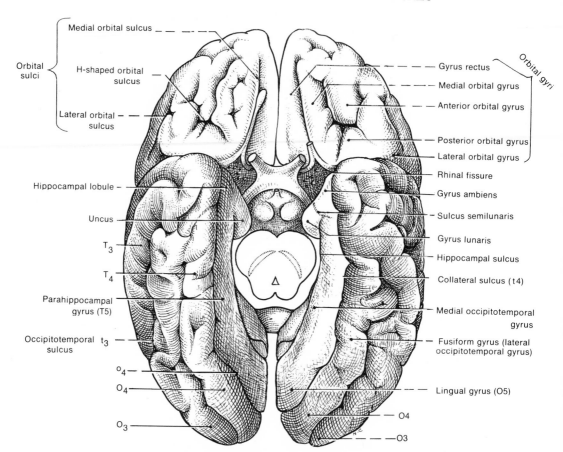

Orbital sulci
- Medial orbital sulcus
- H-shaped orbital sulcus
- Lateral orbital sulcus

Orbital gyri
- Gyrus rectus
- Medial orbital gyrus
- Anterior orbital gyrus
- Posterior orbital gyrus
- Lateral orbital gyrus

Hippocampal lobule
Uncus
T₃
T₄
Parahippocampal gyrus (T5)
Occipitotemporal t₃ sulcus
o₄
O₄
O₃

Rhinal fissure
Gyrus ambiens
Sulcus semilunaris
Gyrus lunaris
Hippocampal sulcus
Collateral sulcus (t4)
Medial occipitotemporal gyrus
Fusiform gyrus (lateral occipitotemporal gyrus)
Lingual gyrus (O5)
O4
O3

The medial occipitotemporal gyrus, lying medial to the collateral sulcus, includes the parahippocampal gyrus and the lingual gyrus.

The lateral occipitotemporal gyrus, located between the collateral sulcus and the occipitotemporal (or inferior temporal) sulcus, extends from the occipital to the temporal pole. Its most frequent alternative names are fusiform gyrus and occipitotemporal gyrus.

INSULA

(After removing frontal, parietal and temporal opercula)

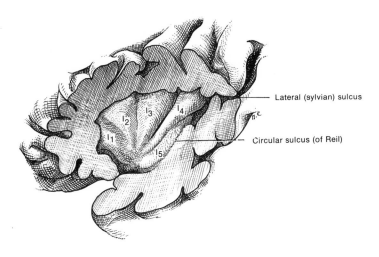

Lateral (sylvian) sulcus

Circular sulcus (of Reil)

TEMPORAL LOBE AND TRANSVERSE TEMPORAL GYRI

(Temporal lobe has been isolated and the specimen slightly turned in order to show the transverse temporal gyri)

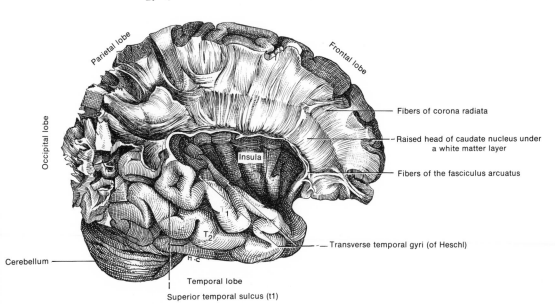

Parietal lobe

Frontal lobe

Occipital lobe

Fibers of corona radiata

Raised head of caudate nucleus under a white matter layer

Insula

Fibers of the fasciculus arcuatus

Transverse temporal gyri (of Heschl)

Cerebellum

Temporal lobe

Superior temporal sulcus (t1)

SCHEMATIC FRONTAL SECTION SHOWING THE RELATIONSHIPS OF
THE MAIN WHITE MATTER FORMATIONS WITH THE BASAL GANGLIA

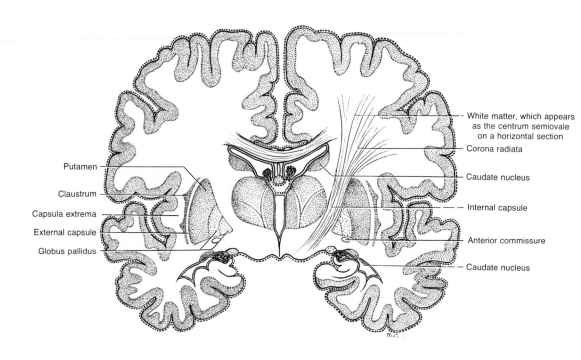

LONG ASSOCIATION FIBERS OF THE HEMISPHERES

PROJECTION OF ASSOCIATION FASCICULI ON MEDIAL ASPECT OF RIGHT HEMISPHERE

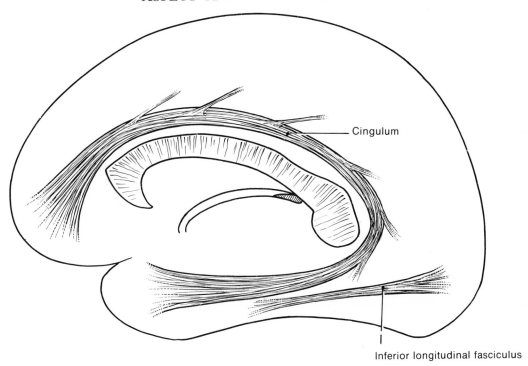

Cingulum

Inferior longitudinal fasciculus

LOCATION OF ASSOCIATION FASCICULI ON FRONTAL SECTION OF THE HEMISPHERES

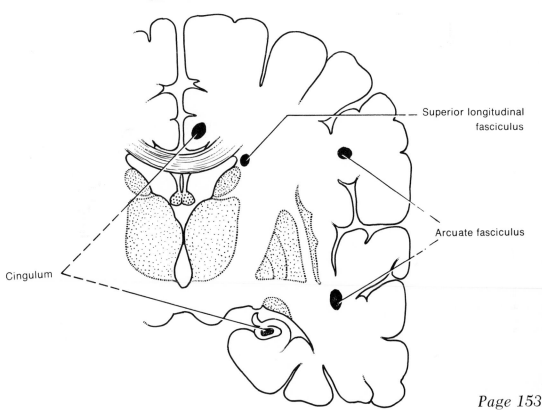

Superior longitudinal fasciculus

Arcuate fasciculus

Cingulum

Diagram of the Fornix

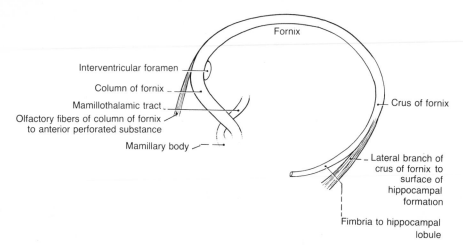

Fornix

Interventricular foramen

Column of fornix

Mamillothalamic tract

Olfactory fibers of column of fornix
to anterior perforated substance

Mamillary body

Crus of fornix

Lateral branch of
crus of fornix to
surface of
hippocampal
formation

Fimbria to hippocampal
lobule

Inferior View of
the Posterior Part of
the Fornix

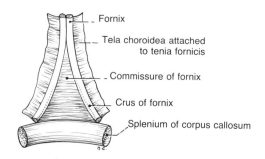

Fornix

Tela choroidea attached
to tenia fornicis

Commissure of fornix

Crus of fornix

Splenium of corpus callosum

Projection of Association Fasciculi on
Lateral Aspect of Right Hemisphere

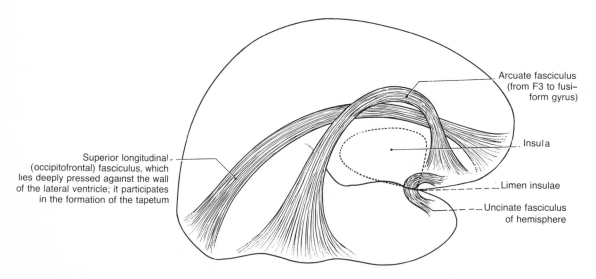

Arcuate fasciculus
(from F3 to fusi–
form gyrus)

Insula

Superior longitudinal
(occipitofrontal) fasciculus, which
lies deeply pressed against the wall
of the lateral ventricle; it participates
in the formation of the tapetum

Limen insulae

Uncinate fasciculus
of hemisphere

STRUCTURE OF THE CEREBRAL CORTEX

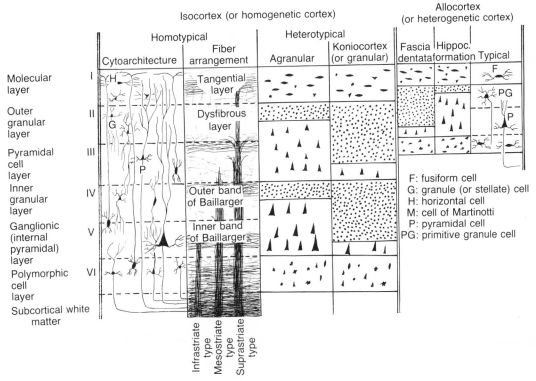

	Isocortex (or homogenetic cortex)				Allocortex (or heterogenetic cortex)		
	Homotypical		Heterotypical		Fascia dentata	Hippoc. formation	Typical
	Cytoarchitecture	Fiber arrangement	Agranular	Koniocortex (or granular)			

Molecular layer — I

Outer granular layer — II

Pyramidal cell layer — III

Inner granular layer — IV

Ganglionic (internal pyramidal) layer — V

Polymorphic cell layer — VI

Subcortical white matter

Tangential layer

Dysfibrous layer

Outer band of Baillarger

Inner band of Baillarger

Infrastriate type — Mesostriate type — Suprastriate type

F: fusiform cell
G: granule (or stellate) cell
H: horizontal cell
M: cell of Martinotti
P: pyramidal cell
PG: primitive granule cell

Allocortex: the 6 cell layers are not recognized — archipallium
Isocortex: the 6 cell layers are always recognized
    homotypical: harmonious proportions of the 6 layers — association cortex
    heterotypical: agranular: predominance of the pyramidal cell layers — motor cortex
        koniocortex: predominance of the granule cell layers — sensory cortex

AREAS OF THE CEREBRAL CORTEX

(The numbers correspond to the cytoarchitectonic areas of Brodmann)

AREAS OF THE ORBITAL SURFACE OF THE FRONTAL LOBE

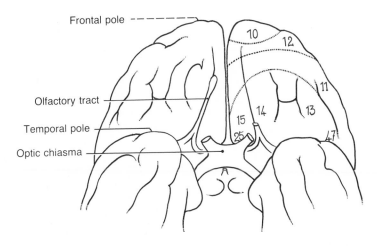

Frontal pole

Olfactory tract

Temporal pole

Optic chiasma

LATERAL ASPECT OF LEFT HEMISPHERE

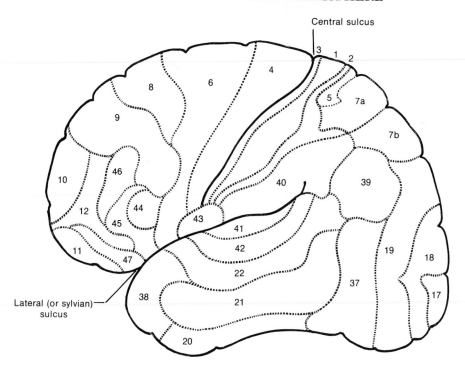

Central sulcus

Lateral (or sylvian) sulcus

MEDIAL ASPECT OF RIGHT HEMISPHERE

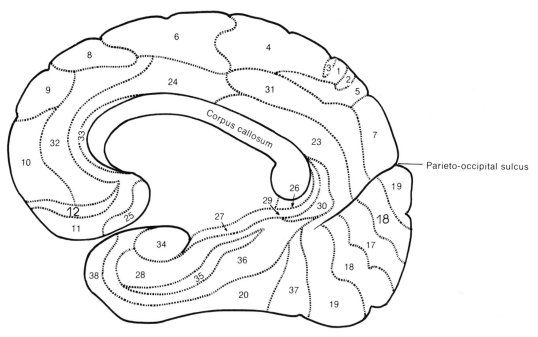

Corpus callosum

Parieto-occipital sulcus

The *cortical areas* are territories showing particular architectonic characteristics (arrangement of the cell bodies and the fibers). They often have specific functions; when this is the case and if their boundaries are well defined, they may be called *centers*. The word "zona" is usually applied, meaning a functional area not well bounded morphologically.

SECTION OF THE CIRCULAR FORMATIONS
OF THE THRESHOLD OF THE HEMISPHERE

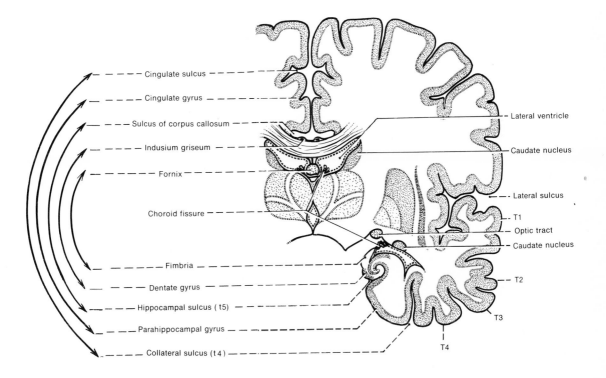

Schematic frontal section of a cerebral hemisphere intended to show the correspondence of the medial concentric formations.

These limbic formations (practically all archipallial) are included between the cingulate and collateral sulci on the one hand and the choroid fissure on the other.

CAVITIES OF THE BRAIN

LATERAL PROJECTION OF THE LATERAL AND THIRD VENTRICLES

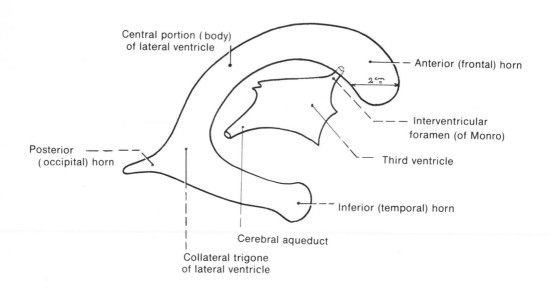

Central portion (body) of lateral ventricle

Anterior (frontal) horn

2 cm

Interventricular foramen (of Monro)

Third ventricle

Posterior (occipital) horn

Inferior (temporal) horn

Cerebral aqueduct

Collateral trigone of lateral ventricle

FRONTAL SECTION OF THE BRAIN SHOWING THE MAIN RELATIONSHIPS OF THE VENTRICULAR CAVITIES

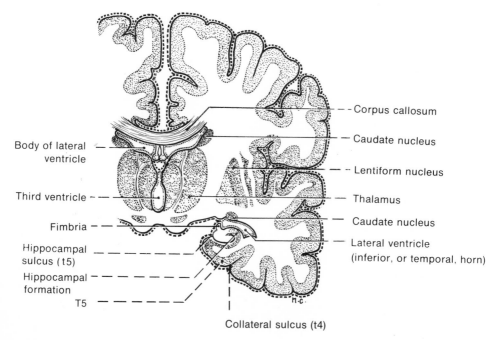

Corpus callosum

Caudate nucleus

Body of lateral ventricle

Lentiform nucleus

Third ventricle

Thalamus

Caudate nucleus

Fimbria

Lateral ventricle (inferior, or temporal, horn)

Hippocampal sulcus (t5)

Hippocampal formation

T5

Collateral sulcus (t4)

FRONTAL SECTION THROUGH THE POSTERIOR (OCCIPITAL) HORN OF THE LATERAL VENTRICLE

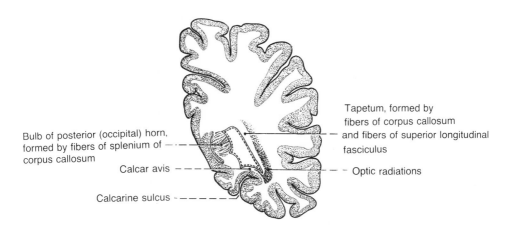

Bulb of posterior (occipital) horn, formed by fibers of splenium of corpus callosum

Calcar avis

Calcarine sulcus

Tapetum, formed by fibers of corpus callosum and fibers of superior longitudinal fasciculus

Optic radiations

SCHEMATIC HORIZONTAL SECTION OF THE INFERIOR (TEMPORAL) HORN OF THE LATERAL VENTRICLE

DRAWING OF A SPECIMEN OF THE INFERIOR HORN, CORRESPONDING TO THE OPPOSITE DIAGRAM

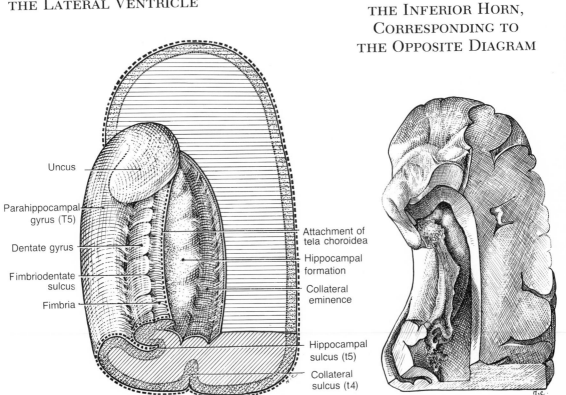

Uncus

Parahippocampal gyrus (T5)

Dentate gyrus

Fimbriodentate sulcus

Fimbria

Attachment of tela choroidea

Hippocampal formation

Collateral eminence

Hippocampal sulcus (t5)

Collateral sulcus (t4)

SECTIONS OF THE CEREBRAL HEMISPHERES

Horizontal Section Passing Through the Genu and the Splenium of the Corpus Callosum

(The letters indicate the levels of the frontal sections that ensue)

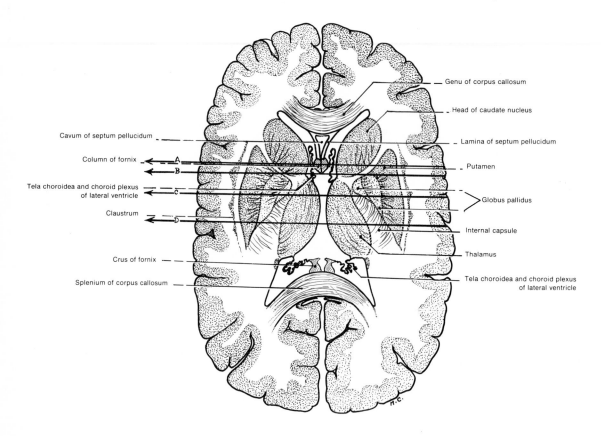

FRONTAL SECTION "A" AT THE LEVEL OF THE ANTERIOR COMMISSURE

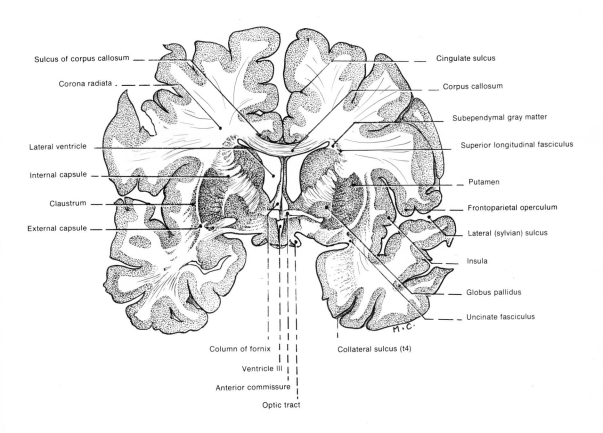

Sulcus of corpus callosum

Corona radiata

Lateral ventricle

Internal capsule

Claustrum

External capsule

Cingulate sulcus

Corpus callosum

Subependymal gray matter

Superior longitudinal fasciculus

Putamen

Frontoparietal operculum

Lateral (sylvian) sulcus

Insula

Globus pallidus

Uncinate fasciculus

Column of fornix

Ventricle III

Anterior commissure

Optic tract

Collateral sulcus (t4)

M.C.

FRONTAL SECTION "B" JUST BEHIND THE ANTERIOR COMMISSURE

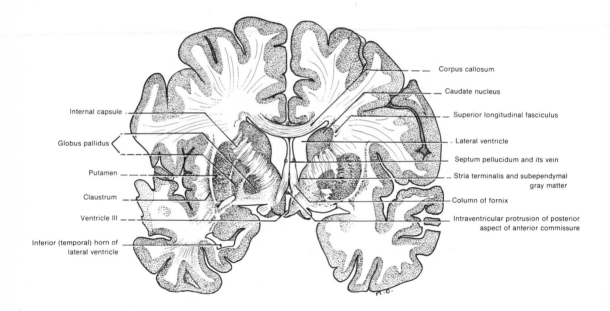

Corpus callosum

Caudate nucleus

Superior longitudinal fasciculus

Lateral ventricle

Septum pellucidum and its vein

Stria terminalis and subependymal gray matter

Column of fornix

Intraventricular protrusion of posterior aspect of anterior commissure

Internal capsule

Globus pallidus

Putamen

Claustrum

Ventricle III

Inferior (temporal) horn of lateral ventricle

Frontal Section "C" Through the Mamillary Bodies

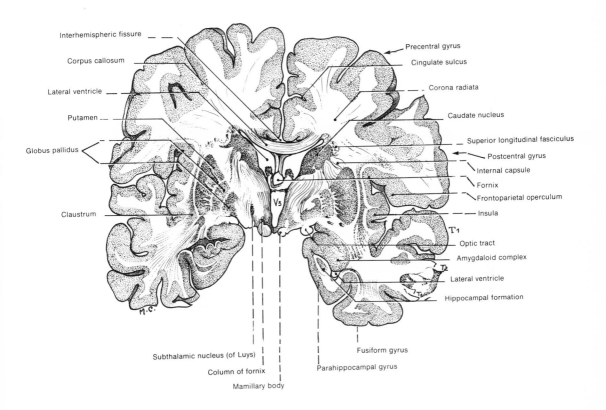

Interhemispheric fissure

Corpus callosum

Lateral ventricle

Putamen

Globus pallidus

Claustrum

Precentral gyrus

Cingulate sulcus

Corona radiata

Caudate nucleus

Superior longitudinal fasciculus

Postcentral gyrus

Internal capsule

Fornix

Frontoparietal operculum

Insula

T₁

Optic tract

Amygdaloid complex

T₂

Lateral ventricle

T₃

Hippocampal formation

V₃

Subthalamic nucleus (of Luys)

Column of fornix

Mamillary body

Fusiform gyrus

Parahippocampal gyrus

M.C.

FRONTAL SECTION "D" THROUGH THE MIDDLE PART OF THE THALAMUS

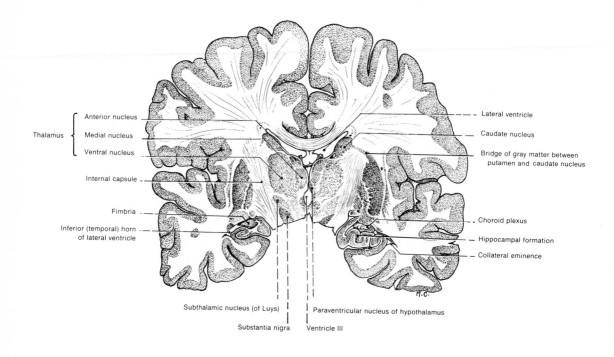

Thalamus
- Anterior nucleus
- Medial nucleus
- Ventral nucleus

Internal capsule

Fimbria

Inferior (temporal) horn of lateral ventricle

Lateral ventricle

Caudate nucleus

Bridge of gray matter between putamen and caudate nucleus

Choroid plexus

Hippocampal formation

Collateral eminence

Subthalamic nucleus (of Luys)

Substantia nigra

Paraventricular nucleus of hypothalamus

Ventricle III

INTRACORTICAL CIRCUITS[*]

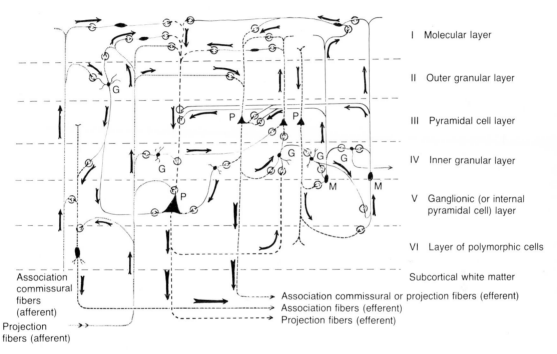

I Molecular layer

II Outer granular layer

III Pyramidal cell layer

IV Inner granular layer

V Ganglionic (or internal pyramidal cell) layer

VI Layer of polymorphic cells

Subcortical white matter

Association commissural fibers (afferent)

Projection fibers (afferent)

Association commissural or projection fibers (efferent)
Association fibers (efferent)
Projection fibers (efferent)

G: granule cell
M: cell of Martinotti
P: pyramidal cell
O: synapse

[*]*Diagram of the intracortical circuits modified from Lorente de Nó, R.: The structure of the cerebral cortex. In Fulton, J. F. (ed.): Physiology of the Nervous System. 3rd ed. New York, New York University Press, 1949, p. 296.*

Blood Supply of the Central Nervous System

DIAGRAM OF THE BLOOD SUPPLY OF THE BRAIN

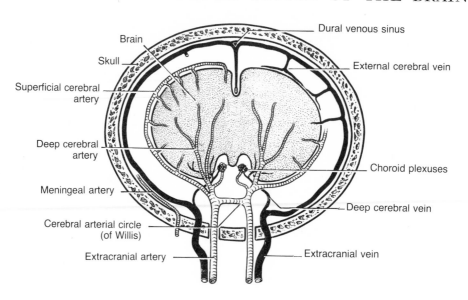

Brain

Skull

Superficial cerebral artery

Deep cerebral artery

Meningeal artery

Cerebral arterial circle (of Willis)

Extracranial artery

Dural venous sinus

External cerebral vein

Choroid plexuses

Deep cerebral vein

Extracranial vein

MENINGEAL ARTERIES

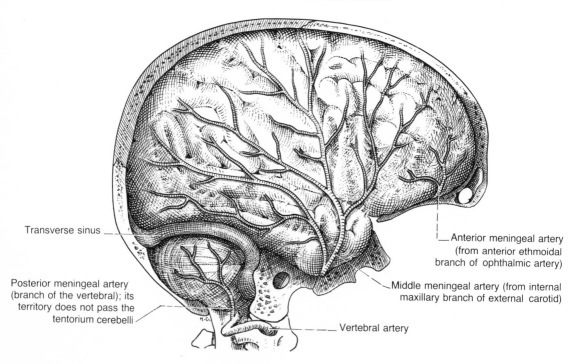

Transverse sinus

Posterior meningeal artery (branch of the vertebral); its territory does not pass the tentorium cerebelli

Anterior meningeal artery (from anterior ethmoidal branch of ophthalmic artery)

Middle meningeal artery (from internal maxillary branch of external carotid)

Vertebral artery

ARTERIES OF THE SPINAL CORD*

ANTERIOR ARTERIAL SPINAL SYSTEM

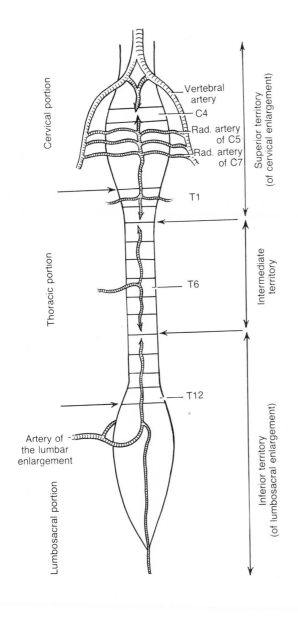

Cervical portion

Vertebral artery

C4

Rad. artery of C5

Rad. artery of C7

Superior territory (of cervical enlargement)

T1

Thoracic portion

Intermediate territory

T6

Inferior territory (of lumbosacral enlargement)

T12

Artery of the lumbar enlargement

Lumbosacral portion

SUPERFICIAL ARTERIAL NETWORK OF THE SPINAL CORD

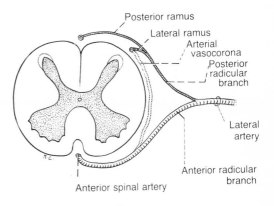

Posterior ramus

Lateral ramus

Arterial vasocorona

Posterior radicular branch

Lateral artery

Anterior radicular branch

Anterior spinal artery

The artery of the lumbar enlargement is usually single, found on the left or right side; it corresponds to a lateral artery of T 10 to L 2.

*Based in part on Lazorthes, G.: Vascularisation et Circulation Cérébrales. Paris, Masson et Cie., 1961.

DIAGRAM OF THE SUPERFICIAL AND DEEP
ARTERIAL BLOOD SUPPLY OF
THE SPINAL CORD

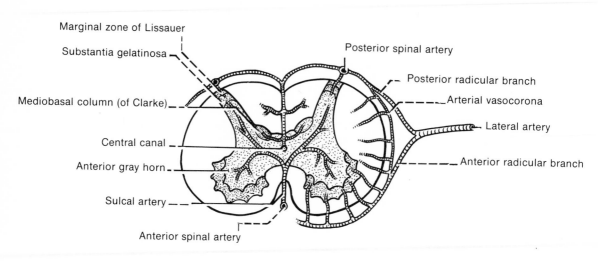

Marginal zone of Lissauer

Substantia gelatinosa

Posterior spinal artery

Posterior radicular branch

Mediobasal column (of Clarke)

Arterial vasocorona

Lateral artery

Central canal

Anterior gray horn

Anterior radicular branch

Sulcal artery

Anterior spinal artery

TERRITORY OF THE SUPERFICIAL
ARTERIAL NETWORK

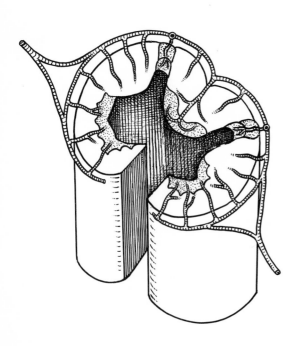

DEEP ARTERIAL
TERRITORY, OR
TERRITORY OF THE
ANTERIOR SPINAL
ARTERIAL SYSTEM

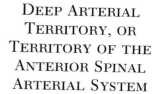

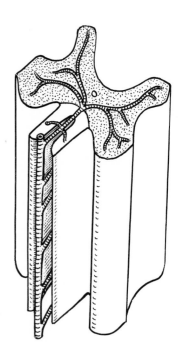

Artificial isolation of the superficial and deep arterial territories of the spinal cord.

CEREBRAL ARTERIES

INFERIOR ASPECT OF THE BRAIN

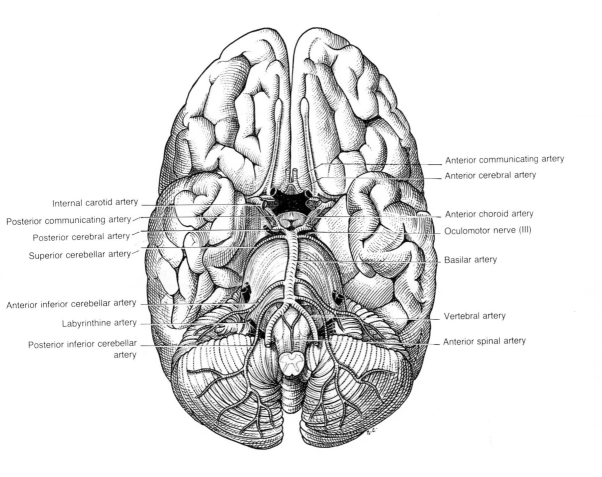

Anterior communicating artery

Anterior cerebral artery

Internal carotid artery

Posterior communicating artery

Posterior cerebral artery

Superior cerebellar artery

Anterior choroid artery

Oculomotor nerve (III)

Basilar artery

Anterior inferior cerebellar artery

Labyrinthine artery

Posterior inferior cerebellar artery

Vertebral artery

Anterior spinal artery

CEREBRAL ARTERIAL CIRCLE (OF WILLIS)

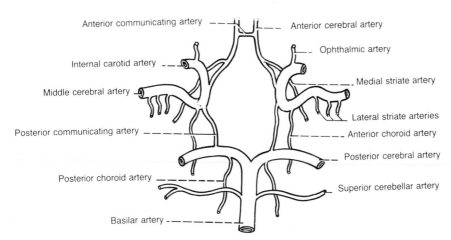

Anterior communicating artery

Anterior cerebral artery

Internal carotid artery

Ophthalmic artery

Middle cerebral artery

Medial striate artery

Lateral striate arteries

Posterior communicating artery

Anterior choroid artery

Posterior cerebral artery

Posterior choroid artery

Superior cerebellar artery

Basilar artery

LATERAL ASPECT OF THE BRAIN

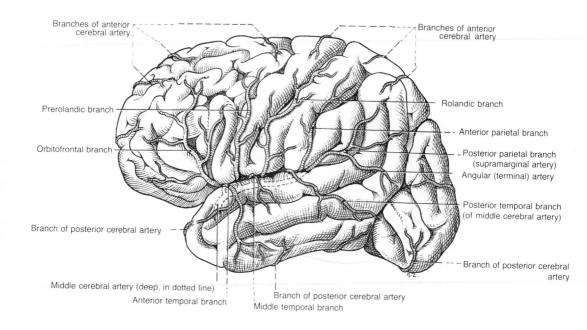

Branches of anterior cerebral artery

Branches of anterior cerebral artery

Prerolandic branch

Rolandic branch

Anterior parietal branch

Orbitofrontal branch

Posterior parietal branch (supramarginal artery)

Angular (terminal) artery

Posterior temporal branch (of middle cerebral artery)

Branch of posterior cerebral artery

Branch of posterior cerebral artery

Middle cerebral artery (deep, in dotted line)

Anterior temporal branch

Branch of posterior cerebral artery

Middle temporal branch

MEDIAL ASPECT OF THE BRAIN

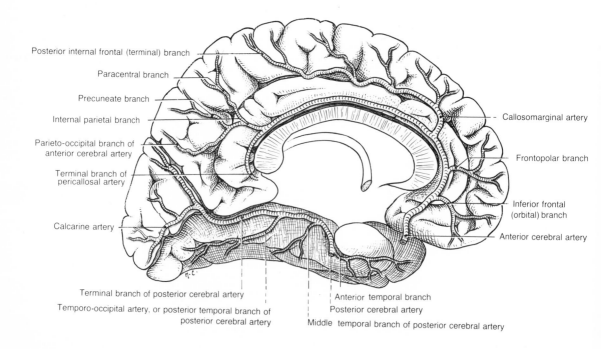

Posterior internal frontal (terminal) branch

Paracentral branch

Precuneate branch

Internal parietal branch

Parieto-occipital branch of anterior cerebral artery

Terminal branch of pericallosal artery

Calcarine artery

Callosomarginal artery

Frontopolar branch

Inferior frontal (orbital) branch

Anterior cerebral artery

Terminal branch of posterior cerebral artery

Temporo-occipital artery, or posterior temporal branch of posterior cerebral artery

Anterior temporal branch

Posterior cerebral artery

Middle temporal branch of posterior cerebral artery

Page 170

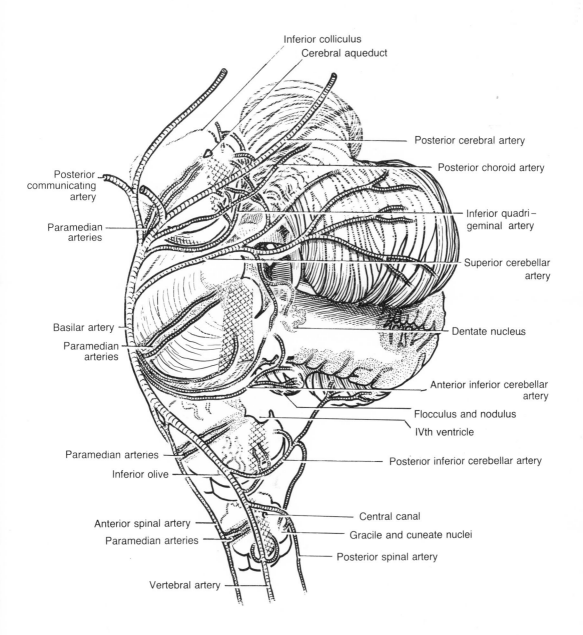

Inferior colliculus
Cerebral aqueduct

Posterior cerebral artery

Posterior choroid artery

Posterior communicating artery

Inferior quadri-geminal artery

Paramedian arteries

Superior cerebellar artery

Basilar artery

Dentate nucleus

Paramedian arteries

Anterior inferior cerebellar artery

Flocculus and nodulus

IVth ventricle

Paramedian arteries

Posterior inferior cerebellar artery

Inferior olive

Anterior spinal artery

Central canal

Gracile and cuneate nuclei

Paramedian arteries

Posterior spinal artery

Vertebral artery

According to Lazorthes, the most poorly irrigated areas of the brain stem are the areas between the territories of the paramedian and vertebral arteries in the medulla, and the areas between the territories of the paramedian and short circumferential arteries in the pontine and mesencephalic regions.

Arterial Territories of the Brain
(Medial aspect of the right hemisphere)

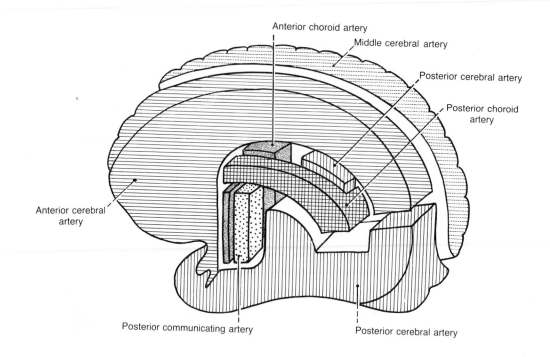

Anterior choroid artery

Middle cerebral artery

Posterior cerebral artery

Posterior choroid artery

Anterior cerebral artery

Posterior communicating artery

Posterior cerebral artery

Arterial Supply of the Basal Ganglia
(Medial aspect)

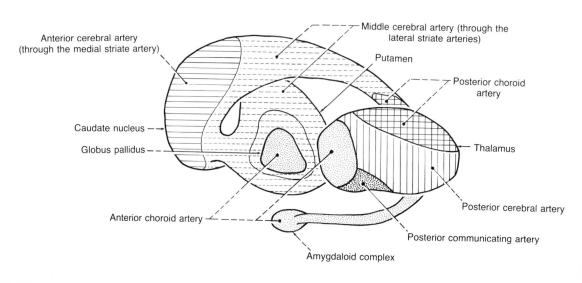

Anterior cerebral artery
(through the medial striate artery)

Middle cerebral artery (through the
lateral striate arteries)

Putamen

Posterior choroid artery

Caudate nucleus

Globus pallidus

Thalamus

Anterior choroid artery

Posterior cerebral artery

Posterior communicating artery

Amygdaloid complex

Page 172

DURAL VENOUS SINUSES AND THE CEREBRAL VEINS

DURAL VENOUS SINUSES ON THE FLOOR OF THE SKULL

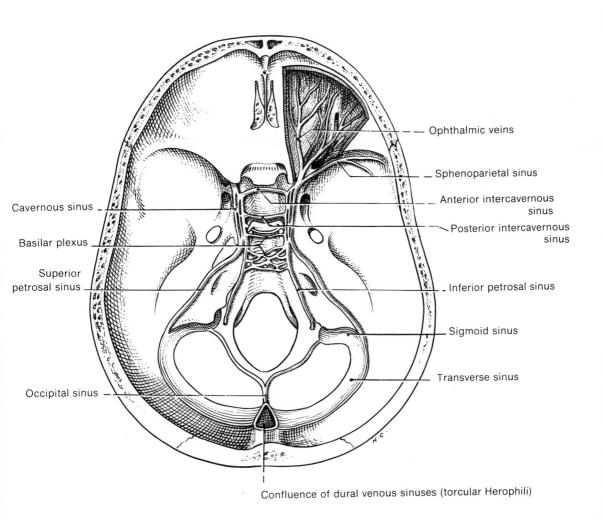

Ophthalmic veins

Sphenoparietal sinus

Anterior intercavernous sinus

Posterior intercavernous sinus

Cavernous sinus

Basilar plexus

Superior petrosal sinus

Inferior petrosal sinus

Sigmoid sinus

Transverse sinus

Occipital sinus

Confluence of dural venous sinuses (torcular Herophili)

CEREBRAL VEINS[*]

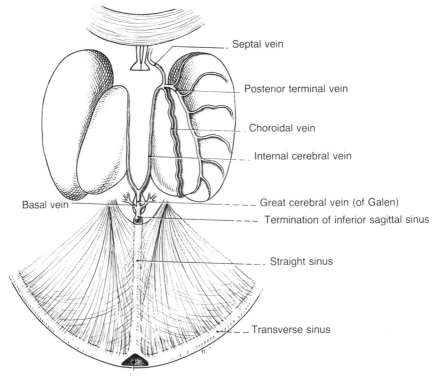

Superior sagittal sinus

Posterior terminal vein

Septal vein

Choroidal vein

Internal cerebral vein

Basal vein

Great cerebral vein (of Galen)

Inferior sagittal sinus

Straight sinus

Transverse sinus

Internal jugular vein

DEEP CEREBRAL VEINS

Septal vein

Posterior terminal vein

Choroidal vein

Internal cerebral vein

Basal vein

Great cerebral vein (of Galen)

Termination of inferior sagittal sinus

Straight sinus

Transverse sinus

Confluence of dural venous sinuses

[*]From Lazorthes, G.: Vascularisation et Circulation Cérébrales. Paris, Masson et Cie., 1961, p. 144.

RELATIONS OF THE BLOOD
VESSELS PENETRATING THE BRAIN*

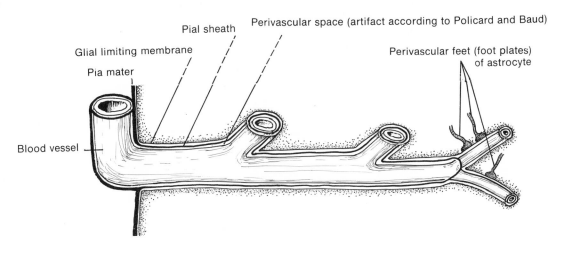

BLOOD-BRAIN BARRIER

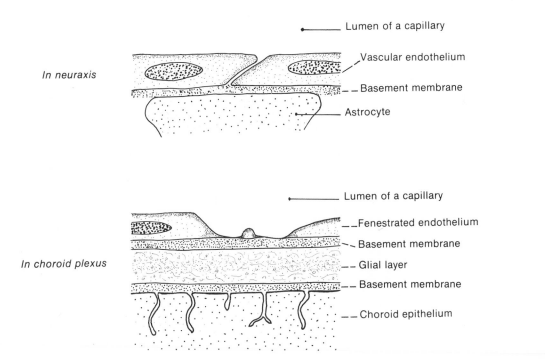

*From Policard, A., and Baud, C. A.: Les Structures Inframicroscopiques Normales et Pathologiques des Cellules et des Tissus. Paris, Masson et Cie., 1958, p. 244.

Protection of the Central Nervous System

SCHEMATIC CIRCULATION OF THE CEREBROSPINAL FLUID (C.S.F.)

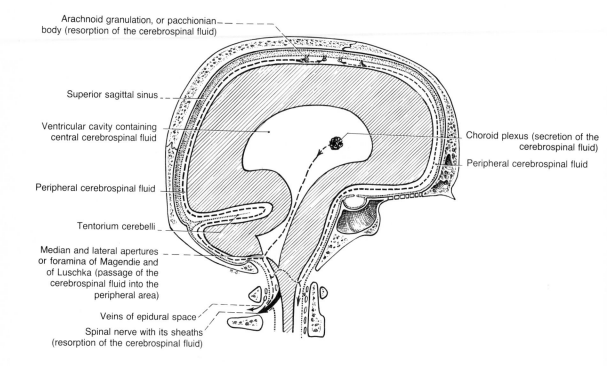

Arachnoid granulation, or pacchionian body (resorption of the cerebrospinal fluid)

Superior sagittal sinus

Ventricular cavity containing central cerebrospinal fluid

Choroid plexus (secretion of the cerebrospinal fluid)

Peripheral cerebrospinal fluid

Peripheral cerebrospinal fluid

Tentorium cerebelli

Median and lateral apertures or foramina of Magendie and of Luschka (passage of the cerebrospinal fluid into the peripheral area)

Veins of epidural space

Spinal nerve with its sheaths (resorption of the cerebrospinal fluid)

SPINAL MENINGES

SCHEMATIC TRANSVERSE SECTION OF THE VERTEBRAL CANAL AND ITS CONTENTS

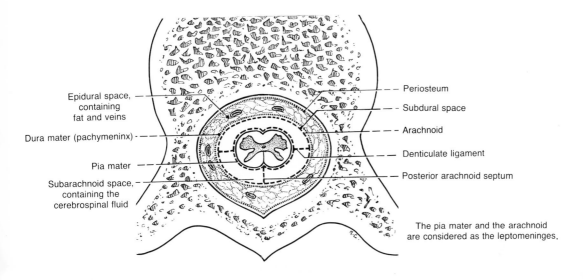

Epidural space, containing fat and veins

Dura mater (pachymeninx)

Pia mater

Subarachnoid space, containing the cerebrospinal fluid

Periosteum

Subdural space

Arachnoid

Denticulate ligament

Posterior arachnoid septum

The pia mater and the arachnoid are considered as the leptomeninges.

POSTERIOR ASPECT OF A SPINAL SEGMENT WITH ITS COVERINGS, SHOWING THE ATTACHMENTS OF THE DENTICULATE LIGAMENT

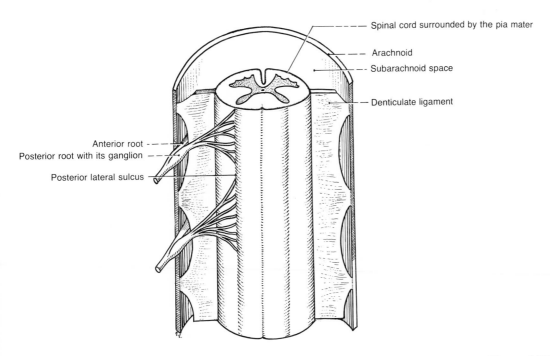

Spinal cord surrounded by the pia mater

Arachnoid

Subarachnoid space

Denticulate ligament

Anterior root

Posterior root with its ganglion

Posterior lateral sulcus

CRANIAL MENINGES

PROTECTING ELEMENTS OF THE BRAIN IN THE CALVARIA (OR SKULL CAP)

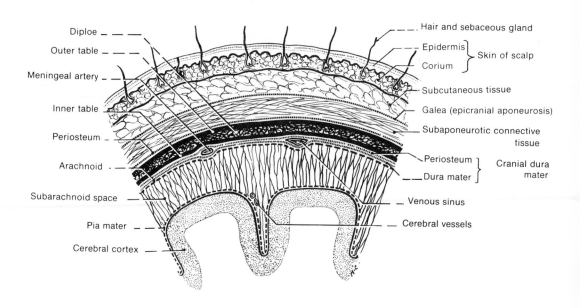

Diploe — — —
Outer table — — —
Meningeal artery — —
Inner table —
Periosteum —
Arachnoid -
Subarachnoid space —
Pia mater — — —
Cerebral cortex — —

— — — Hair and sebaceous gland
— — Epidermis ⎱ Skin of scalp
— Corium ⎰
— Subcutaneous tissue
— Galea (epicranial aponeurosis)
— Subaponeurotic connective tissue
— Periosteum ⎱ Cranial dura
— — Dura mater ⎰ mater
— Venous sinus
— Cerebral vessels

TENTORIUM CEREBELLI

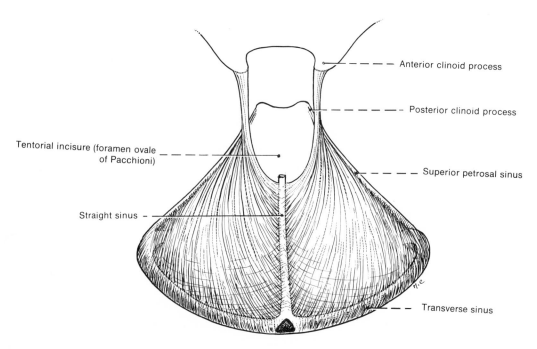

Tentorial incisure (foramen ovale of Pacchioni) — — —
Straight sinus -

— — — Anterior clinoid process
— — — Posterior clinoid process
— — — Superior petrosal sinus
— — Transverse sinus

Page 178

Falx and Tentoria

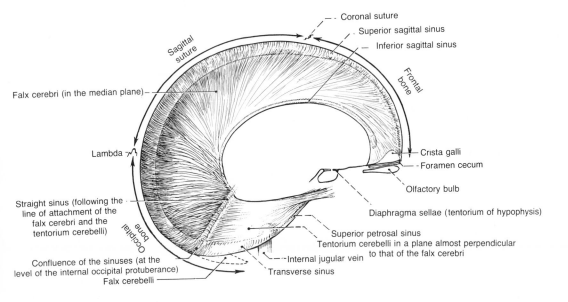

- Coronal suture
- Superior sagittal sinus
- Inferior sagittal sinus

Sagittal suture

Frontal bone

Falx cerebri (in the median plane)

Lambda

Crista galli

Foramen cecum

Olfactory bulb

Diaphragma sellae (tentorium of hypophysis)

Straight sinus (following the line of attachment of the falx cerebri and the tentorium cerebelli)

Occipital bone

Superior petrosal sinus

Tentorium cerebelli in a plane almost perpendicular to that of the falx cerebri

Internal jugular vein

Confluence of the sinuses (at the level of the internal occipital protuberance)

Falx cerebelli

Transverse sinus

Median Section of the Pituitary Fossa (Sella Turcica), Showing the Diaphragma Sellae (Tentorium of Hypophysis)

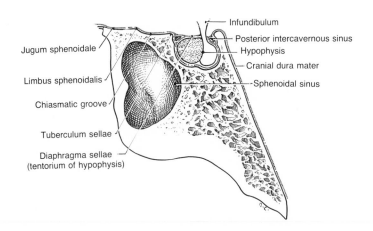

Infundibulum

Jugum sphenoidale

Posterior intercavernous sinus

Hypophysis

Limbus sphenoidalis

Cranial dura mater

Chiasmatic groove

Sphenoidal sinus

Tuberculum sellae

Diaphragma sellae (tentorium of hypophysis)

SUBARACHNOID CISTERNS

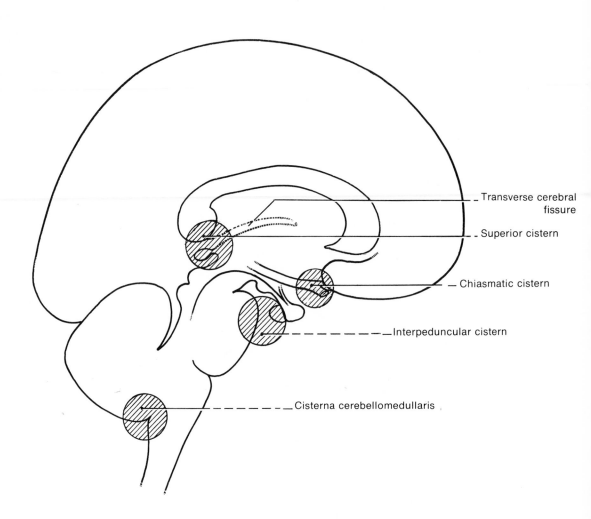

Transverse cerebral fissure

Superior cistern

Chiasmatic cistern

Interpeduncular cistern

Cisterna cerebellomedullaris

The small cisterns of the lamina terminalis, of the pons and of the corpus callosum are not represented on this diagram.

On the lateral aspect of the brain, the cistern of the lateral cerebral fossa appears. It is also called the sylvian or anterolateral cistern.

STRUCTURE OF THE MENINGES

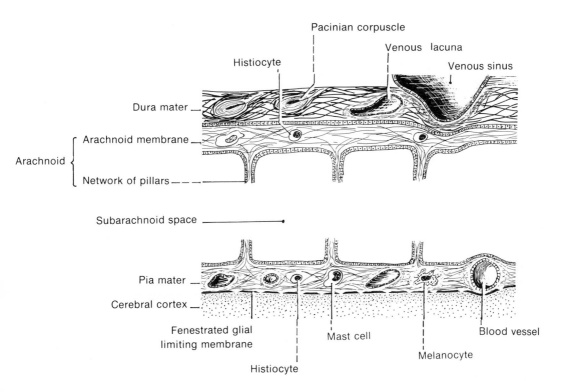

Pacinian corpuscle

Histiocyte

Venous lacuna

Venous sinus

Dura mater

Arachnoid membrane

Arachnoid

Network of pillars

Subarachnoid space

Pia mater

Cerebral cortex

Fenestrated glial limiting membrane

Mast cell

Histiocyte

Melanocyte

Blood vessel

Arachnoid Granulation (or Pacchionian Body)

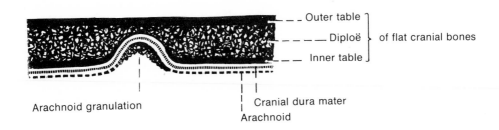

Outer table

Diploë — of flat cranial bones

Inner table

Arachnoid granulation

Cranial dura mater

Arachnoid

PYRAMIDAL TRACTS

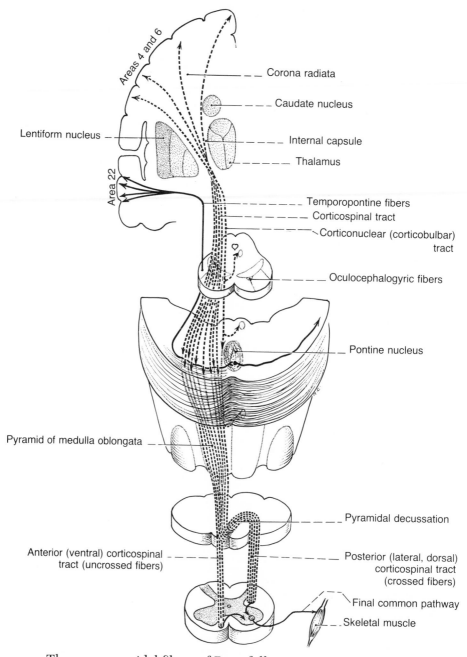

Areas 4 and 6

Corona radiata

Caudate nucleus

Lentiform nucleus

Internal capsule

Thalamus

Area 22

Temporopontine fibers

Corticospinal tract

Corticonuclear (corticobulbar) tract

Oculocephalogyric fibers

Pontine nucleus

Pyramid of medulla oblongata

Pyramidal decussation

Anterior (ventral) corticospinal tract (uncrossed fibers)

Posterior (lateral, dorsal) corticospinal tract (crossed fibers)

Final common pathway

Skeletal muscle

The parapyramidal fibers of Bucy follow a course superimposable on the anterior corticospinal tract.

CORTICORUBROSPINAL PATHWAY

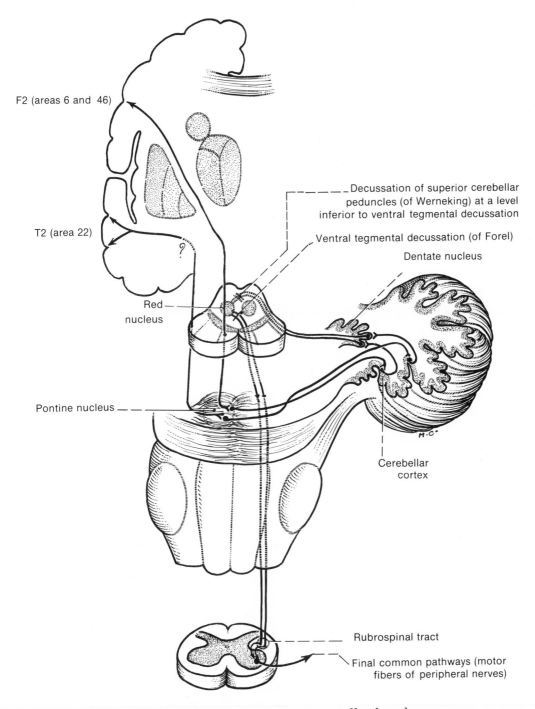

F2 (areas 6 and 46)

T2 (area 22)

Red nucleus

Pontine nucleus

Decussation of superior cerebellar peduncles (of Werneking) at a level inferior to ventral tegmental decussation

Ventral tegmental decussation (of Forel)

Dentate nucleus

Cerebellar cortex

Rubrospinal tract

Final common pathways (motor fibers of peripheral nerves)

Bucy and Klüver have shown experimentally that there are no direct fibers from area 22 to the pontine nucleus in the monkey. Thus, one is obliged to admit the existence of a striate or subthalamic relay.

THE EXTRAPYRAMIDAL PATHWAYS

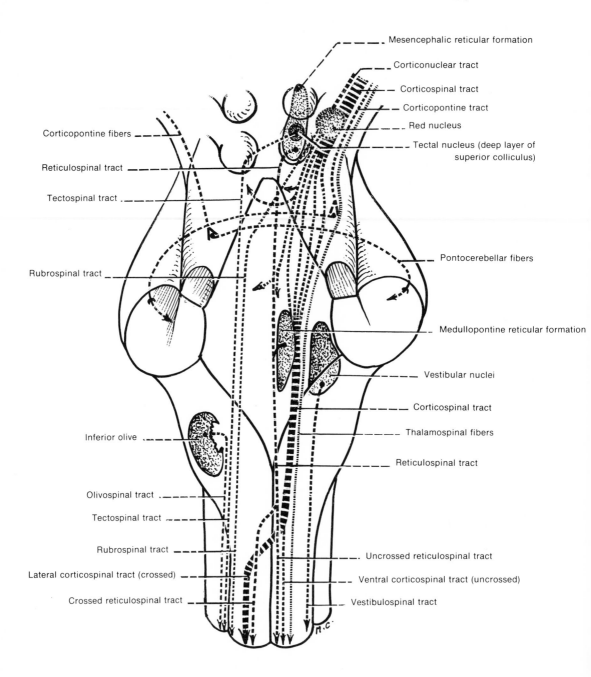

Mesencephalic reticular formation

Corticonuclear tract

Corticospinal tract

Corticopontine tract

Red nucleus

Tectal nucleus (deep layer of superior colliculus)

Corticopontine fibers

Reticulospinal tract

Tectospinal tract

Pontocerebellar fibers

Rubrospinal tract

Medullopontine reticular formation

Vestibular nuclei

Corticospinal tract

Thalamospinal fibers

Reticulospinal tract

Inferior olive

Olivospinal tract

Tectospinal tract

Rubrospinal tract

Uncrossed reticulospinal tract

Lateral corticospinal tract (crossed)

Ventral corticospinal tract (uncrossed)

Crossed reticulospinal tract

Vestibulospinal tract

RED NUCLEUS AND ITS CONNECTIONS

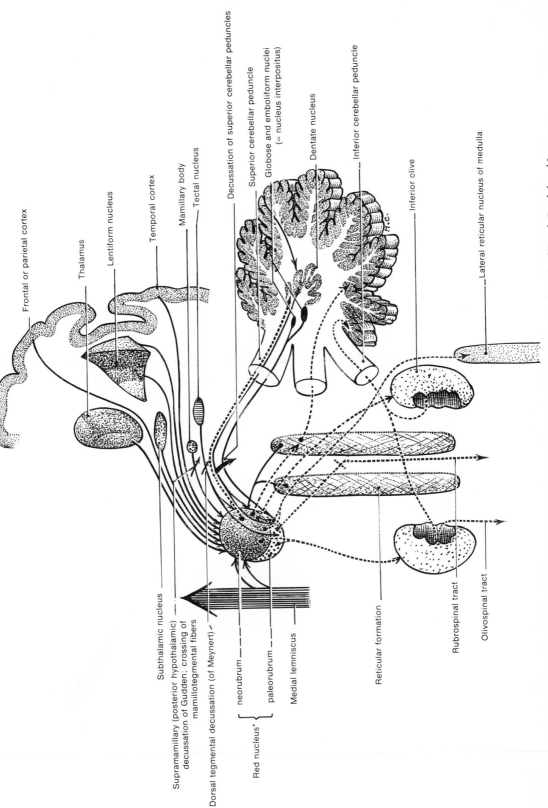

Frontal or parietal cortex

Thalamus

Lentiform nucleus

Temporal cortex

Mamillary body

Tectal nucleus

Decussation of superior cerebellar peduncles

Superior cerebellar peduncle

Globose and emboliform nuclei (= nucleus interpositus)

Dentate nucleus

Inferior cerebellar peduncle

Inferior olive

Lateral reticular nucleus of medulla

Subthalamic nucleus

Supramamillary (posterior hypothalamic) decussation of Gudden: crossing of mamillotegmental fibers

Dorsal tegmental decussation (of Meynert)

Red nucleus* { neorubrum

paleorubrum

Medial lemniscus

Reticular formation

Rubrospinal tract

Olivospinal tract

*Diagram of the connections of the red nucleus based on the morphological work of Cajal, Brodal and Jansen, Walberg, Kappers, and the experimental conclusions of Pompéiano, Albe-Fessard and Massion.

PATHWAYS OF GENERAL SOMESTHETIC SENSIBILITY

These pathways include three neurons:
1st neuron: periphery to nucleus
2nd neuron: nucleus to thalamus
3rd neuron: thalamus to cortex

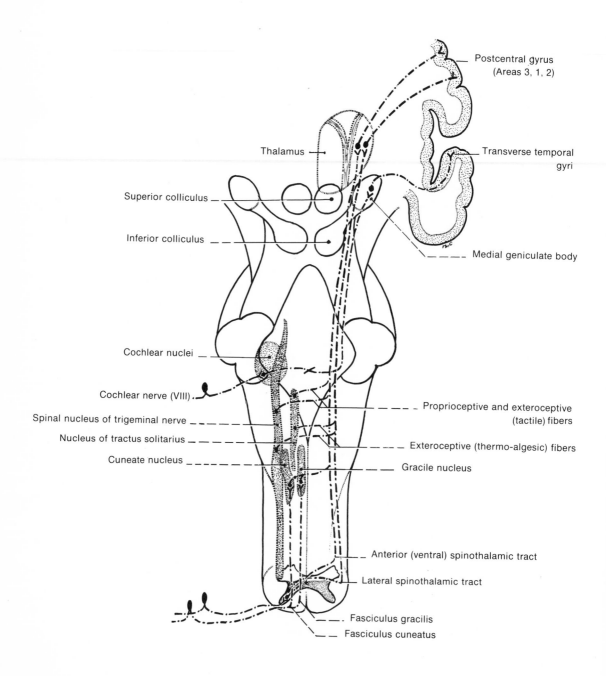

Postcentral gyrus (Areas 3, 1, 2)

Thalamus

Transverse temporal gyri

Superior colliculus

Inferior colliculus

Medial geniculate body

Cochlear nuclei

Cochlear nerve (VIII)

Proprioceptive and exteroceptive (tactile) fibers

Spinal nucleus of trigeminal nerve

Nucleus of tractus solitarius

Exteroceptive (thermo-algesic) fibers

Cuneate nucleus

Gracile nucleus

Anterior (ventral) spinothalamic tract

Lateral spinothalamic tract

Fasciculus gracilis

Fasciculus cuneatus

CEREBELLAR PATHWAYS,
AFFERENT FIBERS TO
CEREBELLUM

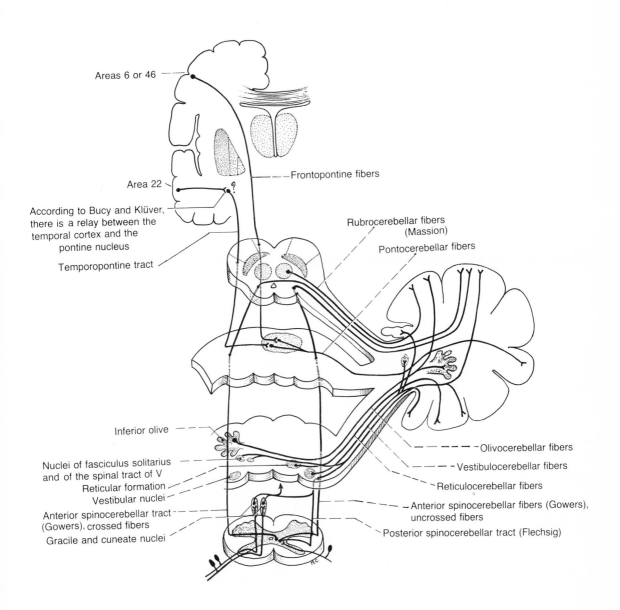

Areas 6 or 46

Frontopontine fibers

Area 22

According to Bucy and Klüver, there is a relay between the temporal cortex and the pontine nucleus

Temporoportine tract

Rubrocerebellar fibers (Massion)

Pontocerebellar fibers

Inferior olive

Nuclei of fasciculus solitarius and of the spinal tract of V

Reticular formation

Vestibular nuclei

Anterior spinocerebellar tract (Gowers), crossed fibers

Gracile and cuneate nuclei

Olivocerebellar fibers

Vestibulocerebellar fibers

Reticulocerebellar fibers

Anterior spinocerebellar fibers (Gowers), uncrossed fibers

Posterior spinocerebellar tract (Flechsig)

Anterior spinocerebellar tract (Gowers):
   the fibers crossed in the spinal cord cross in the brain stem
   the fibers uncrossed in the spinal cord do not cross in the brain stem

CEREBELLAR PATHWAYS, AFFERENT FIBERS FROM CEREBELLUM

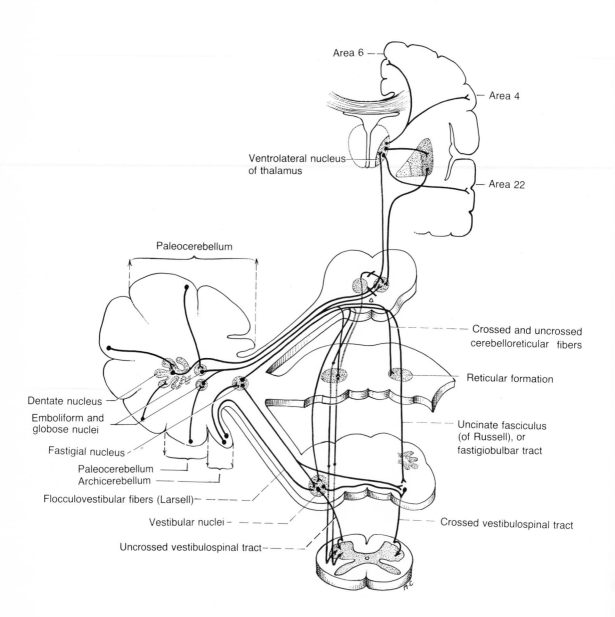

Area 6

Area 4

Area 22

Ventrolateral nucleus of thalamus

Paleocerebellum

Crossed and uncrossed cerebelloreticular fibers

Reticular formation

Dentate nucleus

Emboliform and globose nuclei

Uncinate fasciculus (of Russell), or fastigiobulbar tract

Fastigial nucleus

Paleocerebellum
Archicerebellum

Flocculovestibular fibers (Larsell)

Vestibular nuclei

Crossed vestibulospinal tract

Uncrossed vestibulospinal tract

ASSOCIATION FIBERS AND PATHWAYS

TABLE OF THE ASSOCIATION FASCICULI

1. *Longitudinal association fasciculi*

Cortical level: Cingulum, see pages 153 and 194
   Superior longitudinal (fronto-occipital) fasciculus, see page 154
   Inferior longitudinal (temporo-occipital) fasciculus, see page 153
   Arcuate fasciculus, see page 154
   Uncinate (temporofrontal) fasciculus, located at the level of the limen insulae, see page 154
   Fornix, see pages 154 and 193

Subcortical level: Medial forebrain bundle
   Stria terminalis (stria semicircularis), see page 192
   Stria medullaris of the thalamus, see page 192

Brain stem: Medial longitudinal fasciculus, see pages 127 to 131 and 190
   Dorsal longitudinal fasciculus, see page 130
   Central tegmental tract, see pages 128, 129 and 130

Spinal cord: the fasciculi proprii are pathways more than fasciculi, see page 116

2. *Short fasciculi*

Cortical level: Arcuate (short association) fibers

Internuclear: They are located in the whole neuraxis; they may be individualized as is the ansa lenticularis (page 146) or not (connections between thalamic nuclei for instance); in the latter example, they form laminae or fields of white matter in which the fibers are not oriented and thus show a reticular or plexiform aspect (medullary lamina of the thalamus, see page 146).

Reticular formation: Besides its functional aspect, it is to be considered as an association pathway with many elements.

3. *Commissures*

Crossing of the nerve pathways is a general feature of the central nervous system; thus, commissural fibers are found in the whole length of the neuraxis. Besides the decussations of the great pathways which we will not concern ourselves with in this section, there are groups of association fibers crossing the median plane which, strictly speaking, are the commissures.

Corpus callosum, see page 195
Fornical (hippocampal) commissure, see page 193
Anterior commissure, see page 191
Posterior commissure, see page 191; located between mesencephalon and diencephalon, below the stalk of the pineal body
Supra-optic commissures, page 195
   Ventral supra-optic commissure (of Gudden)
   Dorsal supra-optic commissure (of Meynert)
   Anterior hypothalamic commissure (of Ganser)
Posterior subthalamic commissure (of Forel) between the two subthalamic regions
Posterior hypothalamic commissure (or supramamillary, or transverse fibers of tuber)

Habenular commissure
Tegmental decussations, see pages 131 and 185:
  Ventral tegmental decussation (of Forel)
  Dorsal tegmental decussation (of Meynert)
Decussation of brachia conjunctiva (or superior cerebellar peduncles), see pages 131 and 185
Decussations of the superior and inferior colliculi
Decussations of cranial nerves
Commissural fibers in the spinal cord

It is interesting to note that the specialization of certain fasciculi is such that they are integrated into one functional complex (e.g., stria terminalis into rhinencephalon).

MEDIAL LONGITUDINAL FASCICULUS

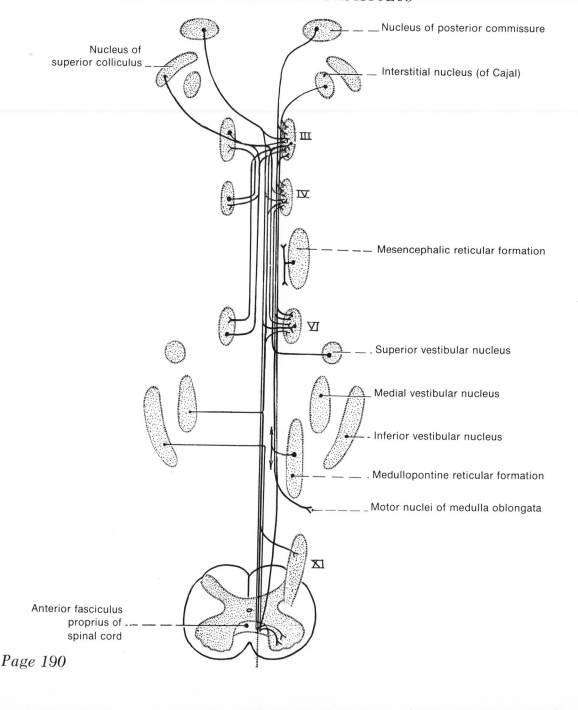

Nucleus of superior colliculus

Nucleus of posterior commissure

Interstitial nucleus (of Cajal)

III

IV

Mesencephalic reticular formation

VI

Superior vestibular nucleus

Medial vestibular nucleus

Inferior vestibular nucleus

Medullopontine reticular formation

Motor nuclei of medulla oblongata

XI

Anterior fasciculus proprius of spinal cord

ANTERIOR COMMISSURE*

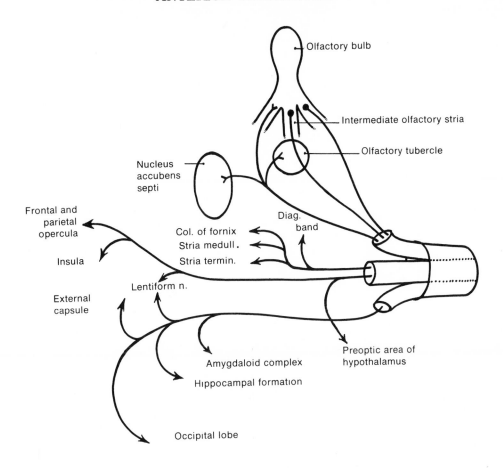

Olfactory bulb

Intermediate olfactory stria

Olfactory tubercle

Nucleus
accubens
septi

Diag.
band

Frontal and
parietal
opercula

Col. of fornix
Stria medull.
Stria termin.

Insula

Lentiform n.

External
capsule

Preoptic area of
hypothalamus

Amygdaloid complex

Hippocampal formation

Occipital lobe

POSTERIOR COMMISSURE

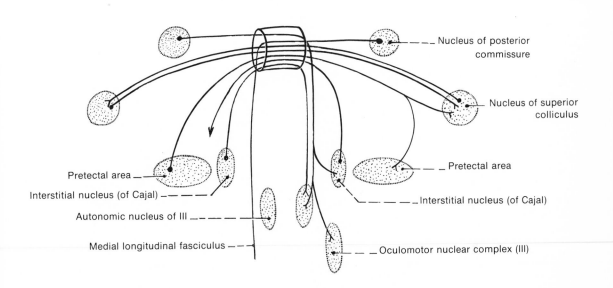

Nucleus of posterior
commissure

Nucleus of superior
colliculus

Pretectal area

Pretectal area

Interstitial nucleus (of Cajal)

Interstitial nucleus (of Cajal)

Autonomic nucleus of III

Medial longitudinal fasciculus

Oculomotor nuclear complex (III)

°*From the works of Brodal and Foroglou.*

STRIA TERMINALIS AND STRIA MEDULLARIS
OF THE THALAMUS*

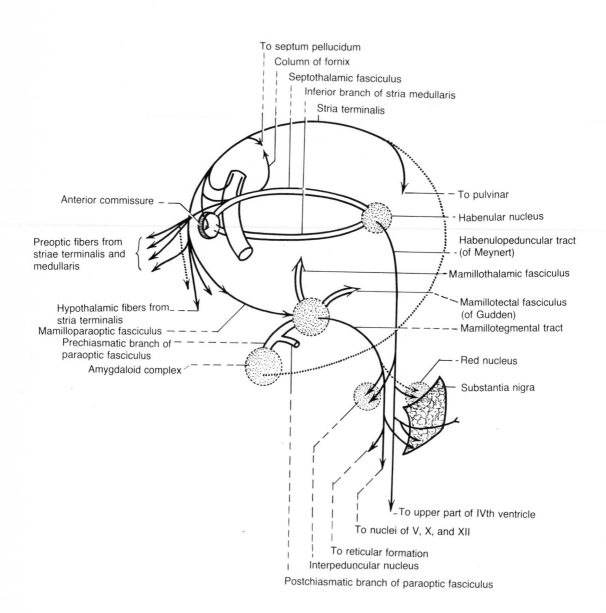

To septum pellucidum
Column of fornix
Septothalamic fasciculus
Inferior branch of stria medullaris
Stria terminalis

Anterior commissure

Preoptic fibers from
striae terminalis and
medullaris

Hypothalamic fibers from
stria terminalis
Mamilloparaoptic fasciculus
Prechiasmatic branch of
paraoptic fasciculus
Amygdaloid complex

To pulvinar
Habenular nucleus
Habenulopeduncular tract
(of Meynert)
Mamillothalamic fasciculus
Mamillotectal fasciculus
(of Gudden)
Mamillotegmental tract

Red nucleus
Substantia nigra

To upper part of IVth ventricle
To nuclei of V, X, and XII
To reticular formation
Interpeduncular nucleus
Postchiasmatic branch of paraoptic fasciculus

*From Foroglou, G. P.:
  Étude macroscopique de la commissure blanche antérieure et des voies olfactives chez le mouton. Arch.
    Anat. Histol. Embryol., 38:67-79, 1955.
  Concerning the mammilloparaoptic bundle, otherwise called bundle in "A." Acta Anat., 31:531-538, 1957.
  Étude comparative des voies olfactives centrales. Thèse de Médecine, Lausanne, 1959.

FORNIX

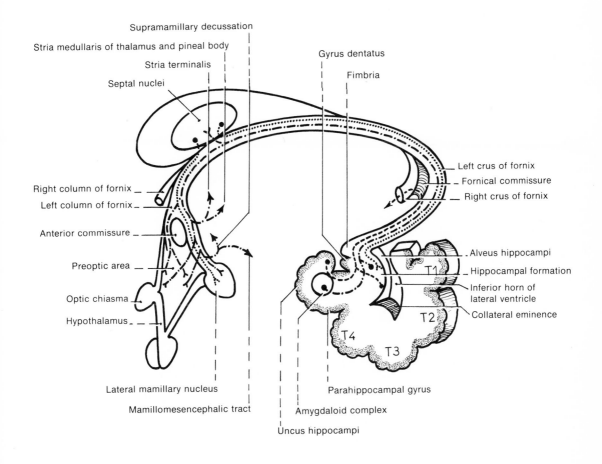

Supramamillary decussation

Stria medullaris of thalamus and pineal body

Stria terminalis

Septal nuclei

Gyrus dentatus

Fimbria

Right column of fornix

Left column of fornix

Anterior commissure

Preoptic area

Optic chiasma

Hypothalamus

Left crus of fornix

Fornical commissure

Right crus of fornix

Alveus hippocampi

Hippocampal formation

Inferior horn of lateral ventricle

Collateral eminence

T1

T2

T3

T4

Lateral mamillary nucleus

Mamillomesencephalic tract

Amygdaloid complex

Parahippocampal gyrus

Uncus hippocampi

DIAGRAM OF THE CINGULUM AND ITS MAIN RELATIONSHIPS*

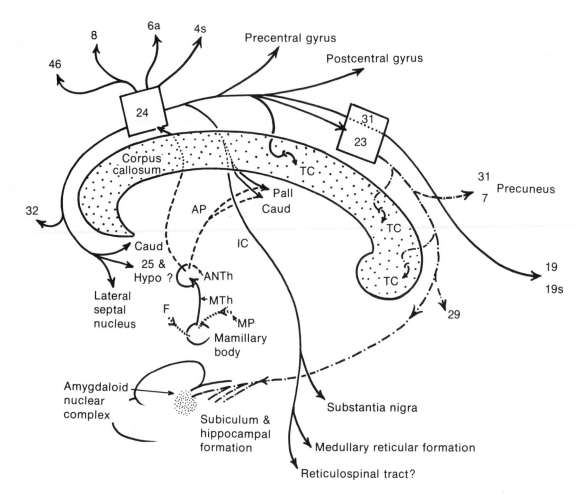

ANTh: anterior nucleus of thalamus
AP   : ansa peduncularis
Caud : caudate nucleus
Hypo : hypothalamus
IC   : internal capsule
MP   : mamillary peduncle
MTh : mamillothalamic tract
Pall : pallidum
TC   : transcallosal fibers

(The numbers refer to
Brodman's cortical areas.)

*According to the works of Cajal, Clark (1932, 1933), Locke and Kruper (1965), McCulloch (1944), Papez (1937), Rose et al. (1947), and Ward (1948).

SUPRA-OPTIC COMMISSURES*

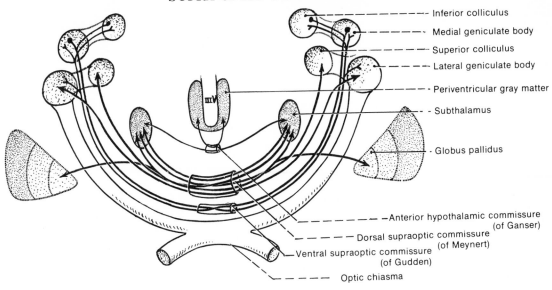

Inferior colliculus
Medial geniculate body
Superior colliculus
Lateral geniculate body
Periventricular gray matter
Subthalamus
Globus pallidus

Anterior hypothalamic commissure
(of Ganser)
Dorsal supraoptic commissure
(of Meynert)
Ventral supraoptic commissure
(of Gudden)
Optic chiasma

CORPUS CALLOSUM

Superior aspect of a specimen
   On the left side, dissection of superior callosal radiations
   On the right side, superior callosal radiations, insula and a part of basal ganglia were
      removed to display the inferior callosal radiations from the rostrum and the splenium
      of the corpus callosum

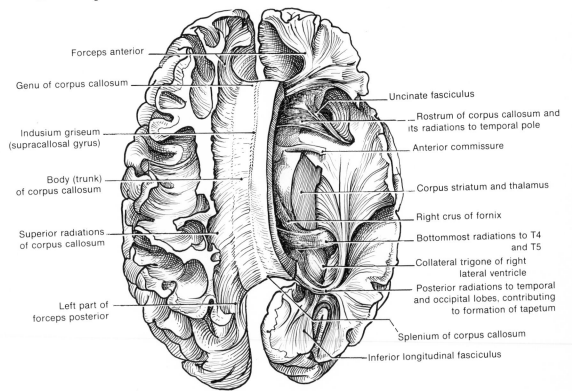

Forceps anterior
Genu of corpus callosum
Indusium griseum
(supracallosal gyrus)
Body (trunk)
of corpus callosum
Superior radiations
of corpus callosum
Left part of
forceps posterior

Uncinate fasciculus
Rostrum of corpus callosum and
its radiations to temporal pole
Anterior commissure
Corpus striatum and thalamus
Right crus of fornix
Bottommost radiations to T4
and T5
Collateral trigone of right
lateral ventricle
Posterior radiations to temporal
and occipital lobes, contributing
to formation of tapetum
Splenium of corpus callosum
Inferior longitudinal fasciculus

From Kuntz, A.: A Textbook of Neuroanatomy. 5th ed. Philadelphia, Lea & Febiger, 1950, p. 348.

Part Four

Cranial Nerves and Special Sense Organs

Morphological Structures Related to Olfaction

EXTERNAL NOSE

TYPES OF NOSES

Straight nose
(Augustus)
Horizontal base

Greek nose
(Venus de Milo)
Horizontal base

Arched nose
(Dante)
Aryan type
Base inclined downward

Upturned nose
(Socrates)
Base inclined upward

TYPES OF NOSTRILS

Caucasian
(sagittal orifice)

Mongoloid
(oblique orifice)

Negroid
(transverse orifice)

SKELETON OF THE NASAL PYRAMID

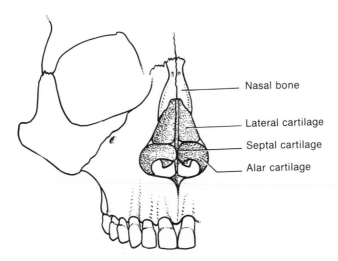

- Nasal bone
- Lateral cartilage
- Septal cartilage
- Alar cartilage

BASE OF THE EXTERNAL NOSE

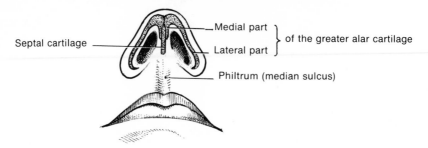

Septal cartilage

Medial part ⎫
Lateral part ⎬ of the greater alar cartilage

Philtrum (median sulcus)

LATERAL ASPECT OF THE SKELETON OF THE NASAL PYRAMID

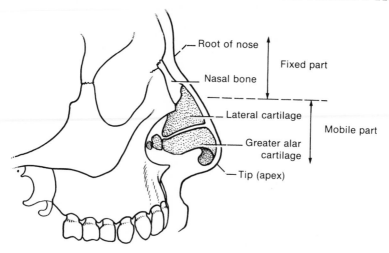

Root of nose

Fixed part

Nasal bone

Lateral cartilage

Mobile part

Greater alar cartilage

Tip (apex)

MUSCLES OF THE NOSE
(supplied by the facial nerve)

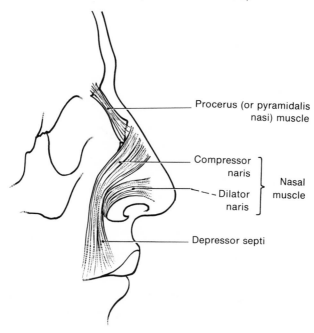

Procerus (or pyramidalis nasi) muscle

Compressor naris ⎫
                  ⎬ Nasal muscle
Dilator naris ⎭

Depressor septi

NASAL CAVITY

SKELETON OF THE NASAL SEPTUM

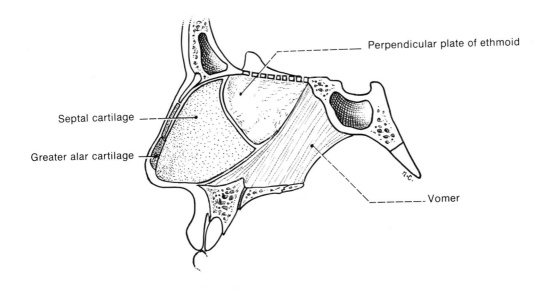

Perpendicular plate of ethmoid

Septal cartilage

Greater alar cartilage

Vomer

SKELETON OF THE LATERAL WALL OF THE RIGHT NASAL CAVITY

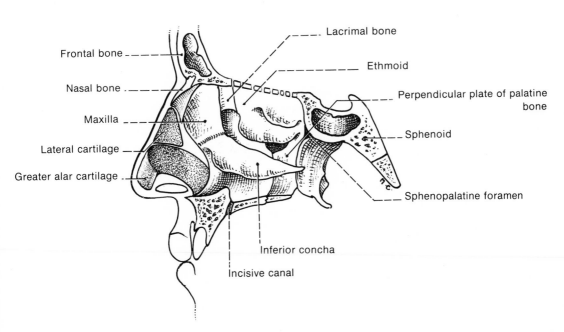

Lacrimal bone

Frontal bone

Ethmoid

Nasal bone

Perpendicular plate of palatine bone

Maxilla

Lateral cartilage

Sphenoid

Greater alar cartilage

Sphenopalatine foramen

Inferior concha

Incisive canal

Mucous Membrane of the Nasal Cavity

Medial Wall of the Left Nasal Cavity (or Septal Wall)

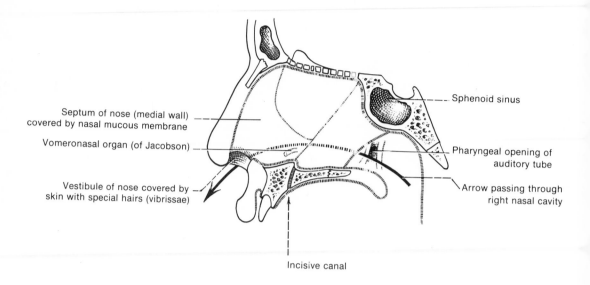

Septum of nose (medial wall) covered by nasal mucous membrane

Vomeronasal organ (of Jacobson)

Vestibule of nose covered by skin with special hairs (vibrissae)

Sphenoid sinus

Pharyngeal opening of auditory tube

Arrow passing through right nasal cavity

Incisive canal

Lateral Wall of the Right Nasal Cavity

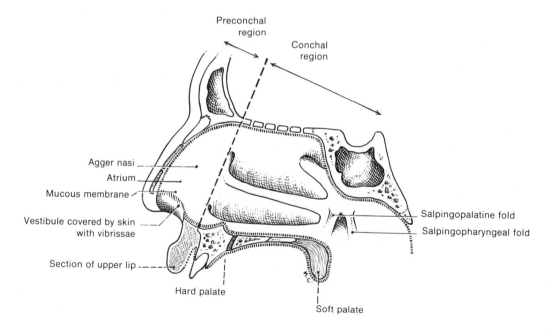

Preconchal region

Conchal region

Agger nasi

Atrium

Mucous membrane

Vestibule covered by skin with vibrissae

Section of upper lip

Hard palate

Soft palate

Salpingopalatine fold

Salpingopharyngeal fold

Section of the mucous membrane is shown by the dotted line.

PARANASAL SINUSES

FRONTAL SECTION OF THE SKULL SHOWING THE PARANASAL SINUSES

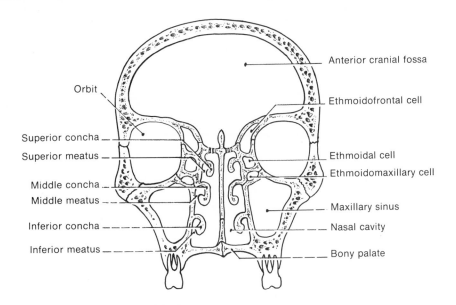

Anterior cranial fossa
Orbit
Ethmoidofrontal cell
Superior concha
Superior meatus
Ethmoidal cell
Ethmoidomaxillary cell
Middle concha
Middle meatus
Maxillary sinus
Inferior concha
Nasal cavity
Inferior meatus
Bony palate

SCHEME OF THE LATERAL WALL OF THE RIGHT NASAL CAVITY SHOWING THE OPENINGS OF THE PARANASAL SINUSES

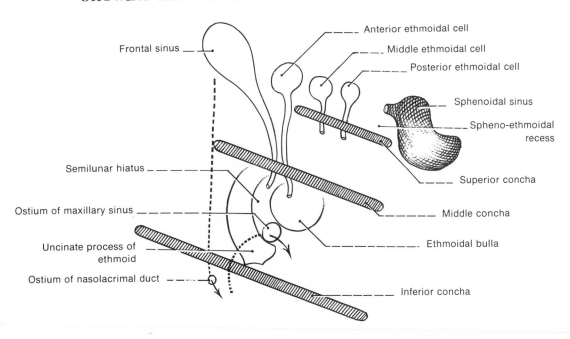

Frontal sinus
Anterior ethmoidal cell
Middle ethmoidal cell
Posterior ethmoidal cell
Sphenoidal sinus
Spheno-ethmoidal recess
Semilunar hiatus
Ostium of maxillary sinus
Superior concha
Uncinate process of ethmoid
Middle concha
Ostium of nasolacrimal duct
Ethmoidal bulla
Inferior concha

The arrow going out of the maxillary sinus indicates the level of the floor of this sinus located below the ostium.

SENSORY NERVES AND ARTERIES OF
THE NASAL CAVITY

ARTERIES AND NERVES OF THE NASAL SEPTUM

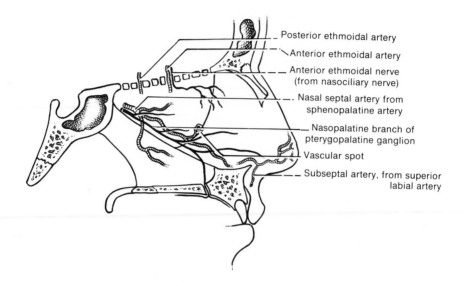

Only the anterior and posterior ethmoidal arteries, branches of the ophthalmic artery, are related to the internal carotid system.

ARTERIES AND NERVES OF THE LATERAL WALL

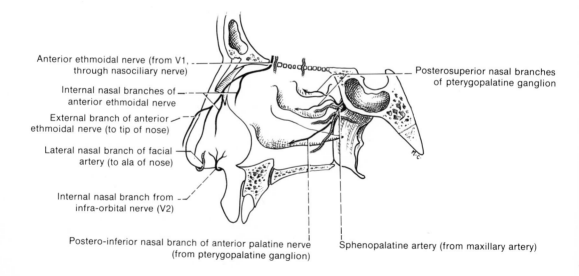

APPARATUS OF THE OLFACTORY SENSE

The olfactory mucosa has a yellowish color. It covers the middle and the superior conchae, the upper part of the septum, and the cribriform plate of the ethmoid.

OLFACTORY NEUROEPITHELIUM

The sensory cells are located between the sustentacular cells and the basal cells. The olfactory neuroepithelium is a columnar, pseudo-stratified epithelium.

The *basal cells* are deep, stellate, and connected to each other in network fashion, and form a discontinuous layer. It is not yet known if these cells are nervous or connective, or if they ought to be considered as substitute cells (Cajal).

The *sustentacular cells* are elongated epithelial cells, including yellow granules and mucigenic vacuoles. They possess no vibratile cilia, as opposed to the rest of the cells of the respiratory mucosa.

The bodies of the *olfactory cells* are staggered, which results in their pseudostratified appearance. Each cell is formed according to the following scheme: a cell body including nucleus, and possessing (on the nasal side) an olfactory rod, the distal end of which is dilated into a small vesicle supporting five or six small cilia; on the opposite side, an axonal process passing through the lamina propria to the cribriform plate of the ethmoid bone.

MUCOUS MEMBRANE OF THE OLFACTORY AREA

ELECTRON MICROSCOPY OF THE OLFACTORY CELLS*

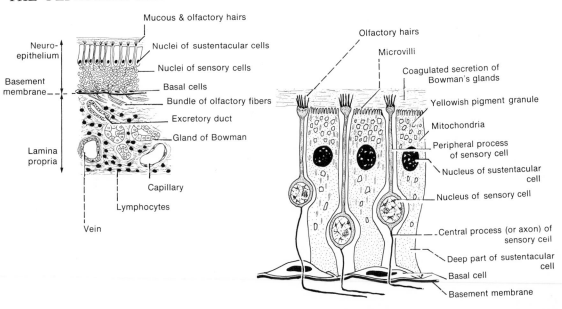

Redrawn from Rhodin, J. A. G.: An Atlas of Ultrastructure. Philadelphia, W. B. Saunders Company, 1963, p. 164; and from Bloom, G.: Studies on the olfactory epithelium of the frog and the toad with aid of light and electron microscopy. Z. Zellforsch., 41:89-100, 1954.

The fibers originating from the sensory cells combine in groups of about 20 rami for each nasal cavity (8 to 12 for the medial and the lateral walls). These rami are the olfactory nerves, strictly speaking. Surrounded by a sheath originating from the cranial dura mater, they pass through the cribriform plate and enter the olfactory bulb in two parallel rows, depending on their septal or lateral origin. The olfactory nerves end at this level.

Macroscopically the olfactory bulb lies on the cribriform plate of the ethmoid, maintained in place by a formation of the dura mater, the tentorium of the olfactory bulb (see page 179). The olfactory tract connects the olfactory bulb to the anterior perforated substance and is in contact with the olfactory sulcus of the orbital surface of the frontal lobe (see page 201).

STRUCTURE OF THE OLFACTORY BULB IN MAN

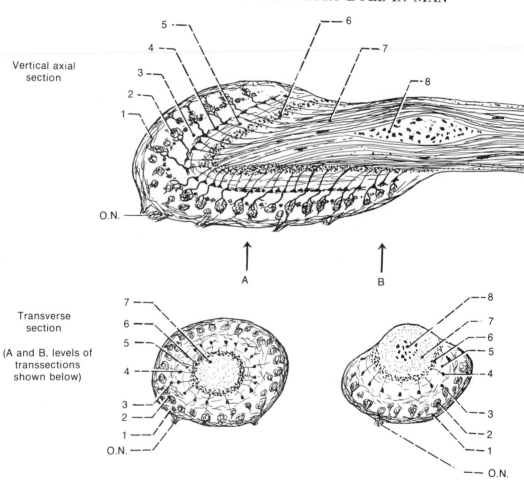

Vertical axial section

Transverse section

(A and B, levels of transsections shown below)

1. Superficial (or fibrillar) layer
2. Layer of the glomeruli
3. External plexiform layer
4. Layer of the mitral cells
5. Internal plexiform layer

6. Granular layer
7. Layer of the fibers of the olfactory tract
8. Median nucleus (or central body)
O.N., Olfactory nerves

OLFACTORY BULB AND OLFACTORY TRACT

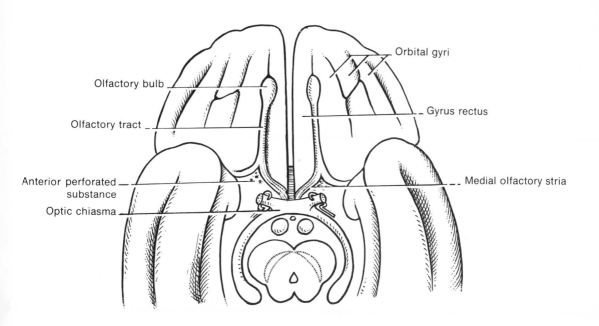

Orbital gyri

Olfactory bulb

Olfactory tract

Gyrus rectus

Anterior perforated substance

Medial olfactory stria

Optic chiasma

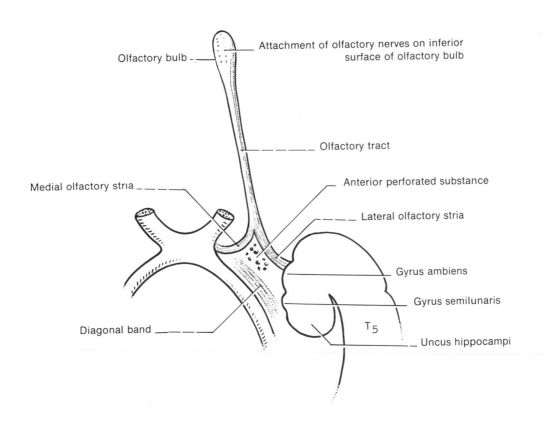

Olfactory bulb

Attachment of olfactory nerves on inferior surface of olfactory bulb

Olfactory tract

Medial olfactory stria

Anterior perforated substance

Lateral olfactory stria

Gyrus ambiens

Gyrus semilunaris

Diagonal band

T5

Uncus hippocampi

RHINENCEPHALON

The rhinencephalon is generally accepted as a complex which includes all the structures related to olfaction. In man this may not be entirely true because some of the structures of the rhinencephalon are thought to have no direct involvement in the sense of smell.

DIAGRAM OF THE OLFACTORY PATHWAYS

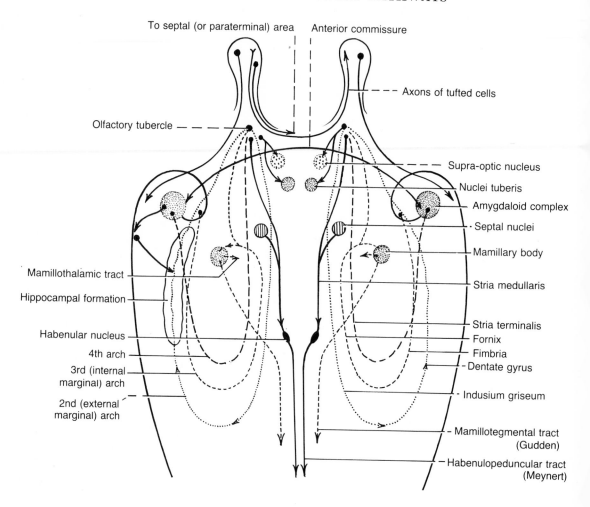

According to Lammers and Gastaut,* all the impulses arrive in the amygdaloid complex by the lateral olfactory stria; for all the arches the direction is, according to them, from the amygdaloid complex to the olfactory tubercle.

The direct connections with the hypothalamus are denied by Ramon y Cajal and Le Gros Clark.

*Gastaut, H., and Lammers, H. J.: Anatomie du Rhinencéphale (Alajouanine, T. [ed.]). Paris, Masson et Cie., 1961.

For didactic reasons the concentric rhinencephalic formations are exposed according to the morphologic diagram of Zuckerkandl, which includes 3 arches:

1st arch, limbic lobe of Broca

2nd arch, external marginal arch (hippocampal limbus)

3rd arch, internal marginal arch (medullary limbus), or fornix system

Sometimes the stria terminalis is considered as the 4th arch of the rhinencephalic formations.

DIAGRAM OF THE CONCENTRIC RHINENCEPHALIC FORMATIONS

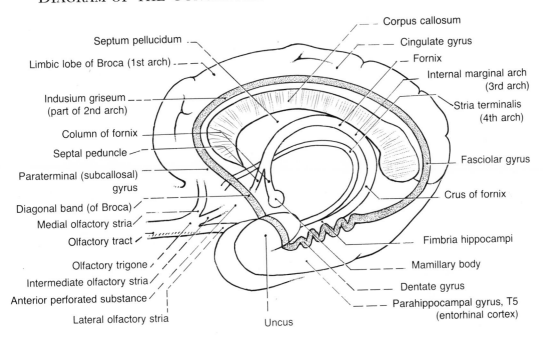

DIAGRAM OF THE CORTICAL OLFACTORY AREAS

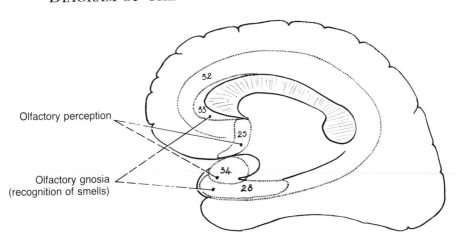

Morphological Structures Related to Vision

The morphological structures contributing to vision may be grouped under various headings:

Peripheral receptor apparatus, that is, the eyeball and its adnexa. This section includes a sensory element, the retina, and some organs of protection and accommodation.

Sensory transmission apparatus: optic nerve.

Oculomotor apparatus, formed by extrinsic muscles of the eye and three motor nerves.

Pathways and centers of vision and visual accommodation.

BONY ORBIT

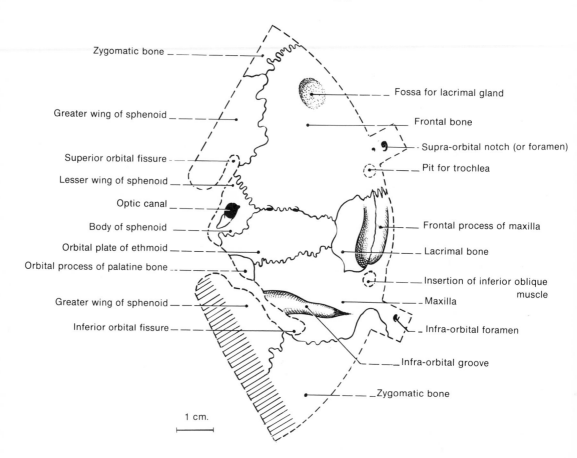

BONES OF THE ORBIT*

From O'Rahilly, R.: Anat. Rec., 141:315-316, 1961. To reconstruct a normal orbit, it suffices to cut the border of this figure and to attach the striped part to the corresponding portion of the orbital wall (zygomatic bone and greater wing of the sphenoid).

POSITION OF THE EYEBALL

ANTERIOR ASPECT OF THE BASE OF THE ORBIT

(The numbers indicate the distance, in millimeters, from the
projection of the eyeball to the margin of the orbit)

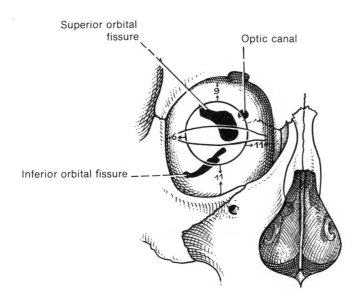

HORIZONTAL SECTION OF THE ORBIT SHOWING THE LACK OF LATERAL PROTECTION

(On the other hand, this anatomical arrangement allows for more
extensive lateral vision)

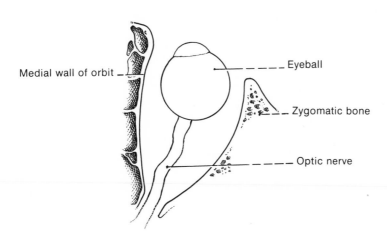

THE DEVELOPMENT OF THE EYE

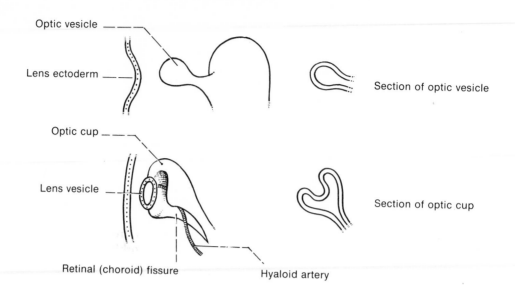

Optic vesicle

Lens ectoderm

Section of optic vesicle

Optic cup

Lens vesicle

Section of optic cup

Retinal (choroid) fissure

Hyaloid artery

The external lamina of the optic cup gives rise to the pigmented cell layer. The internal lamina gives rise to the neurosensory retina. The pigmented cell layer covers the posterior surface of the iris and extends to the margin of the pupil.

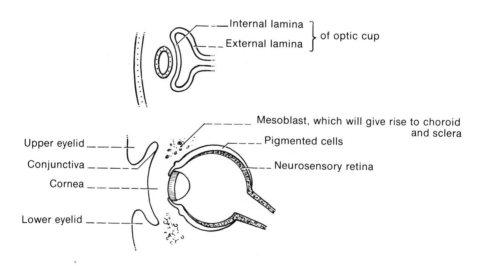

Internal lamina ⎱
                 ⎰ of optic cup
External lamina

Mesoblast, which will give rise to choroid and sclera

Upper eyelid

Pigmented cells

Conjunctiva

Neurosensory retina

Cornea

Lower eyelid

EXTERNAL CONFIGURATION OF THE EYEBALL

LATERAL ASPECT

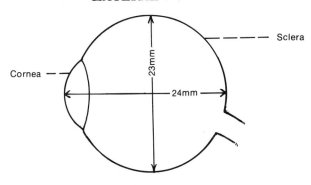

UPPER ASPECT

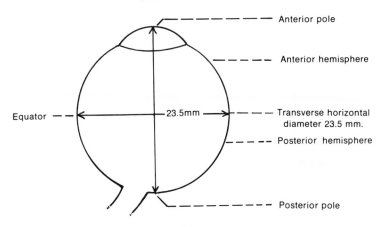

Meridian: imaginary line from pole to pole. The various meridians are designated according to the imaginary face of a clock superimposed on the cornea.

The distance between the pupillary openings varies around 60 mm.

POSTERIOR ASPECT

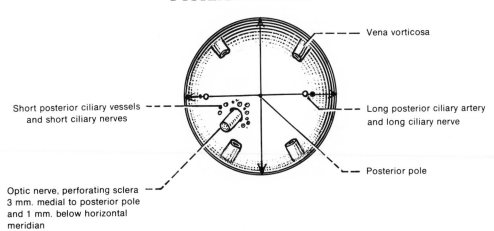

FIBROUS TUNIC OF THE EYEBALL

MAIN DIMENSIONS OF THE FIBROUS TUNIC (IN MILLIMETERS)

LIMBUS OF THE CORNEA AND SCLEROCORNEAL JUNCTION

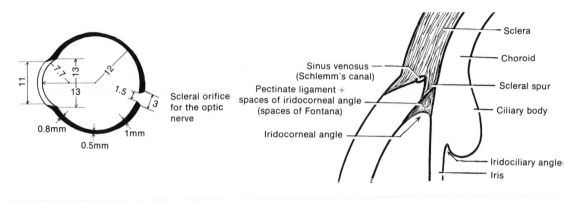

Scleral orifice for the optic nerve

Sinus venosus (Schlemm's canal)

Pectinate ligament + spaces of iridocorneal angle (spaces of Fontana)

Iridocorneal angle

Sclera

Choroid

Scleral spur

Ciliary body

Iridociliary angle

Iris

ANTERIOR ASPECT OF THE EYEBALL

A linear light beam of a slit lamp readily shows:

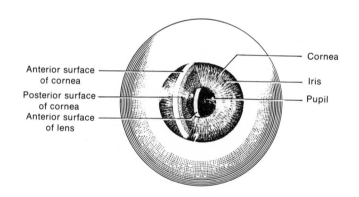

Anterior surface of cornea

Posterior surface of cornea

Anterior surface of lens

Cornea

Iris

Pupil

NERVE SUPPLY OF THE CORNEA

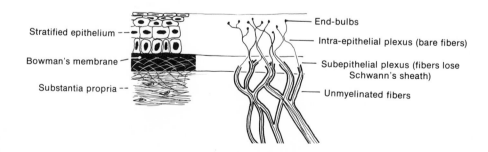

Stratified epithelium

Bowman's membrane

Substantia propria

End-bulbs

Intra-epithelial plexus (bare fibers)

Subepithelial plexus (fibers lose Schwann's sheath)

Unmyelinated fibers

VASCULAR TUNIC OF THE EYEBALL (UVEA)

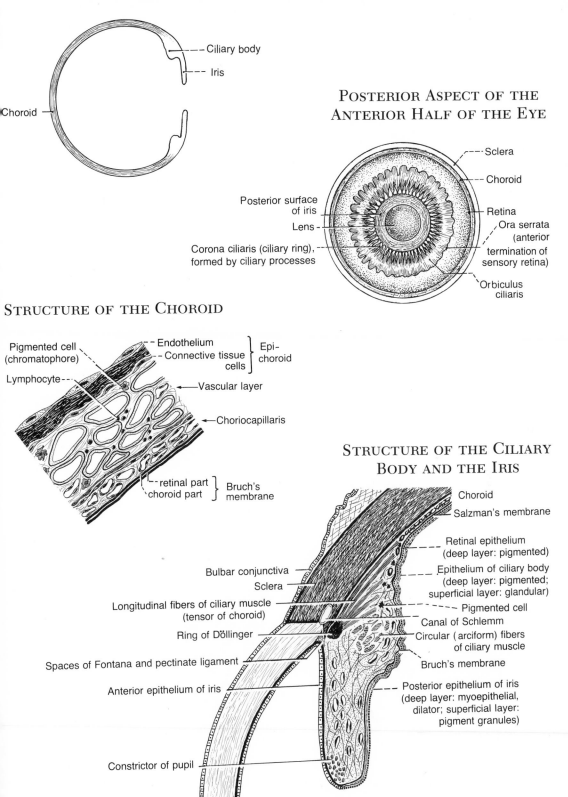

Ciliary body

Iris

Choroid

POSTERIOR ASPECT OF THE ANTERIOR HALF OF THE EYE

Sclera

Choroid

Retina

Ora serrata (anterior termination of sensory retina)

Posterior surface of iris

Lens

Corona ciliaris (ciliary ring), formed by ciliary processes

Orbiculus ciliaris

STRUCTURE OF THE CHOROID

Pigmented cell (chromatophore)

Endothelium
Connective tissue cells } Epi-choroid

Lymphocyte

Vascular layer

Choriocapillaris

retinal part
choroid part } Bruch's membrane

STRUCTURE OF THE CILIARY BODY AND THE IRIS

Choroid

Salzman's membrane

Retinal epithelium (deep layer: pigmented)

Epithelium of ciliary body (deep layer: pigmented; superficial layer: glandular)

Bulbar conjunctiva

Sclera

Longitudinal fibers of ciliary muscle (tensor of choroid)

Ring of Döllinger

Spaces of Fontana and pectinate ligament

Anterior epithelium of iris

Pigmented cell

Canal of Schlemm

Circular (arciform) fibers of ciliary muscle

Bruch's membrane

Posterior epithelium of iris (deep layer: myoepithelial, dilator; superficial layer: pigment granules)

Constrictor of pupil

Page 215

VESSELS AND NERVES OF THE VASCULAR TUNIC OF THE EYEBALL

Arteries

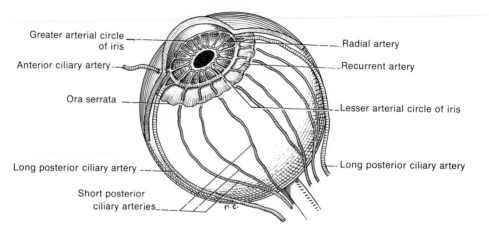

Greater arterial circle of iris

Anterior ciliary artery

Ora serrata

Long posterior ciliary artery

Short posterior ciliary arteries

Radial artery

Recurrent artery

Lesser arterial circle of iris

Long posterior ciliary artery

Veins

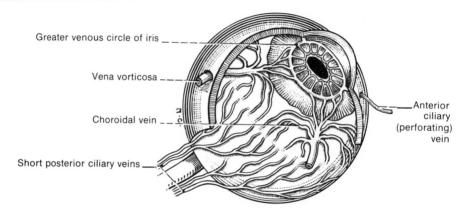

Greater venous circle of iris

Vena vorticosa

Choroidal vein

Short posterior ciliary veins

Anterior ciliary (perforating) vein

Nerves

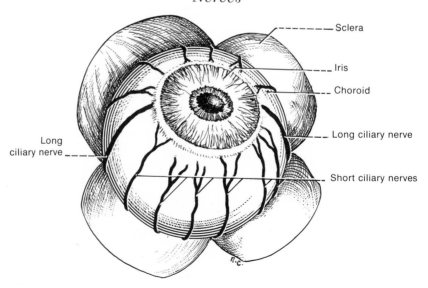

Sclera

Iris

Choroid

Long ciliary nerve

Short ciliary nerves

Long ciliary nerve

INTERNAL (SENSORY) TUNIC OF THE EYE
AND OPTIC NERVE

SAGITTAL SECTION OF THE RETINA

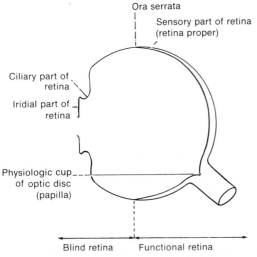

Ora serrata

Sensory part of retina (retina proper)

Ciliary part of retina

Iridial part of retina

Physiologic cup of optic disc (papilla)

Blind retina   Functional retina

ANTERIOR ASPECT OF THE POSTERIOR HALF OF THE EYE

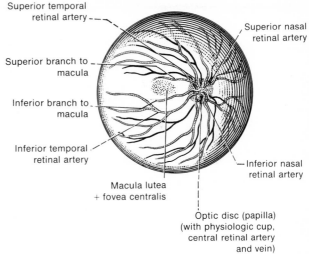

Superior temporal retinal artery

Superior nasal retinal artery

Superior branch to macula

Inferior branch to macula

Inferior temporal retinal artery

Inferior nasal retinal artery

Macula lutea + fovea centralis

Optic disc (papilla) (with physiologic cup, central retinal artery and vein)

(The veins are shown in black.)

LONGITUDINAL SECTION OF THE OPTIC NERVE AT THE POINT WHERE IT EMERGES FROM THE EYEBALL

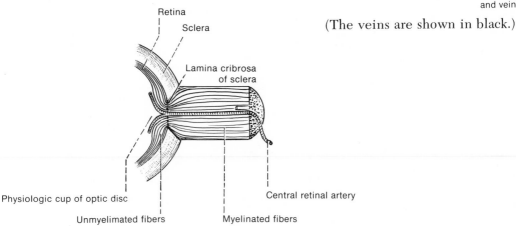

Retina

Sclera

Lamina cribrosa of sclera

Physiologic cup of optic disc

Unmyelimated fibers

Myelinated fibers

Central retinal artery

STRUCTURE OF THE RETINA

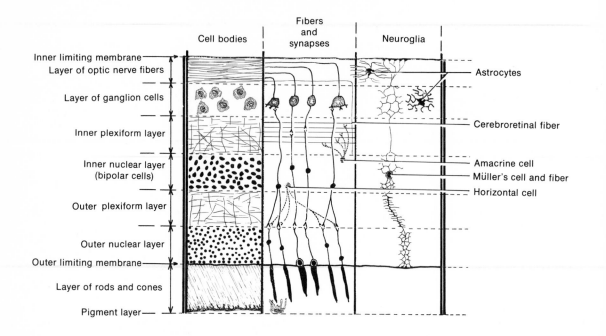

Cell bodies

Fibers and synapses

Neuroglia

Inner limiting membrane
Layer of optic nerve fibers

Layer of ganglion cells

Inner plexiform layer

Inner nuclear layer (bipolar cells)

Outer plexiform layer

Outer nuclear layer

Outer limiting membrane

Layer of rods and cones

Pigment layer

Astrocytes

Cerebroretinal fiber

Amacrine cell
Müller's cell and fiber
Horizontal cell

FINE STRUCTURE OF THE PHOTORECEPTORS

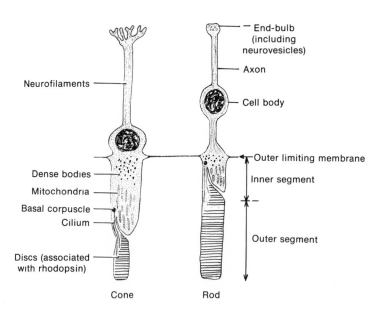

End-bulb (including neurovesicles)

Axon

Cell body

Neurofilaments

Dense bodies
Mitochondria
Basal corpuscle
Cilium

Discs (associated with rhodopsin)

Outer limiting membrane

Inner segment

Outer segment

Cone

Rod

SAGITTAL SECTION OF THE ANTERIOR
HALF OF THE EYE

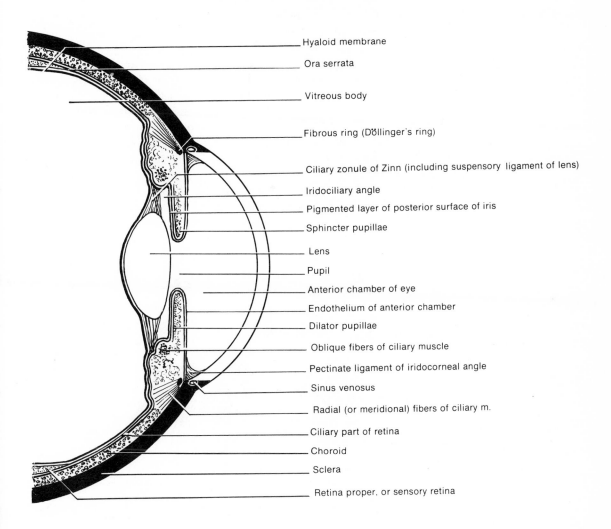

Hyaloid membrane

Ora serrata

Vitreous body

Fibrous ring (Döllinger's ring)

Ciliary zonule of Zinn (including suspensory ligament of lens)

Iridociliary angle

Pigmented layer of posterior surface of iris

Sphincter pupillae

Lens

Pupil

Anterior chamber of eye

Endothelium of anterior chamber

Dilator pupillae

Oblique fibers of ciliary muscle

Pectinate ligament of iridocorneal angle

Sinus venosus

Radial (or meridional) fibers of ciliary m.

Ciliary part of retina

Choroid

Sclera

Retina proper, or sensory retina

DIOPTRIC MEDIA OF THE EYE

To reach the retina, a light beam has to pass through a series of dioptric media:

Cornea: See fibrous tunic of the eyeball, page 214.

Aqueous humor: This fills the anterior and posterior chambers. The anterior chamber is the space between the anterior surface of the iris and the cornea; the posterior chamber is the space located between the iris and the lens.

The aqueous humor is secreted by the epithelium of the ciliary surface of the posterior chamber; it passes through the pupil to the anterior chamber; its resorption by the sinus venosus (Schlemm's canal) takes place at the iridocorneal angle.

Vitreous body: It occupies the area located behind the lens. It is enclosed by the hyaloid membrane. During embryonic life the hyaloid artery passes through the vitreous body; the remains of this artery are the hyaloid canal (of Stilling, or of Cloquet). The vitreous body is a transparent gel composed of collagenous fibers, vitreous cells and pseudocells (atrophic cells).

Lens: This is interposed between the aqueous humor and the vitreous body; it is held in place by the ciliary zonule of Zinn (suspensory ligament of the lens).

MERIDIONAL SECTION OF THE LENS

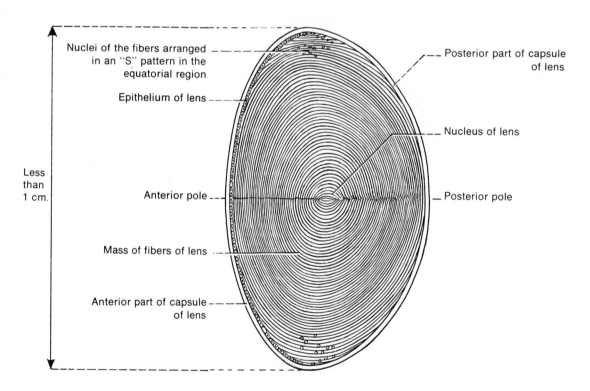

Nuclei of the fibers arranged in an "S" pattern in the equatorial region

Epithelium of lens

Posterior part of capsule of lens

Nucleus of lens

Less than 1 cm.

Anterior pole

Posterior pole

Mass of fibers of lens

Anterior part of capsule of lens

°From Babuchin, cited by Testut, L., and Latarjet, A.: Traité d'Anatomie Humaine. 9th ed. Paris, Gaston Doin et Cie., 1949, p. 644.

EYELIDS AND CONJUNCTIVA

SAGITTAL SECTION OF THE EYELIDS

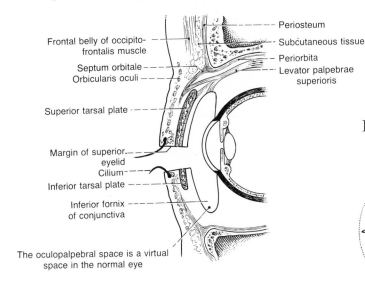

- Frontal belly of occipito-frontalis muscle
- Septum orbitale
- Orbicularis oculi
- Superior tarsal plate
- Margin of superior eyelid
- Cilium
- Inferior tarsal plate
- Inferior fornix of conjunctiva

The oculopalpebral space is a virtual space in the normal eye

- Periosteum
- Subcutaneous tissue
- Periorbita
- Levator palpebrae superioris

PALPEBRAL FISSURE (RIMA)

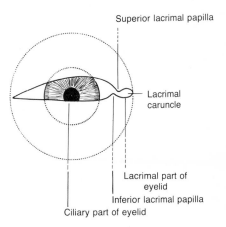

- Superior lacrimal papilla
- Lacrimal caruncle
- Lacrimal part of eyelid
- Inferior lacrimal papilla
- Ciliary part of eyelid

ORBICULARIS OCULI

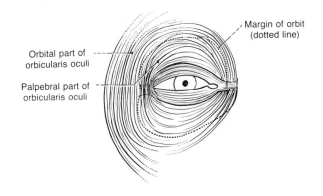

- Margin of orbit (dotted line)
- Orbital part of orbicularis oculi
- Palpebral part of orbicularis oculi

SAGITTAL SECTION OF THE LACRIMAL CARUNCLE

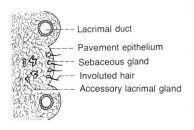

- Lacrimal duct
- Pavement epithelium
- Sebaceous gland
- Involuted hair
- Accessory lacrimal gland

Winckler divides the palpebral part into:
    preseptal part
    pretarsal part
    marginal part (ciliary bundle)
        (This last is also divided into preciliary and retrociliary portions; see page 222.)
Only the fibers of the marginal part are inserted into the two palpebral ligaments.

GLANDS OF THE EYELIDS

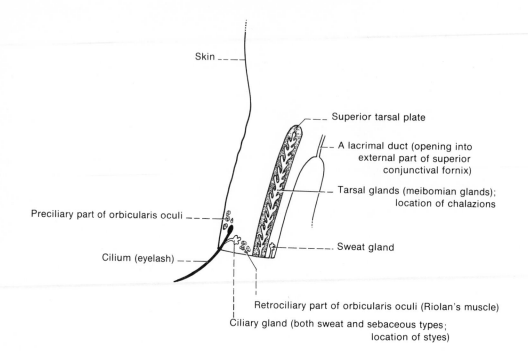

Skin

Superior tarsal plate

A lacrimal duct (opening into external part of superior conjunctival fornix)

Tarsal glands (meibomian glands); location of chalazions

Preciliary part of orbicularis oculi

Sweat gland

Cilium (eyelash)

Retrociliary part of orbicularis oculi (Riolan's muscle)

Ciliary gland (both sweat and sebaceous types; location of styes)

ORBITAL SEPTUM

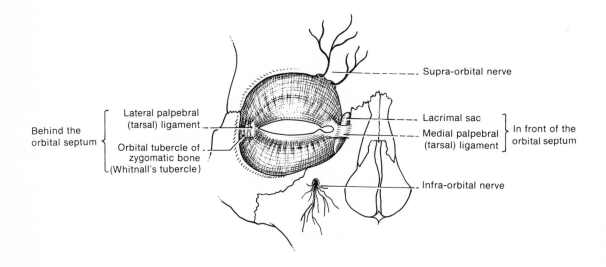

Supra-orbital nerve

Behind the orbital septum

Lateral palpebral (tarsal) ligament

Orbital tubercle of zygomatic bone (Whitnall's tubercle)

Lacrimal sac

Medial palpebral (tarsal) ligament

In front of the orbital septum

Infra-orbital nerve

PALPEBRAL (TARSAL) LIGAMENTS AND LACRIMAL SAC

Anterior Aspect of the Medial Palpebral Ligament

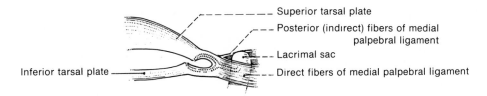

- Superior tarsal plate
- Posterior (indirect) fibers of medial palpebral ligament
- Lacrimal sac
- Inferior tarsal plate
- Direct fibers of medial palpebral ligament

Horizontal Section

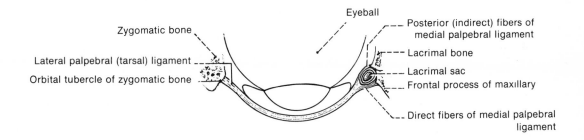

- Zygomatic bone
- Lateral palpebral (tarsal) ligament
- Orbital tubercle of zygomatic bone
- Eyeball
- Posterior (indirect) fibers of medial palpebral ligament
- Lacrimal bone
- Lacrimal sac
- Frontal process of maxillary
- Direct fibers of medial palpebral ligament

Lateral Aspect of the Medial Wall of the Orbit

The tarsal plates have been retracted in order to show the posterior aspect of the medial palpebral ligament, which is covered by the lacrimal part of the orbicularis oculi (Horner's muscle).

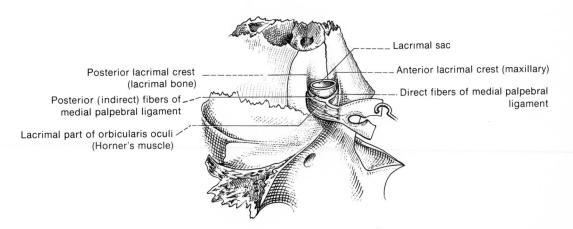

- Posterior lacrimal crest (lacrimal bone)
- Posterior (indirect) fibers of medial palpebral ligament
- Lacrimal part of orbicularis oculi (Horner's muscle)
- Lacrimal sac
- Anterior lacrimal crest (maxillary)
- Direct fibers of medial palpebral ligament

MUSCLES OF THE ORBIT

Origin of the Extrinsic Muscles of the Eye at the Level of the Apex of the Orbit

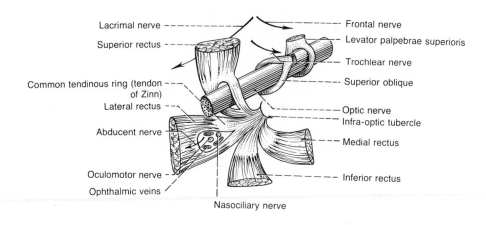

Lacrimal nerve

Superior rectus

Common tendinous ring (tendon of Zinn)

Lateral rectus

Abducent nerve

Oculomotor nerve

Ophthalmic veins

Frontal nerve

Levator palpebrae superioris

Trochlear nerve

Superior oblique

Optic nerve

Infra-optic tubercle

Medial rectus

Inferior rectus

Nasociliary nerve

Scleral Attachment of the Oblique Muscles

Scleral Attachment of the Rectus Muscles

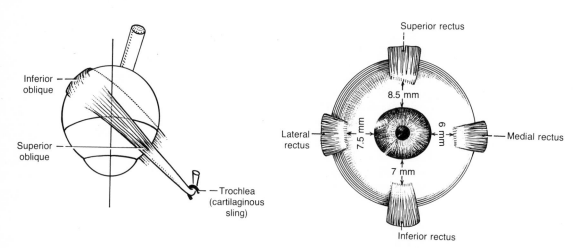

Inferior oblique

Superior oblique

Trochlea (cartilaginous sling)

Superior rectus

8.5 mm

Lateral rectus

7.5 mm

6 mm

Medial rectus

7 mm

Inferior rectus

In the orbit there are also smooth muscles:

Superior and inferior palpebral (tarsal) muscles (Müller's muscles); these are the tensors of the fornices, and influence the tonus of the eyelids

Orbital muscle (tensor of the periorbita, or Müller's muscle), which is located in the inferior orbital fissure

ORBITAL FAT AND FASCIAE

MUSCULAR SHEATHS

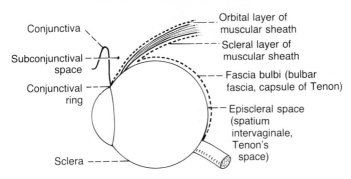

Conjunctiva

Subconjunctival space

Conjunctival ring

Sclera

Orbital layer of muscular sheath

Scleral layer of muscular sheath

Fascia bulbi (bulbar fascia, capsule of Tenon)

Episcleral space (spatium intervaginale, Tenon's space)

CHECK LIGAMENTS AND INTERMUSCULAR FASCIAE

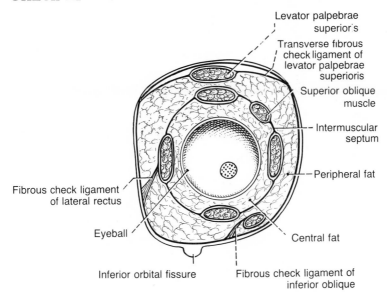

Levator palpebrae superioris

Transverse fibrous check ligament of levator palpebrae superioris

Superior oblique muscle

Intermuscular septum

Peripheral fat

Fibrous check ligament of lateral rectus

Eyeball

Inferior orbital fissure

Central fat

Fibrous check ligament of inferior oblique

FAT OF THE BASE OF THE ORBIT

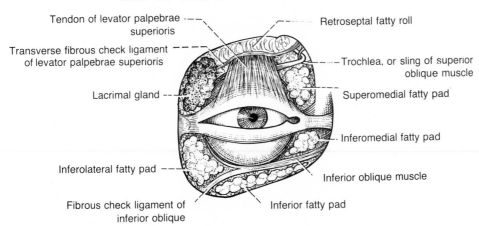

Tendon of levator palpebrae superioris

Transverse fibrous check ligament of levator palpebrae superioris

Lacrimal gland

Inferolateral fatty pad

Fibrous check ligament of inferior oblique

Retroseptal fatty roll

Trochlea, or sling of superior oblique muscle

Superomedial fatty pad

Inferomedial fatty pad

Inferior oblique muscle

Inferior fatty pad

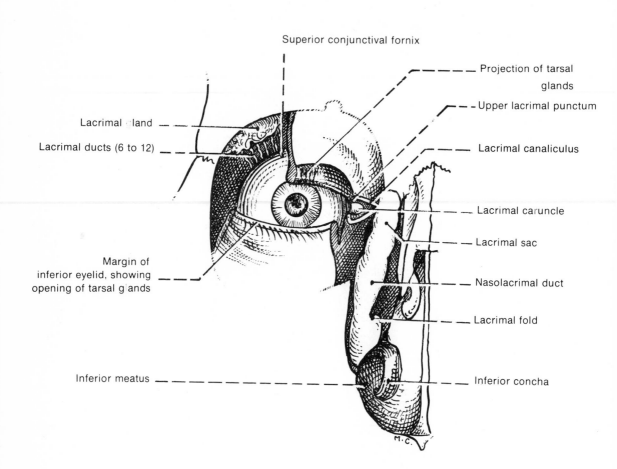

Superior conjunctival fornix

Projection of tarsal glands

Upper lacrimal punctum

Lacrimal gland

Lacrimal ducts (6 to 12)

Lacrimal canaliculus

Lacrimal caruncle

Lacrimal sac

Margin of inferior eyelid, showing opening of tarsal glands

Nasolacrimal duct

Lacrimal fold

Inferior meatus

Inferior concha

MOTOR NERVES OF THE EYEBALL

NUCLEI OF THE MOTOR NERVES OF THE EYE

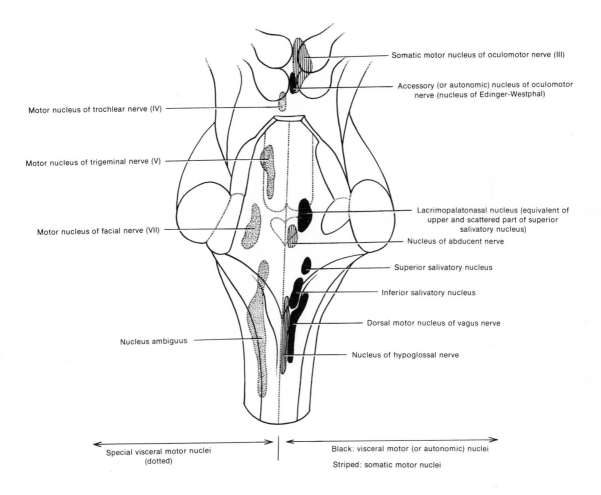

The nuclei of the trochlear nerves must be considered as part of the special visceral motor nuclei (Kappers, C. U. A.: Anatomie Comparée du Système Nerveux. Paris, Masson et Cie., 1947).

Section of the Midbrain Through the Nuclei of the Oculomotor Nerves

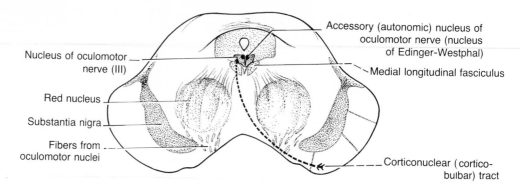

Accessory (autonomic) nucleus of oculomotor nerve (nucleus of Edinger-Westphal)

Nucleus of oculomotor nerve (III)

Medial longitudinal fasciculus

Red nucleus

Substantia nigra

Fibers from oculomotor nuclei

Corticonuclear (cortico-bulbar) tract

Section Through the Inferior Colliculus and the Nuclei of the Trochlear Nerves (IV)

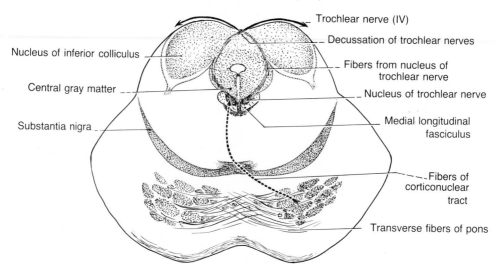

Trochlear nerve (IV)

Decussation of trochlear nerves

Nucleus of inferior colliculus

Fibers from nucleus of trochlear nerve

Central gray matter

Nucleus of trochlear nerve

Medial longitudinal fasciculus

Substantia nigra

Fibers of corticonuclear tract

Transverse fibers of pons

Section of the Pons Through the Nuclei of the Abducent Nerve (VI)

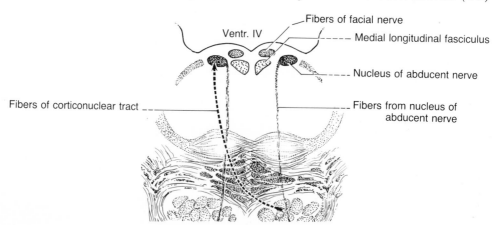

Fibers of facial nerve

Ventr. IV

Medial longitudinal fasciculus

Nucleus of abducent nerve

Fibers of corticonuclear tract

Fibers from nucleus of abducent nerve

EMERGENCE OF THE MOTOR NERVES OF THE EYE

Ventral Aspect of the Brain Stem

Lateral Aspect of the Brain Stem

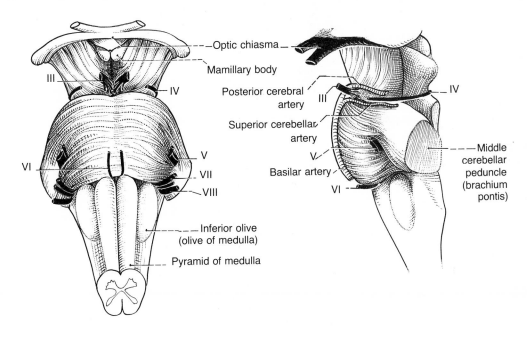

Optic chiasma

Mamillary body

Posterior cerebral artery

Superior cerebellar artery

Basilar artery

III

IV

V

VI

VII

VIII

Inferior olive (olive of medulla)

Pyramid of medulla

Middle cerebellar peduncle (brachium pontis)

Dorsal Aspect of the Brain Stem

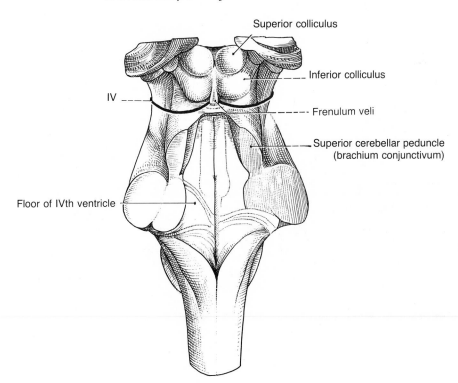

Superior colliculus

Inferior colliculus

Frenulum veli

Superior cerebellar peduncle (brachium conjunctivum)

IV

Floor of IVth ventricle

PASSAGE OF NERVES THROUGH THE SUBARACHNOID SPACE AND THE DURA MATER

Superior Aspect

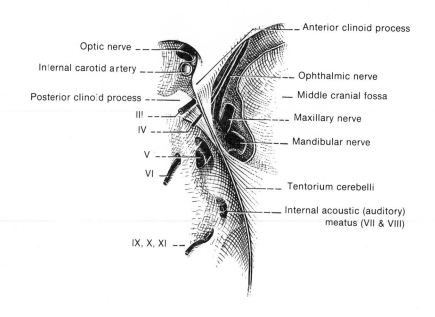

Optic nerve

Internal carotid artery

Posterior clinoid process

III

IV

V

VI

IX, X, XI

Anterior clinoid process

Ophthalmic nerve

Middle cranial fossa

Maxillary nerve

Mandibular nerve

Tentorium cerebelli

Internal acoustic (auditory) meatus (VII & VIII)

Medial Aspect

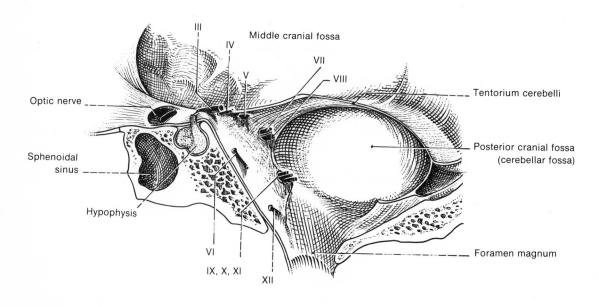

III

IV

V

VII

VIII

Middle cranial fossa

Optic nerve

Sphenoidal sinus

Hypophysis

VI

IX, X, XI

XII

Tentorium cerebelli

Posterior cranial fossa (cerebellar fossa)

Foramen magnum

Passage of Nerves Through the Cavernous Sinus

Frontal Section Through the Cavernous Sinuses

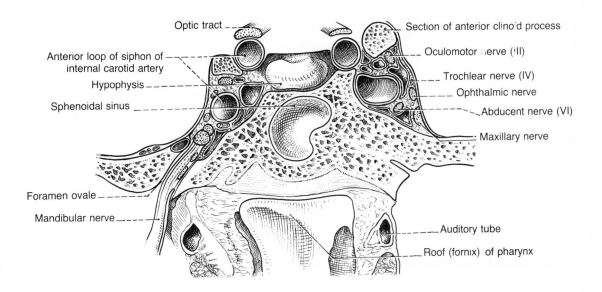

Optic tract

Anterior loop of siphon of internal carotid artery

Hypophysis

Sphenoidal sinus

Foramen ovale

Mandibular nerve

Section of anterior clinoid process

Oculomotor nerve (III)

Trochlear nerve (IV)

Ophthalmic nerve

Abducent nerve (VI)

Maxillary nerve

Auditory tube

Roof (fornix) of pharynx

Arrangement of the Nerves in the Cavernous Sinus

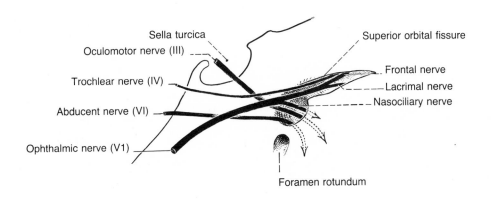

Sella turcica

Oculomotor nerve (III)

Trochlear nerve (IV)

Abducent nerve (VI)

Ophthalmic nerve (V1)

Superior orbital fissure

Frontal nerve

Lacrimal nerve

Nasociliary nerve

Foramen rotundum

PASSAGE OF STRUCTURES THROUGH THE SUPERIOR ORBITAL FISSURE

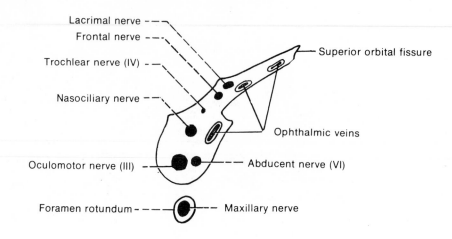

- Lacrimal nerve
- Frontal nerve
- Trochlear nerve (IV)
- Nasociliary nerve
- Superior orbital fissure
- Ophthalmic veins
- Oculomotor nerve (III)
- Abducent nerve (VI)
- Foramen rotundum
- Maxillary nerve

INTRA-ORBITAL PASSAGE

Oculomotor Nerve (III)

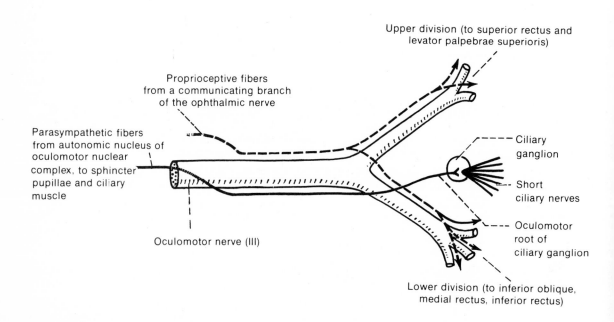

Upper division (to superior rectus and levator palpebrae superioris)

Proprioceptive fibers from a communicating branch of the ophthalmic nerve

Parasympathetic fibers from autonomic nucleus of oculomotor nuclear complex, to sphincter pupillae and ciliary muscle

Ciliary ganglion

Short ciliary nerves

Oculomotor root of ciliary ganglion

Oculomotor nerve (III)

Lower division (to inferior oblique, medial rectus, inferior rectus)

Trochlear Nerve (IV)

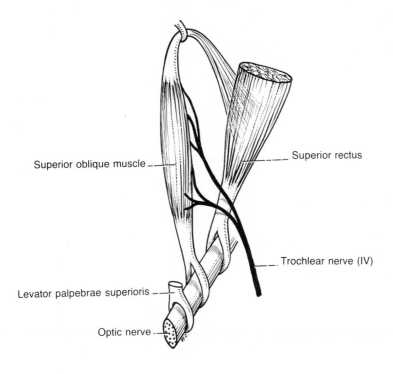

Superior oblique muscle —

Superior rectus

Trochlear nerve (IV)

Levator palpebrae superioris —

Optic nerve —

Abducent Nerve (VI)

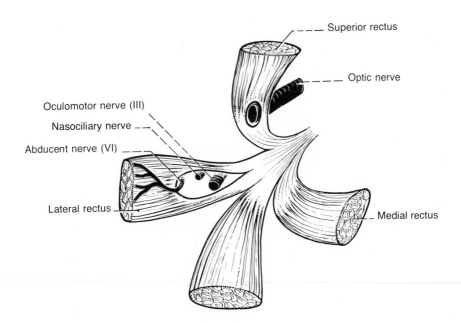

Superior rectus

Optic nerve

Oculomotor nerve (III)

Nasociliary nerve —

Abducent nerve (VI) —

Lateral rectus —

Medial rectus

DIAGRAM OF THE MOTOR NERVES OF THE EYEBALL

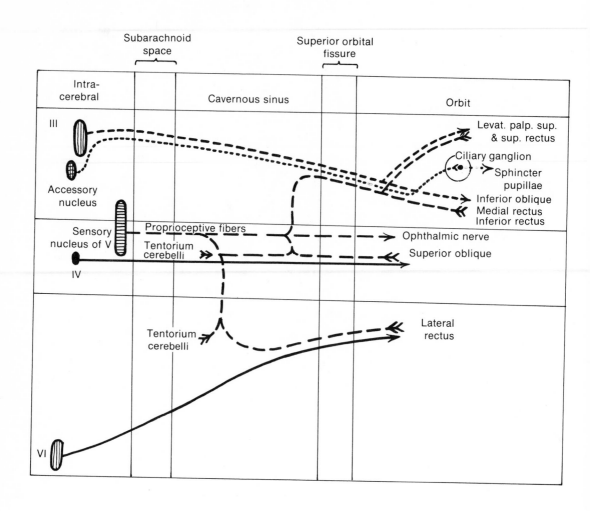

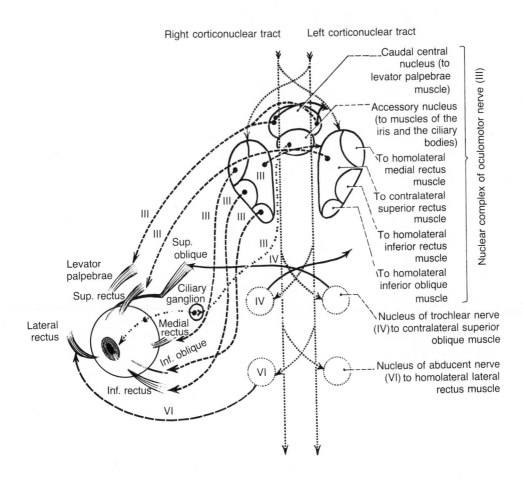

Right corticonuclear tract   Left corticonuclear tract

Caudal central nucleus (to levator palpebrae muscle)

Accessory nucleus (to muscles of the iris and the ciliary bodies)

To homolateral medial rectus muscle

To contralateral superior rectus muscle

To homolateral inferior rectus muscle

To homolateral inferior oblique muscle

Nuclear complex of oculomotor nerve (III)

Nucleus of trochlear nerve (IV) to contralateral superior oblique muscle

Nucleus of abducent nerve (VI) to homolateral lateral rectus muscle

Sup. oblique

Levator palpebrae

Sup. rectus

Ciliary ganglion

Lateral rectus

Medial rectus

Inf. oblique

Inf. rectus

From the works of Warwick, R.: Representation of the extraocular muscles in the oculomotor nuclei of the monkey. J. Comp. Neurol., 98:449-504, 1953.

OCULOCEPHALOGYRIC CENTERS AND PATHWAYS

EXTRAPYRAMIDAL AND OCULOCEPHALOGYRIC CORTICAL AREAS

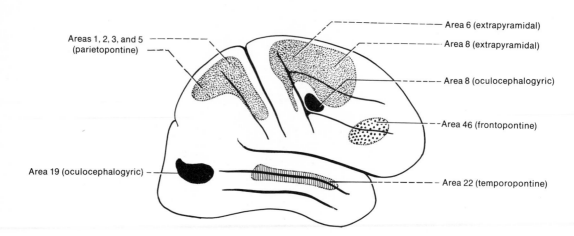

Areas 1, 2, 3, and 5 (parietopontine)

Area 6 (extrapyramidal)

Area 8 (extrapyramidal)

Area 8 (oculocephalogyric)

Area 46 (frontopontine)

Area 19 (oculocephalogyric)

Area 22 (temporopontine)

ANATOMICAL DIAGRAM OF THE OCULOCEPHALOGYRIC PATHWAYS

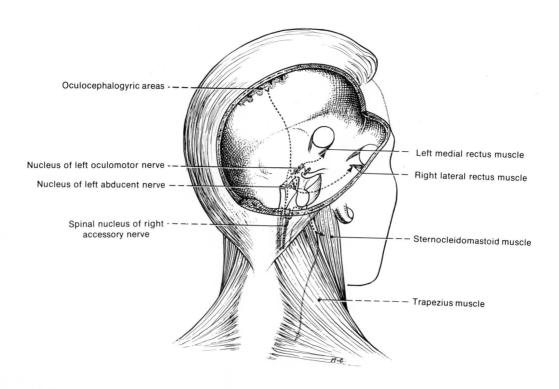

Oculocephalogyric areas

Nucleus of left oculomotor nerve

Nucleus of left abducent nerve

Spinal nucleus of right accessory nerve

Left medial rectus muscle

Right lateral rectus muscle

Sternocleidomastoid muscle

Trapezius muscle

PATHWAYS AND CENTERS OF VISION

DIAGRAM OF SENSORY VISUAL PATHWAYS

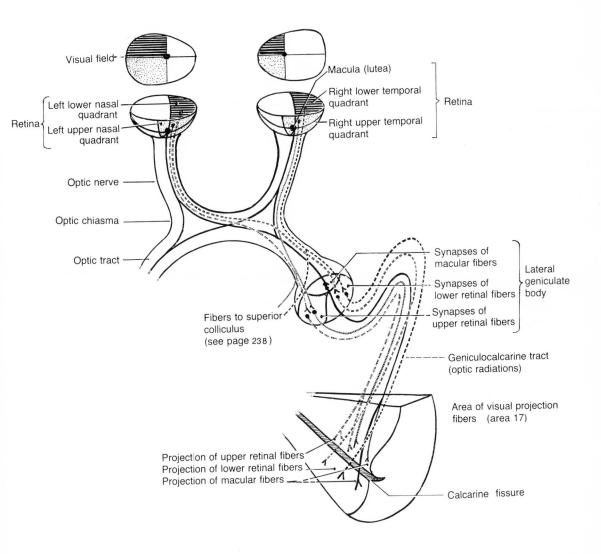

In the temporal lobe, the fibers from the lower temporal quadrant of the retina form the most anterior loops; this anatomical arrangement can explain some clinical quadrantanopsias.

The macular fibers have both direct and crossed trajectories.

DIAGRAM OF THE MAIN REFLEX AND ASSOCIATION PATHWAYS CONCERNING VISION

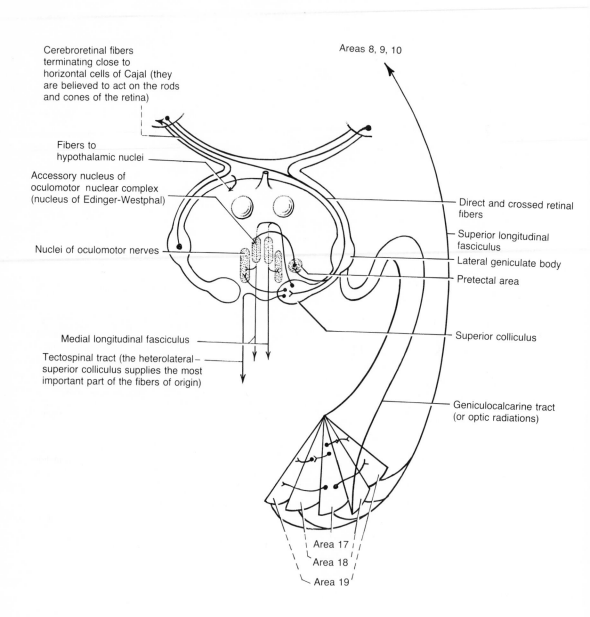

Cerebroretinal fibers terminating close to horizontal cells of Cajal (they are believed to act on the rods and cones of the retina)

Areas 8, 9, 10

Fibers to hypothalamic nuclei

Accessory nucleus of oculomotor nuclear complex (nucleus of Edinger-Westphal)

Nuclei of oculomotor nerves

Direct and crossed retinal fibers

Superior longitudinal fasciculus

Lateral geniculate body

Pretectal area

Medial longitudinal fasciculus

Tectospinal tract (the heterolateral superior colliculus supplies the most important part of the fibers of origin)

Superior colliculus

Geniculocalcarine tract (or optic radiations)

Area 17

Area 18

Area 19

MONOCULAR ACCOMMODATION (LIGHT AND DISTANCE)

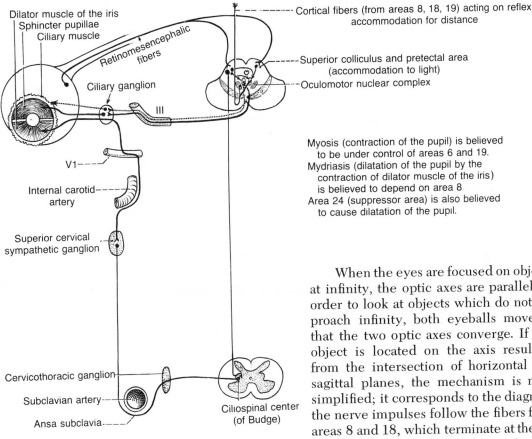

Dilator muscle of the iris
Sphincter pupillae
Ciliary muscle

Retinomesencephalic fibers

Ciliary ganglion

III

V1

Internal carotid artery

Superior cervical sympathetic ganglion

Cervicothoracic ganglion

Subclavian artery

Ansa subclavia

Ciliospinal center (of Budge)

Cortical fibers (from areas 8, 18, 19) acting on reflex accommodation for distance

Superior colliculus and pretectal area (accommodation to light)

Oculomotor nuclear complex

Myosis (contraction of the pupil) is believed to be under control of areas 6 and 19.
Mydriasis (dilatation of the pupil by the contraction of dilator muscle of the iris) is believed to depend on area 8.
Area 24 (suppressor area) is also believed to cause dilatation of the pupil.

BINOCULAR ACCOMMODATION (CONVERGENCE)

Cerebral cortex (areas 8 and 10)

Nucleus of Perlia (caudal central nucleus)

Medial rectus muscle

When the eyes are focused on objects at infinity, the optic axes are parallel. In order to look at objects which do not approach infinity, both eyeballs move so that the two optic axes converge. If this object is located on the axis resulting from the intersection of horizontal and sagittal planes, the mechanism is most simplified; it corresponds to the diagram: the nerve impulses follow the fibers from areas 8 and 18, which terminate at the coordinating center of convergence (caudal central nucleus?); from this center fibers run toward the right and left ventral nuclei of the oculomotor nuclear complex; from these right and left nuclei fibers go toward right and left medial rectus muscles.

But as soon as this axis is deviated from, other complex muscular movements intervene.

The posterior commissure includes the fibers which govern synergic movements such as raising and lowering of the eyes.

According to Warwick,* the very existence of the nucleus of Perlia is uncertain in monkeys, and thus its role in convergence is debatable.

*Warwick, R.: The so-called nucleus of convergence. Brain, 78:92-114, 1955.

CUTANEOUS SENSORY AREAS

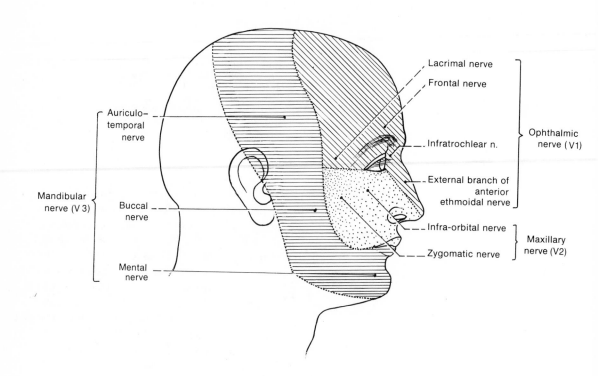

Lacrimal nerve

Frontal nerve

Auriculo–
temporal
nerve

Infratrochlear n.

Ophthalmic
nerve (V1)

External branch of
anterior
ethmoidal nerve

Mandibular
nerve (V 3)

Buccal
nerve

Infra-orbital nerve

Maxillary
nerve (V2)

Zygomatic nerve

Mental
nerve

NUCLEI OF THE TRIGEMINAL NERVE

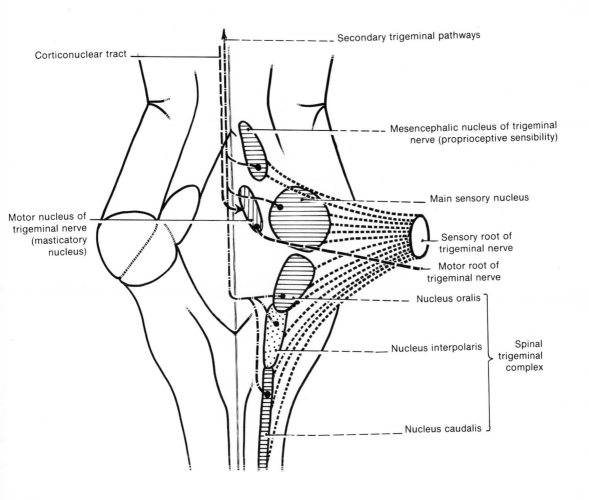

Corticonuclear tract

Secondary trigeminal pathways

Mesencephalic nucleus of trigeminal nerve (proprioceptive sensibility)

Main sensory nucleus

Motor nucleus of trigeminal nerve (masticatory nucleus)

Sensory root of trigeminal nerve

Motor root of trigeminal nerve

Nucleus oralis

Nucleus interpolaris

Spinal trigeminal complex

Nucleus caudalis

(The description of the spinal trigeminal complex according to Olszewski, J.: J. Comp. Neurol., 92:401-413, 1950.)

EMERGENCE OF THE TRIGEMINAL NERVE

See pages 118 and 229.

Page 241

INTRACRANIAL COURSE

The trigeminal nerve, its ganglion and its branches as seen through the dura mater.

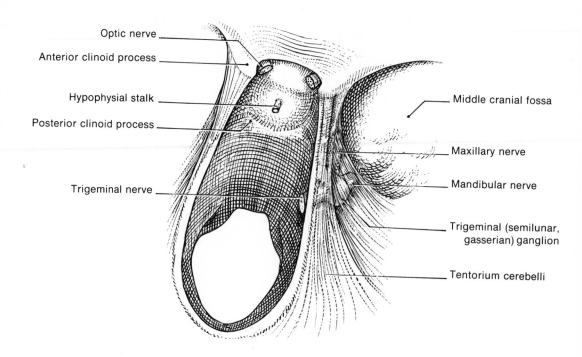

Optic nerve

Anterior clinoid process

Hypophysial stalk

Posterior clinoid process

Trigeminal nerve

Middle cranial fossa

Maxillary nerve

Mandibular nerve

Trigeminal (semilunar, gasserian) ganglion

Tentorium cerebelli

The trigeminal ganglion is lodged in a dural recess, the cavum trigeminale (or Meckel's cave).

OPHTHALMIC NERVE AND CILIARY GANGLION

FRONTAL AND LACRIMAL NERVES

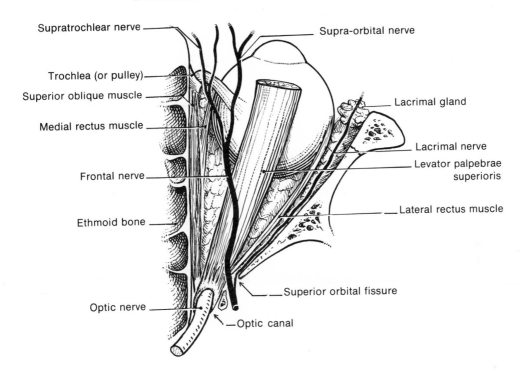

Supratrochlear nerve

Trochlea (or pulley)

Superior oblique muscle

Medial rectus muscle

Frontal nerve

Ethmoid bone

Optic nerve

Optic canal

Supra-orbital nerve

Lacrimal gland

Lacrimal nerve

Levator palpebrae superioris

Lateral rectus muscle

Superior orbital fissure

NASOCILIARY NERVE

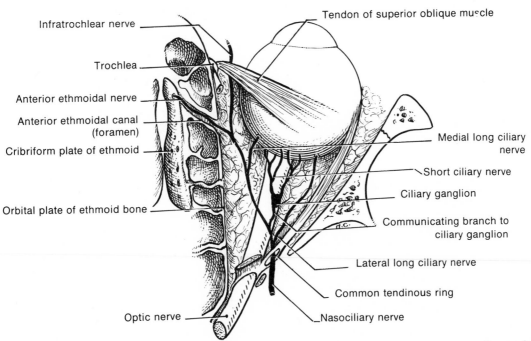

Infratrochlear nerve

Trochlea

Anterior ethmoidal nerve

Anterior ethmoidal canal (foramen)

Cribriform plate of ethmoid

Orbital plate of ethmoid bone

Optic nerve

Tendon of superior oblique muscle

Medial long ciliary nerve

Short ciliary nerve

Ciliary ganglion

Communicating branch to ciliary ganglion

Lateral long ciliary nerve

Common tendinous ring

Nasociliary nerve

Page 243

ANTERIOR ETHMOIDAL NERVE

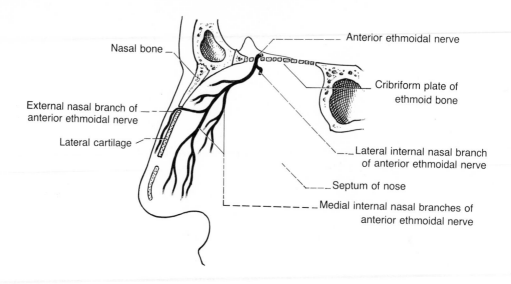

Nasal bone

Anterior ethmoidal nerve

Cribriform plate of
ethmoid bone

External nasal branch of
anterior ethmoidal nerve

Lateral cartilage

Lateral internal nasal branch
of anterior ethmoidal nerve

Septum of nose

Medial internal nasal branches of
anterior ethmoidal nerve

DIAGRAM OF THE CILIARY GANGLION

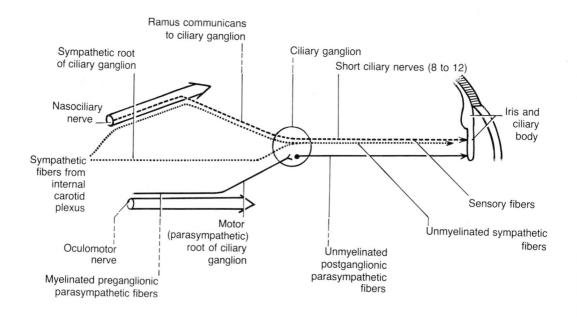

Ramus communicans
to ciliary ganglion

Sympathetic root
of ciliary ganglion

Ciliary ganglion

Short ciliary nerves (8 to 12)

Nasociliary
nerve

Iris and
ciliary
body

Sympathetic
fibers from
internal
carotid
plexus

Oculomotor
nerve

Motor
(parasympathetic)
root of ciliary
ganglion

Sensory fibers

Unmyelinated sympathetic
fibers

Unmyelinated
postganglionic
parasympathetic
fibers

Myelinated preganglionic
parasympathetic fibers

MAXILLARY NERVE AND PTERYGOPALATINE (SPHENOPALATINE) GANGLION

COURSE OF THE MAXILLARY NERVE

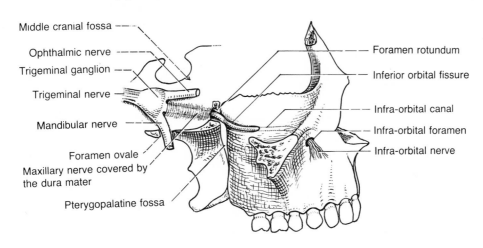

Middle cranial fossa

Ophthalmic nerve

Trigeminal ganglion

Trigeminal nerve

Mandibular nerve

Foramen ovale

Maxillary nerve covered by the dura mater

Pterygopalatine fossa

Foramen rotundum

Inferior orbital fissure

Infra-orbital canal

Infra-orbital foramen

Infra-orbital nerve

BRANCHES OF THE MAXILLARY NERVE

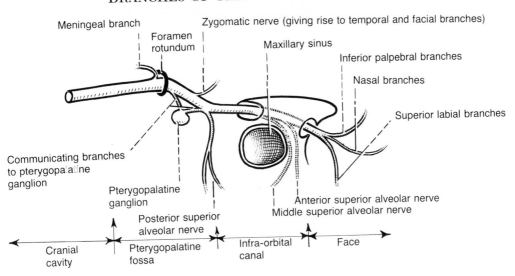

Meningeal branch

Foramen rotundum

Zygomatic nerve (giving rise to temporal and facial branches)

Maxillary sinus

Inferior palpebral branches

Nasal branches

Superior labial branches

Communicating branches to pterygopalatine ganglion

Pterygopalatine ganglion

Posterior superior alveolar nerve

Anterior superior alveolar nerve

Middle superior alveolar nerve

Cranial cavity

Pterygopalatine fossa

Infra-orbital canal

Face

TERMINAL BRANCHES OF THE INFRA-ORBITAL NERVE

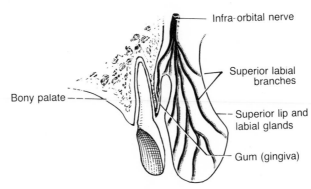

Infra-orbital nerve

Superior labial branches

Superior lip and labial glands

Gum (gingiva)

Bony palate

Page 245

Sensory Nerves of the Palate

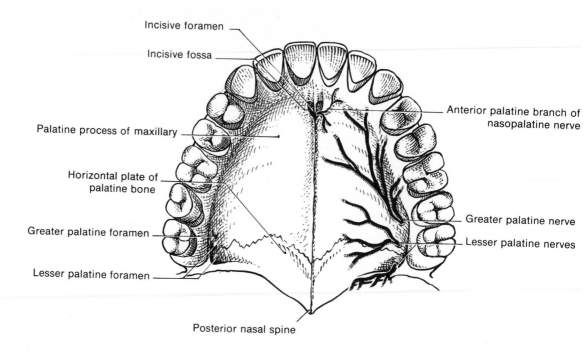

Incisive foramen

Incisive fossa

Palatine process of maxillary

Horizontal plate of palatine bone

Greater palatine foramen

Lesser palatine foramen

Posterior nasal spine

Anterior palatine branch of nasopalatine nerve

Greater palatine nerve

Lesser palatine nerves

Posterior Nerves of the Nasal Cavities

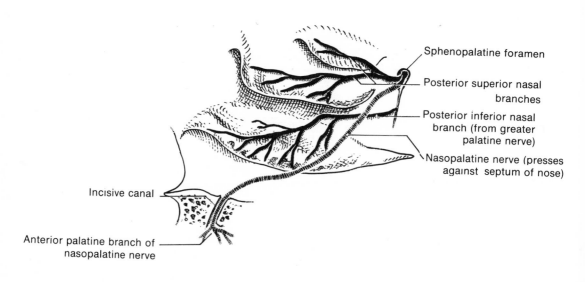

Sphenopalatine foramen

Posterior superior nasal branches

Posterior inferior nasal branch (from greater palatine nerve)

Nasopalatine nerve (presses against septum of nose)

Incisive canal

Anterior palatine branch of nasopalatine nerve

DIAGRAM OF THE PTERYGOPALATINE GANGLION

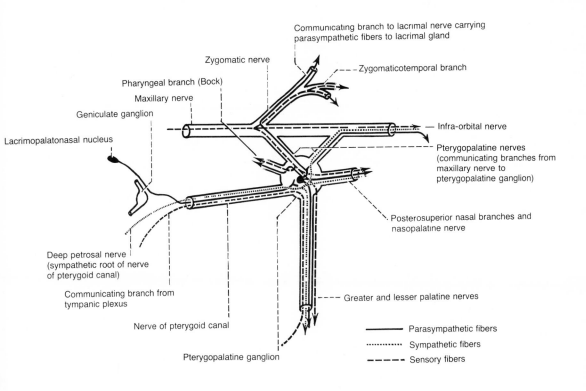

Communicating branch to lacrimal nerve carrying parasympathetic fibers to lacrimal gland

Zygomatic nerve

Zygomaticotemporal branch

Pharyngeal branch (Bock)

Maxillary nerve

Geniculate ganglion

Infra-orbital nerve

Lacrimopalatonasal nucleus

Pterygopalatine nerves (communicating branches from maxillary nerve to pterygopalatine ganglion)

Posterosuperior nasal branches and nasopalatine nerve

Deep petrosal nerve (sympathetic root of nerve of pterygoid canal)

Communicating branch from tympanic plexus

Greater and lesser palatine nerves

Nerve of pterygoid canal

—————— Parasympathetic fibers

················· Sympathetic fibers

– – – – – Sensory fibers

Pterygopalatine ganglion

SUBMANDIBULAR AND OTIC GANGLIA

LATERAL ASPECT OF THE MANDIBULAR NERVE

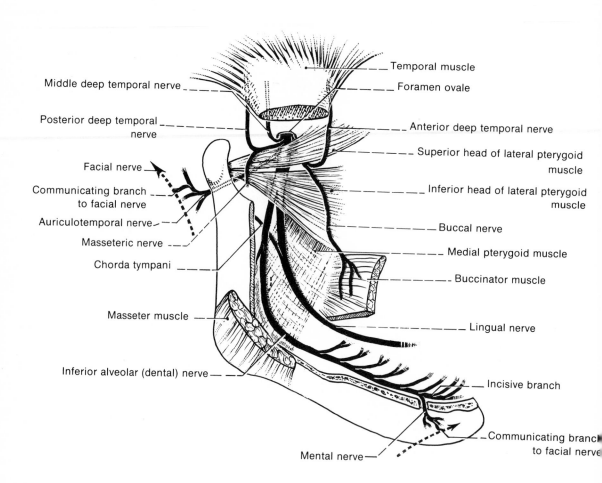

Middle deep temporal nerve

Posterior deep temporal nerve

Facial nerve

Communicating branch to facial nerve

Auriculotemporal nerve

Masseteric nerve

Chorda tympani

Masseter muscle

Inferior alveolar (dental) nerve

Mental nerve

Temporal muscle

Foramen ovale

Anterior deep temporal nerve

Superior head of lateral pterygoid muscle

Inferior head of lateral pterygoid muscle

Buccal nerve

Medial pterygoid muscle

Buccinator muscle

Lingual nerve

Incisive branch

Communicating branch to facial nerve

MEDIAL ASPECT OF THE MANDIBULAR NERVE

Meningeal branch (which follows middle meningeal artery)

Foramen ovale

Mandibular nerve

Otic ganglion

Lateral pterygoid muscle

Tensor veli palatini

Middle meningeal artery

Auriculotemporal nerve

Parotid branches to parotid gland

Maxillary artery

Chorda tympani

Inferior alveolar nerve

Nerve to medial pterygoid, tensor tympani and tensor veli palatini muscles

Lingula of mandible

Mylohyoid nerve (to mylohyoid muscle and anterior belly of digastric)

Lingual nerve

Medial pterygoid muscle

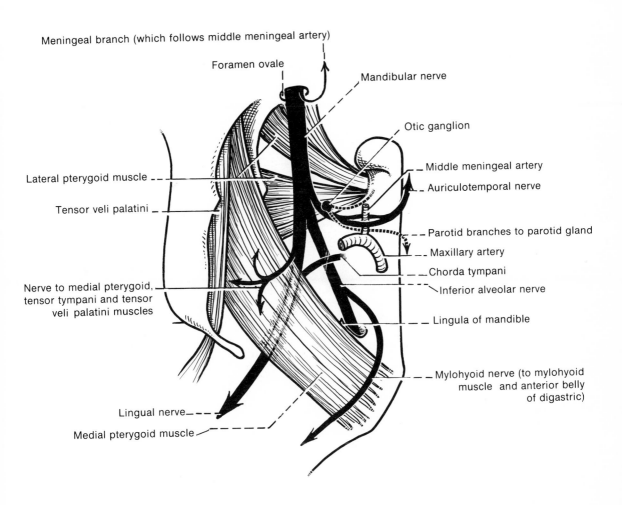

Submandibular and Sublingual Ganglia

Usually the sublingual and the submandibular ganglia are described together as the submandibular ganglion.

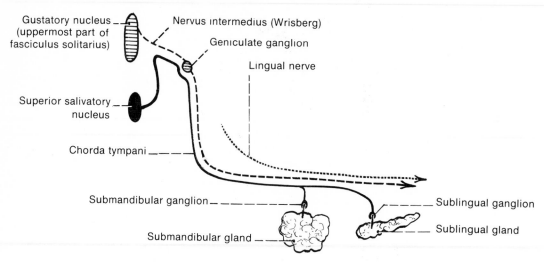

Otic Ganglion

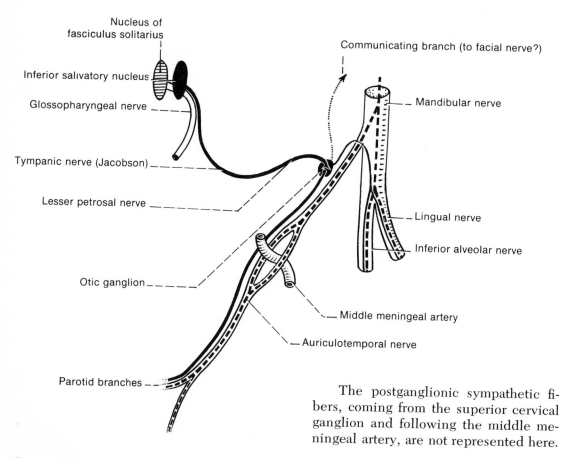

The postganglionic sympathetic fibers, coming from the superior cervical ganglion and following the middle meningeal artery, are not represented here.

DIAGRAM OF THE TRIGEMINAL NERVE

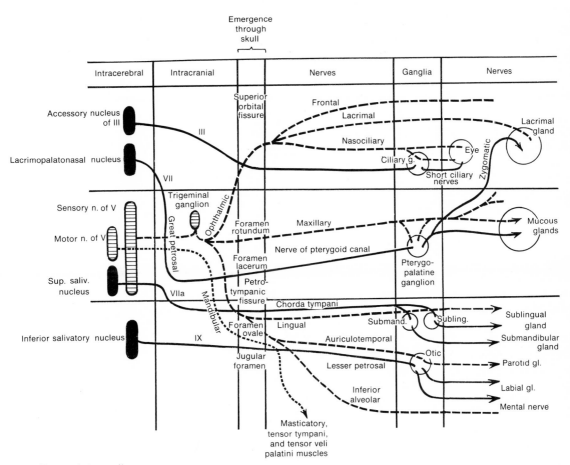

VIIa: Nervus intermedius

The Facial Nerve and the Nervus Intermedius
(Wrisberg)

NUCLEI OF THE FACIAL NERVE
AND NERVUS INTERMEDIUS

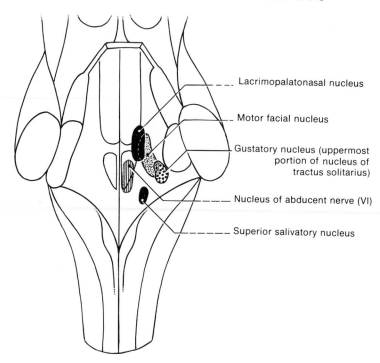

The lacrimopalatonasal nucleus (nuclear complex) is the superior portion of the superior salivatory nucleus which contains cells that give rise to parasympathetic fibers, destined for the pterygopalatine ganglion, and which pass through the greater petrosal nerve.

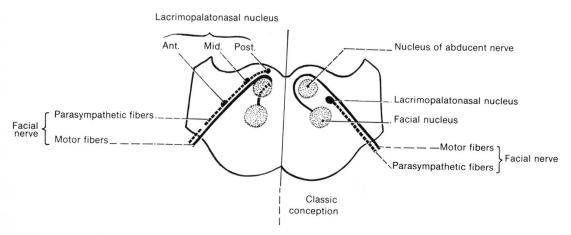

From Eyriès, C., and Chouard, C. H.: Ann. Otolaryng. (Paris), 80:775-802, 1963.

EMERGENCE OF THE FACIAL NERVE
AND NERVUS INTERMEDIUS

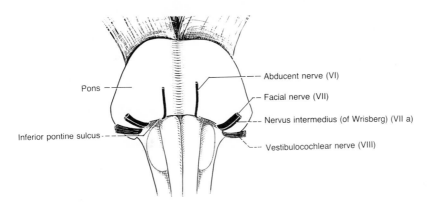

Pons

Inferior pontine sulcus

Abducent nerve (VI)

Facial nerve (VII)

Nervus intermedius (of Wrisberg) (VII a)

Vestibulocochlear nerve (VIII)

INTRACRANIAL COURSE

POSTERIOR ASPECT OF THE PETROUS PART OF THE TEMPORAL BONE

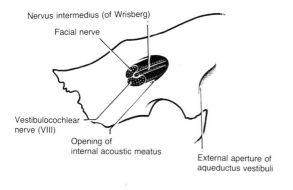

Nervus intermedius (of Wrisberg)

Facial nerve

Vestibulocochlear nerve (VIII)

Opening of internal acoustic meatus

External aperture of aqueductus vestibuli

THE END (FUNDUS) of THE INTERNAL ACOUSTIC MEATUS

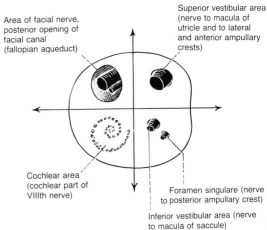

Area of facial nerve, posterior opening of facial canal (fallopian aqueduct)

Superior vestibular area (nerve to macula of utricle and to lateral and anterior ampullary crests)

Cochlear area (cochlear part of VIIIth nerve)

Foramen singulare (nerve to posterior ampullary crest)

Inferior vestibular area (nerve to macula of saccule)

INTRAPETROSAL COURSE

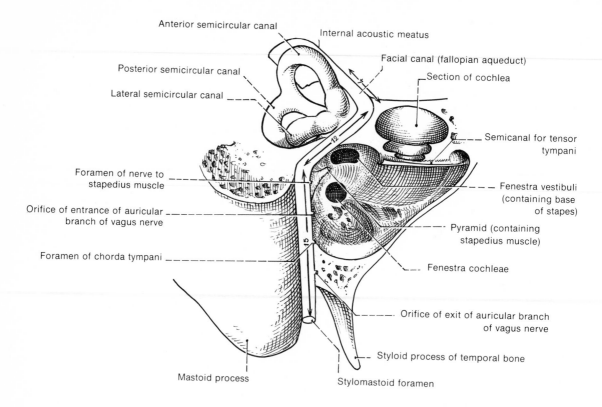

Anterior semicircular canal

Internal acoustic meatus

Posterior semicircular canal

Lateral semicircular canal

Facial canal (fallopian aqueduct)

Section of cochlea

Semicanal for tensor tympani

Foramen of nerve to stapedius muscle

Orifice of entrance of auricular branch of vagus nerve

Foramen of chorda tympani

Fenestra vestibuli (containing base of stapes)

Pyramid (containing stapedius muscle)

Fenestra cochleae

Orifice of exit of auricular branch of vagus nerve

Styloid process of temporal bone

Mastoid process

Stylomastoid foramen

The numbers indicate the average lengths in millimeters of the three parts of the facial canal.

BRANCHES OF THE FACIAL NERVE AND
NERVUS INTERMEDIUS

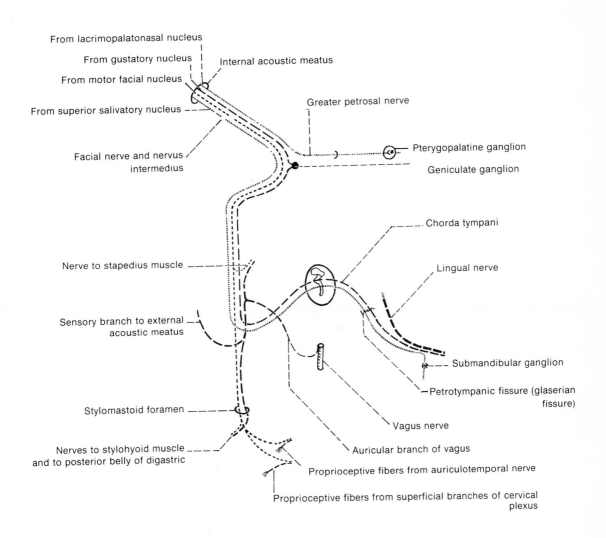

From lacrimopalatonasal nucleus

From gustatory nucleus

Internal acoustic meatus

From motor facial nucleus

From superior salivatory nucleus

Greater petrosal nerve

Facial nerve and nervus intermedius

Pterygopalatine ganglion

Geniculate ganglion

Chorda tympani

Nerve to stapedius muscle

Lingual nerve

Sensory branch to external acoustic meatus

Submandibular ganglion

Petrotympanic fissure (glaserian fissure)

Stylomastoid foramen

Vagus nerve

Nerves to stylohyoid muscle and to posterior belly of digastric

Auricular branch of vagus

Proprioceptive fibers from auriculotemporal nerve

Proprioceptive fibers from superficial branches of cervical plexus

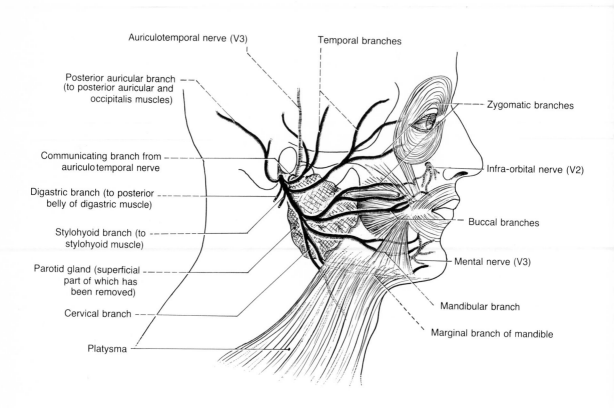

Auriculotemporal nerve (V3)

Temporal branches

Posterior auricular branch
(to posterior auricular and
occipitalis muscles)

Zygomatic branches

Communicating branch from
auriculotemporal nerve

Infra-orbital nerve (V2)

Digastric branch (to posterior
belly of digastric muscle)

Buccal branches

Stylohyoid branch (to
stylohyoid muscle)

Mental nerve (V3)

Parotid gland (superficial
part of which has
been removed)

Mandibular branch

Cervical branch

Marginal branch of mandible

Platysma

Muscles of Facial Expression
Which Are Supplied by the Facial Nerve

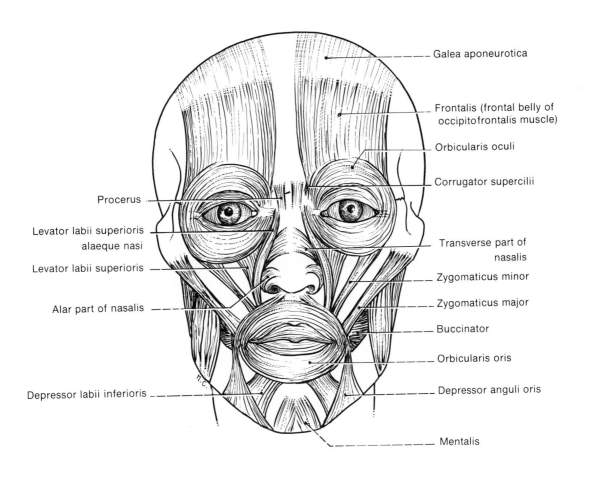

Galea aponeurotica

Frontalis (frontal belly of occipitofrontalis muscle)

Orbicularis oculi

Corrugator supercilii

Procerus

Levator labii superioris alaeque nasi

Levator labii superioris

Alar part of nasalis

Transverse part of nasalis

Zygomaticus minor

Zygomaticus major

Buccinator

Orbicularis oris

Depressor labii inferioris

Depressor anguli oris

Mentalis

DIAGRAM OF FACIAL NERVE AND NERVUS INTERMEDIUS

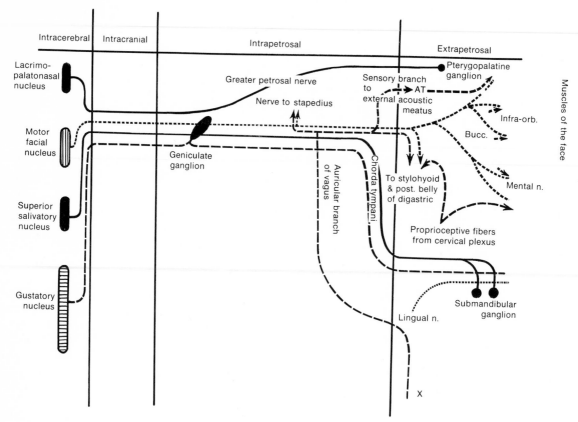

Intracerebral   Intracranial   Intrapetrosal   Extrapetrosal

Lacrimo-palatonasal nucleus

Greater petrosal nerve

Sensory branch to external acoustic meatus

Pterygopalatine ganglion

AT

Infra-orb.

Nerve to stapedius

Bucc.

Motor facial nucleus

Geniculate ganglion

Muscles of the face

Superior salivatory nucleus

To stylohyoid & post. belly of digastric

Mental n.

Auricular branch of vagus

Chorda tympani

Proprioceptive fibers from cervical plexus

Gustatory nucleus

Submandibular ganglion

Lingual n.

X

AT: Auriculo-temporal nerve

Page 258

Morphological Structures Related to Hearing and Equilibrium

EXTERNAL EAR

SUPERFICIAL ASPECT OF THE AURICLE

EXTRINSIC MUSCLES OF THE AURICLE
(the intrinsic muscles of the auricle are not shown here)

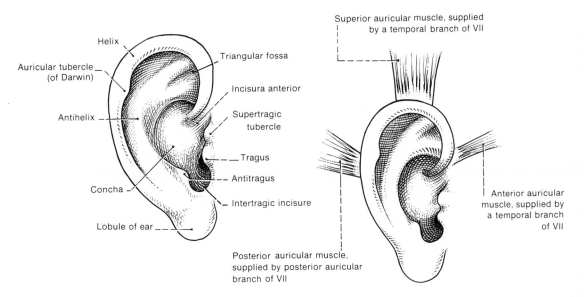

Helix

Auricular tubercle (of Darwin)

Antihelix

Concha

Lobule of ear

Triangular fossa

Incisura anterior

Supertragic tubercle

Tragus

Antitragus

Intertragic incisure

Superior auricular muscle, supplied by a temporal branch of VII

Anterior auricular muscle, supplied by a temporal branch of VII

Posterior auricular muscle, supplied by posterior auricular branch of VII

CARTILAGE OF THE AURICLE

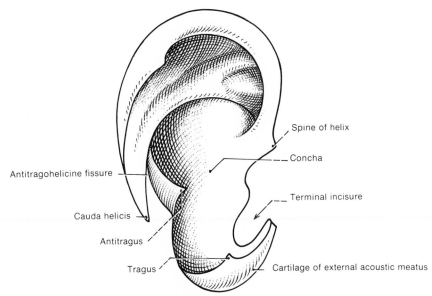

Antitragohelicine fissure

Cauda helicis

Antitragus

Tragus

Spine of helix

Concha

Terminal incisure

Cartilage of external acoustic meatus

ARTERIES OF THE EXTERNAL EAR

SENSORY INNERVATION OF THE EXTERNAL EAR

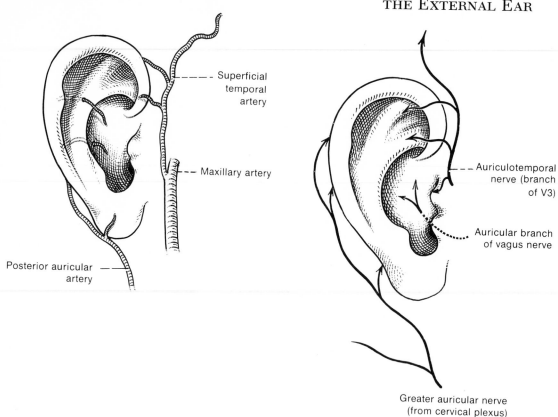

Superficial temporal artery

Maxillary artery

Posterior auricular artery

Auriculotemporal nerve (branch of V3)

Auricular branch of vagus nerve

Greater auricular nerve (from cervical plexus)

LYMPHATIC DRAINAGE OF THE EXTERNAL EAR

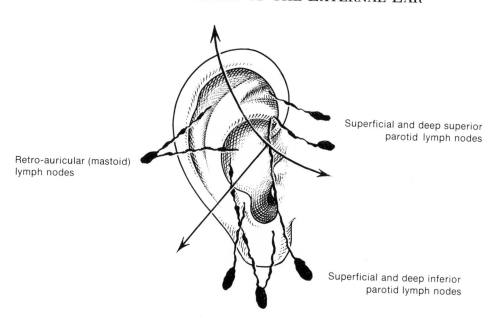

Superficial and deep superior parotid lymph nodes

Retro-auricular (mastoid) lymph nodes

Superficial and deep inferior parotid lymph nodes

EXTERNAL ACOUSTIC MEATUS

Frontal Section through the Long Axis of the External Acoustic Meatus

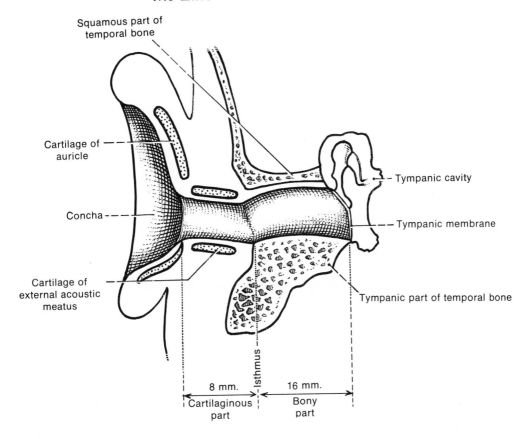

Squamous part of temporal bone

Cartilage of auricle

Concha

Cartilage of external acoustic meatus

Tympanic cavity

Tympanic membrane

Tympanic part of temporal bone

8 mm.
Cartilaginous part

Isthmus

16 mm.
Bony part

Horizontal Section of the External Acoustic Meatus (Inferior Aspect)

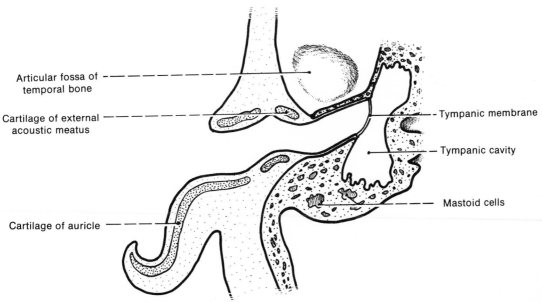

Articular fossa of temporal bone

Cartilage of external acoustic meatus

Cartilage of auricle

Tympanic membrane

Tympanic cavity

Mastoid cells

Page 261

TYMPANIC MEMBRANE

LATERAL ASPECT (CONCAVE)

MEDIAL ASPECT (CONVEX)

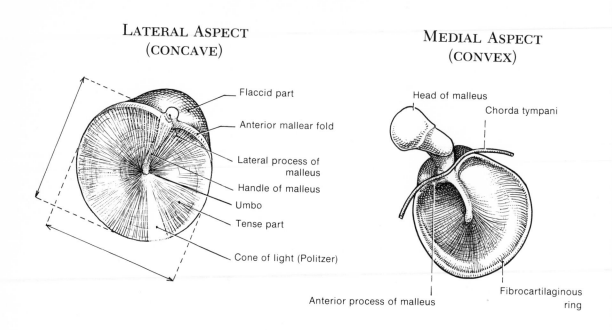

Flaccid part

Anterior mallear fold

Lateral process of malleus

Handle of malleus

Umbo

Tense part

Cone of light (Politzer)

Head of malleus

Chorda tympani

Anterior process of malleus

Fibrocartilaginous ring

FIBROUS LAYERS

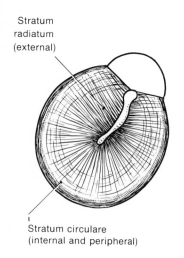

Stratum radiatum (external)

Stratum circulare (internal and peripheral)

VERTICAL SECTION THROUGH THE TYMPANIC MEMBRANE

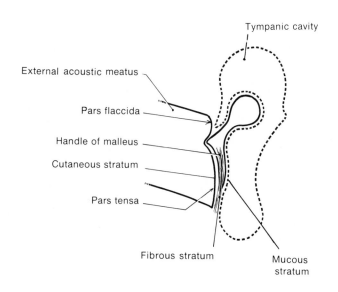

Tympanic cavity

External acoustic meatus

Pars flaccida

Handle of malleus

Cutaneous stratum

Pars tensa

Fibrous stratum

Mucous stratum

MIDDLE EAR

Walls of the Middle Ear

Superior Bony Wall, or Roof, or Tegmental Wall (Left Temporal Bone)

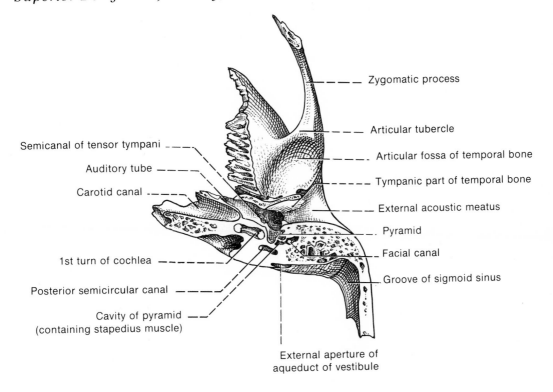

Zygomatic process

Articular tubercle

Articular fossa of temporal bone

Tympanic part of temporal bone

External acoustic meatus

Pyramid

Facial canal

Groove of sigmoid sinus

Semicanal of tensor tympani

Auditory tube

Carotid canal

1st turn of cochlea

Posterior semicircular canal

Cavity of pyramid
(containing stapedius muscle)

External aperture of
aqueduct of vestibule

Inferior Bony Wall, or Floor, or Jugular Wall (Left Temporal Bone)

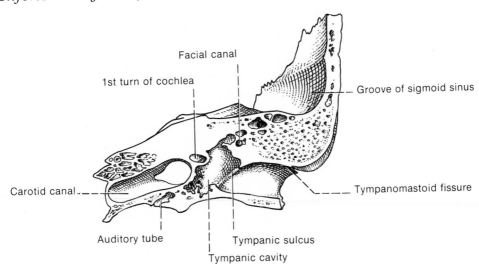

Facial canal

1st turn of cochlea

Groove of sigmoid sinus

Tympanomastoid fissure

Carotid canal

Auditory tube

Tympanic sulcus

Tympanic cavity

Medial Bony Wall, or Labyrinthine Wall (Left Temporal Bone)

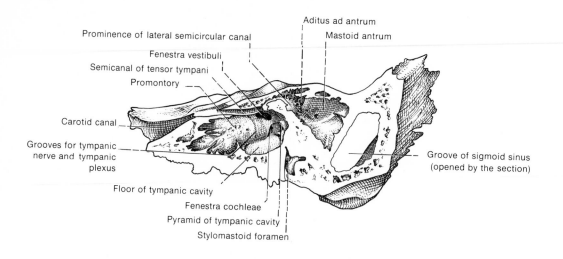

Prominence of lateral semicircular canal

Aditus ad antrum

Mastoid antrum

Fenestra vestibuli

Semicanal of tensor tympani

Promontory

Carotid canal

Grooves for tympanic nerve and tympanic plexus

Groove of sigmoid sinus (opened by the section)

Floor of tympanic cavity

Fenestra cochleae

Pyramid of tympanic cavity

Stylomastoid foramen

Lateral Bony Wall, or Membranous Wall (Left Temporal Bone)

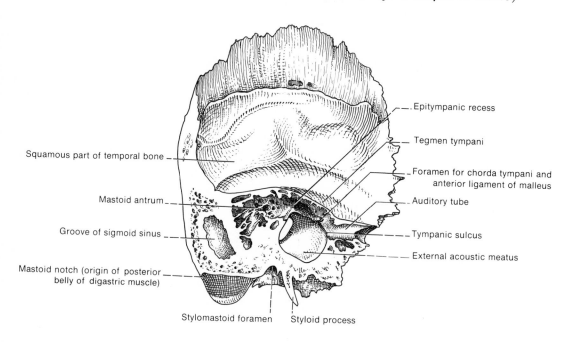

Epitympanic recess

Tegmen tympani

Squamous part of temporal bone

Foramen for chorda tympani and anterior ligament of malleus

Mastoid antrum

Auditory tube

Groove of sigmoid sinus

Tympanic sulcus

External acoustic meatus

Mastoid notch (origin of posterior belly of digastric muscle)

Stylomastoid foramen

Styloid process

Page 264

Posterior Bony Wall, or Mastoid Wall (Right Temporal Bone)

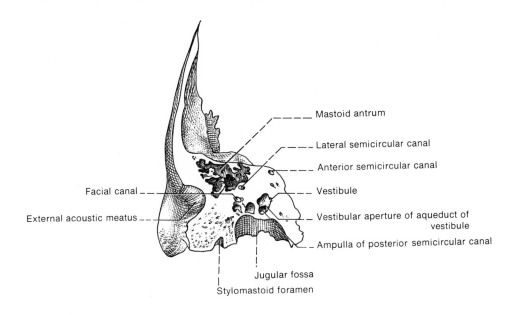

Facial canal

External acoustic meatus

Mastoid antrum

Lateral semicircular canal

Anterior semicircular canal

Vestibule

Vestibular aperture of aqueduct of vestibule

Ampulla of posterior semicircular canal

Jugular fossa

Stylomastoid foramen

Anterior Bony Wall, or Carotid Wall (Right Temporal Bone)

The upper arrow passes through the fenestra vestibuli
The lower arrow passes through the fenestra cochleae

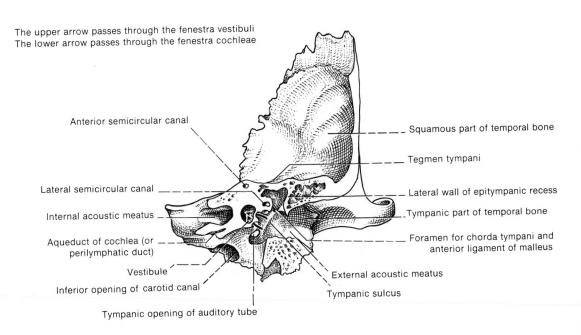

Anterior semicircular canal

Lateral semicircular canal

Internal acoustic meatus

Aqueduct of cochlea (or perilymphatic duct)

Vestibule

Inferior opening of carotid canal

Tympanic opening of auditory tube

Squamous part of temporal bone

Tegmen tympani

Lateral wall of epitympanic recess

Tympanic part of temporal bone

Foramen for chorda tympani and anterior ligament of malleus

External acoustic meatus

Tympanic sulcus

CONTENTS OF THE MIDDLE EAR

Auditory Ossicles

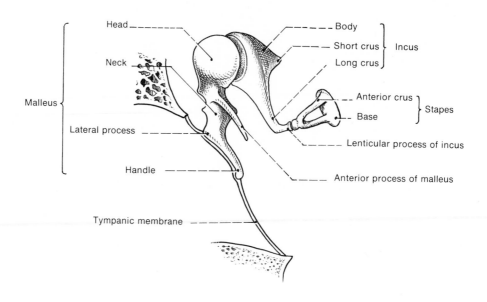

Head — Body
Neck — Short crus ⎫ Incus
— Long crus ⎭
Malleus — Anterior crus ⎫ Stapes
— Base ⎭
Lateral process — Lenticular process of incus
Handle — Anterior process of malleus
Tympanic membrane

Articulations of the Auditory Ossicles

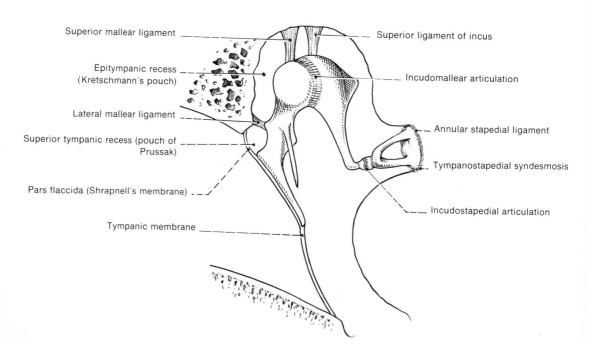

Superior mallear ligament — Superior ligament of incus
Epitympanic recess (Kretschmann's pouch) — Incudomallear articulation
Lateral mallear ligament
Superior tympanic recess (pouch of Prussak) — Annular stapedial ligament
Pars flaccida (Shrapnell's membrane) — Tympanostapedial syndesmosis
Tympanic membrane — Incudostapedial articulation

Medial Aspect

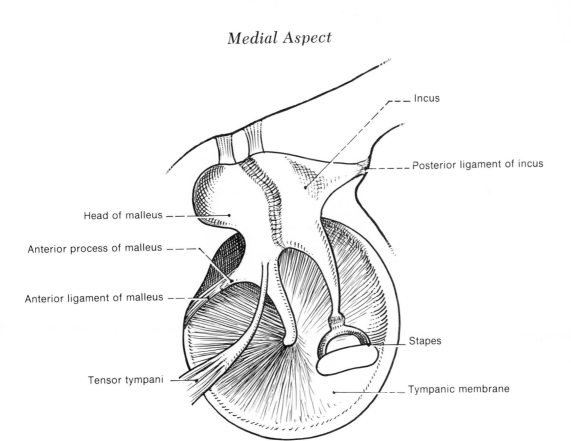

Incus

Posterior ligament of incus

Head of malleus

Anterior process of malleus

Anterior ligament of malleus

Stapes

Tensor tympani

Tympanic membrane

Lateral Aspect after Removing the Tympanic Membrane

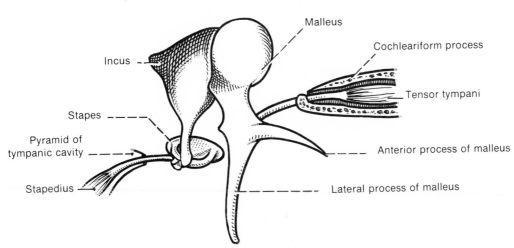

Malleus

Cochleariform process

Incus

Tensor tympani

Stapes

Pyramid of tympanic cavity

Anterior process of malleus

Stapedius

Lateral process of malleus

MUCOUS MEMBRANE OF THE TYMPANIC CAVITY

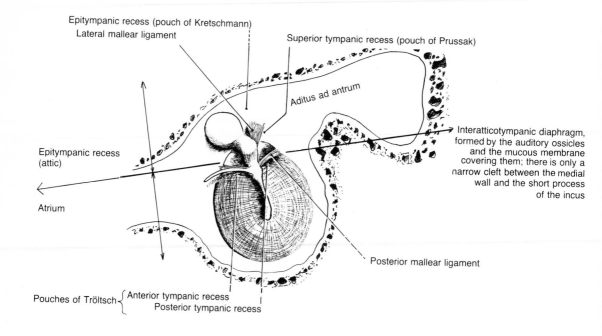

Epitympanic recess (pouch of Kretschmann)
Lateral mallear ligament

Superior tympanic recess (pouch of Prussak)

Aditus ad antrum

Epitympanic recess (attic)

Atrium

Interatticotympanic diaphragm, formed by the auditory ossicles and the mucous membrane covering them; there is only a narrow cleft between the medial wall and the short process of the incus

Posterior mallear ligament

Pouches of Tröltsch { Anterior tympanic recess
Posterior tympanic recess

Pneumatic Cavities Associated with the Middle Ear
(Right Temporal Bone)

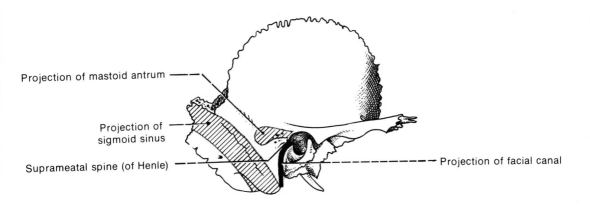

Projection of mastoid antrum

Projection of sigmoid sinus

Suprameatal spine (of Henle)

Projection of facial canal

The tympanic cavity communicates with the air cavities (hollowed out into the bones which form its walls). The most important one are located posteriorly in the mastoid process.

Mastoid (or tympanic) antrum

This is a constant and large cavity, located just behind the tympanic cavity (see pages 264 and 268). The newborn does not possess a mastoid process, but does have a mastoid antrum.

Its average volume is 1 cc. Usually its walls are uneven. The aditus ad antrum establishes extensive communication with the epitympanic recess (attic).

Its main relationship is with the facial nerve, which describes a downward sweep beginning below the floor of the aditus and then lying between the tympanic cavity and the mastoid process.

Mastoid air cells

Located behind and below the mastoid antrum, they are more or less numerous and voluminous, depending on individual differences, and so determine the various types of mastoid process (pneumatic, diploic, etc.). These cells are in relationship with the sigmoid sinus and the vertical (third) part of the facial canal.

Tympanic air cells

They are relatively constant and commonly of small size and are hollowed out mainly in the posterior and inferior parts of the tympanic plate.

Petrous air cells

When they exist, they are located around the labyrinth and may extend to the apex of the petrous temporal. They are usually of very small size and their number varies widely.

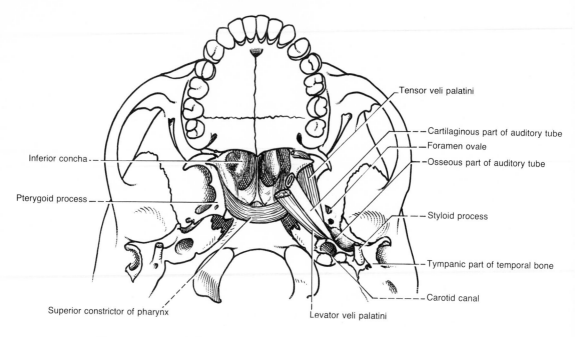

Osseous part of the auditory tube, see also pages 263 and 264
Pharyngeal opening of the auditory tube, see page 202

SEMISCHEMATIC SECTION OF THE MIDDLE PART OF THE LEFT AUDITORY TUBE (ANTERIOR ASPECT)

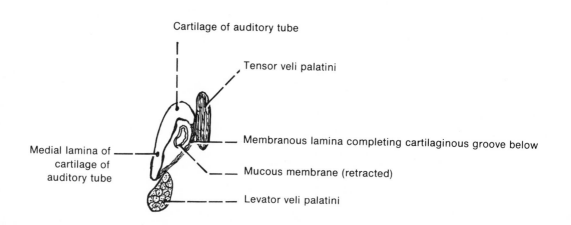

INTERNAL EAR

RIGHT OSSEOUS LABYRINTH

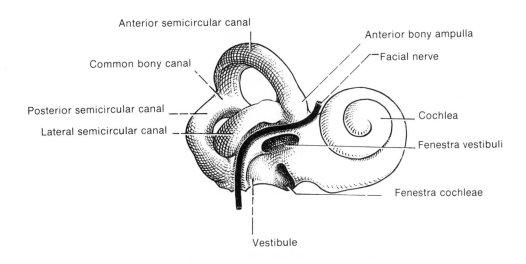

Anterior semicircular canal

Common bony canal

Posterior semicircular canal

Lateral semicircular canal

Anterior bony ampulla

Facial nerve

Cochlea

Fenestra vestibuli

Fenestra cochleae

Vestibule

ORIENTATION OF THE SEMICIRCULAR CANALS IN AN INDIVIDUAL IN THE UPRIGHT POSITION

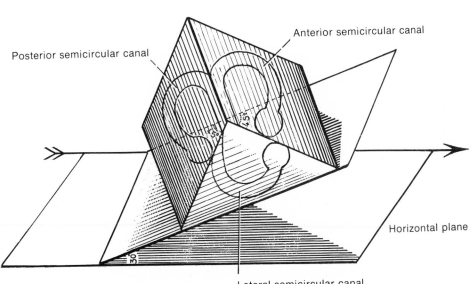

Posterior semicircular canal

Anterior semicircular canal

Horizontal plane

Lateral semicircular canal

Spiral Canal of the Cochlea (a segment of which has been opened)

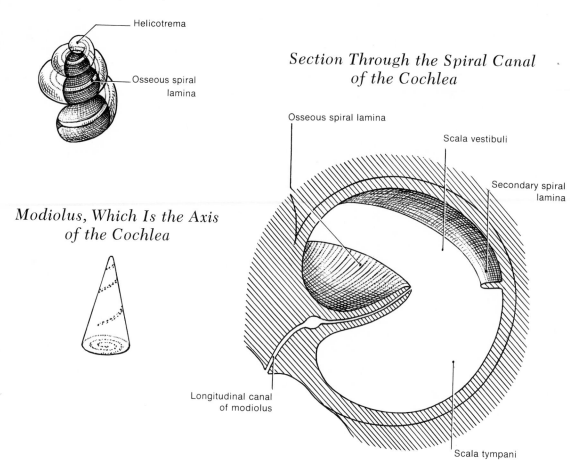

Helicotrema

Osseous spiral lamina

Section Through the Spiral Canal of the Cochlea

Osseous spiral lamina

Scala vestibuli

Secondary spiral lamina

Modiolus, Which Is the Axis of the Cochlea

Longitudinal canal of modiolus

Scala tympani

End (Fundus) of the Internal Acoustic Meatus

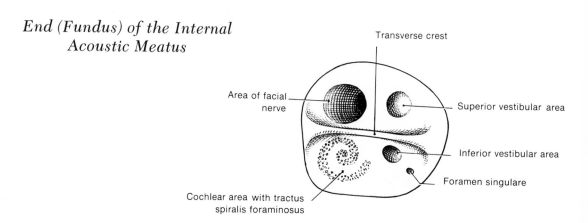

Transverse crest

Area of facial nerve

Superior vestibular area

Inferior vestibular area

Foramen singulare

Cochlear area with tractus spiralis foraminosus

MEMBRANOUS LABYRINTH AND COCHLEAR DUCT

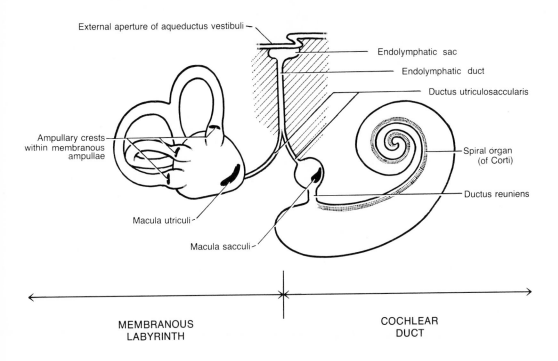

Schematic Section of a Semicircular Canal

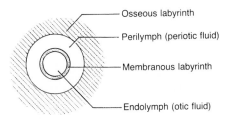

The *endolymph* (otic fluid) fills the membranous labyrinth and the cochlear duct. The *perilymph* (periotic fluid) fills the spaces between the membranous labyrinth, the cochlear duct and the osseous labyrinth.

Section Through the Cochlear Canal

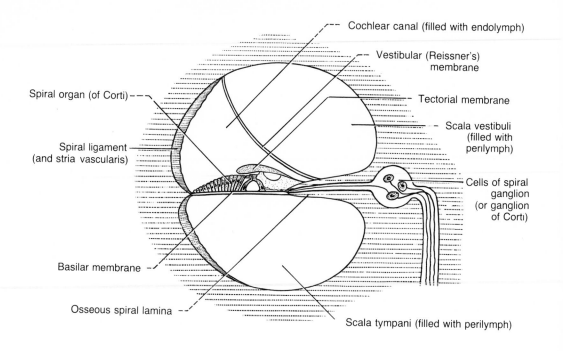

Cochlear canal (filled with endolymph)

Vestibular (Reissner's) membrane

Tectorial membrane

Scala vestibuli (filled with perilymph)

Cells of spiral ganglion (or ganglion of Corti)

Spiral organ (of Corti)

Spiral ligament (and stria vascularis)

Basilar membrane

Osseous spiral lamina

Scala tympani (filled with perilymph)

Diagram of the Cochlea Assumed To Be Unrolled

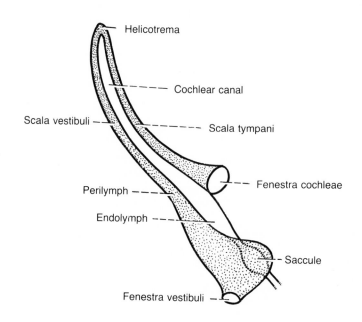

Helicotrema

Cochlear canal

Scala vestibuli

Scala tympani

Fenestra cochleae

Perilymph

Endolymph

Saccule

Fenestra vestibuli

STRUCTURE OF THE SPIRAL ORGAN (OF CORTI)

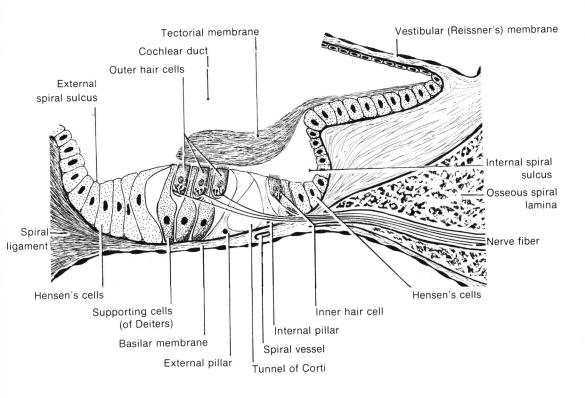

*Ultrastructure of a Hair Cell**

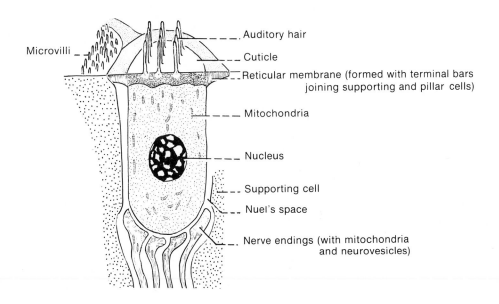

From Engström, H., and Sjöstrand, F. S.: The structure and innervation of the cochlear hair cells. Acta Otolaryng., 44:490-501, 1954.

DIAGRAM OF THE SENSORY EPITHELIAL MEMBRANES OF THE INTERNAL EAR*

Macula   *Crista Ampullaris*   *Spiral Organ of Corti*

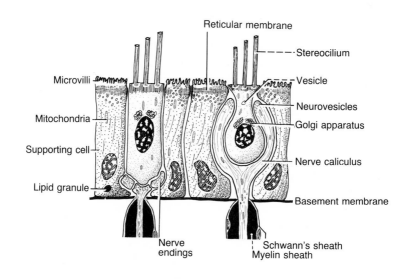

Ultrastructure of Hair Cells of the Maculae and Cristae Ampullares†

TYPE II   TYPE I

From Dubreuil, G., et Canivenc, R.: Manuel Théorique et Pratique d'Histologie. 6th ed. Paris, Vigot Frères, 1967. Vol. 2, p. 415.

†*From Wersäll, J.: Studies on the structure and innervation of the sensory epithelium of cristae ampullares in the guinea pig. A light and electron microscope investigation. Acta Otolaryng. (suppl.) 126:1-85, 1956.*

VESTIBULOCOCHLEAR (STATO-ACOUSTIC) NERVE (VIII)

ORIGIN

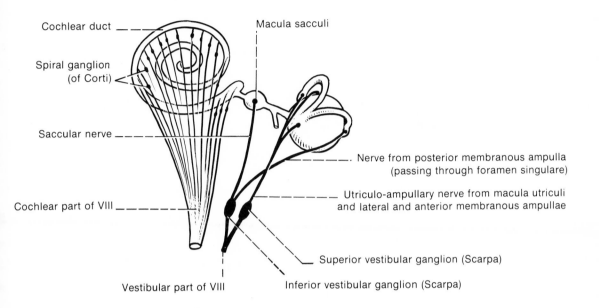

Cochlear duct

Spiral ganglion (of Corti)

Saccular nerve

Cochlear part of VIII

Vestibular part of VIII

Macula sacculi

Nerve from posterior membranous ampulla (passing through foramen singulare)

Utriculo-ampullary nerve from macula utriculi and lateral and anterior membranous ampullae

Superior vestibular ganglion (Scarpa)

Inferior vestibular ganglion (Scarpa)

The nerves of Oort and Hardy are not indicated. It suffices to know the existence of the cochleosaccular fibers (Oort, Weston, Lorente de Nò), and of the cochlear and vestibular efferent fibers (Rasmussen, Portmann, Rossi).

INTRACRANIAL COURSE OF THE VESTIBULOCOCHLEAR NERVE

(Posterior aspect of a frontal section through the posterior
cranial fossa, showing the cerebellopontine region)

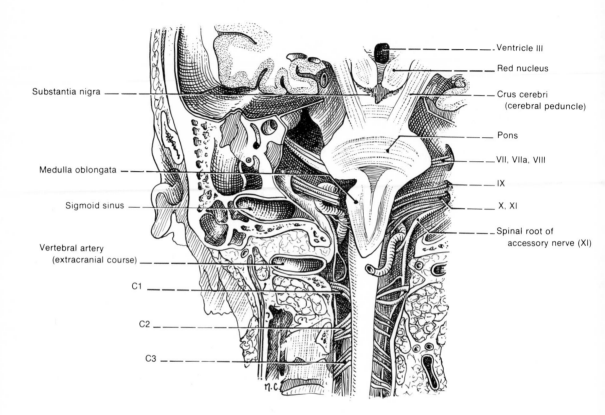

Substantia nigra

Medulla oblongata

Sigmoid sinus

Vertebral artery
(extracranial course)

C1

C2

C3

n.c.

Ventricle III

Red nucleus

Crus cerebri
(cerebral peduncle)

Pons

VII, VIIa, VIII

IX

X, XI

Spinal root of
accessory nerve (XI)

AUDITORY PATHWAYS AND CENTERS

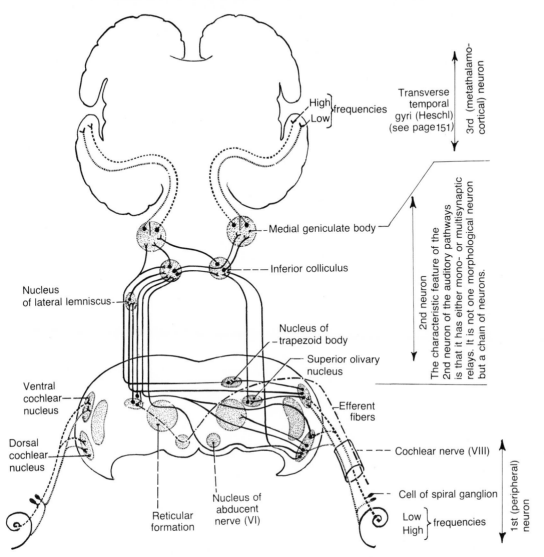

The efferent fibers are thought to be preganglionic to vessels and secretory tissue of the internal ear. According to Rasmussen[*] and Rossi, they do not relay in the nucleus of VI, and they are homo- and contralateral.

Probably the efferent fibers, terminating around the hair cells, are inhibitory.[†]

According to Culler,[‡] high frequencies have a better reception near the base of the cochlea than low ones; this is correlated with the work of Von Békésy.[§]

[*]Rasmussen, G. L: The olivary peduncle and other fiber projections of the superior olivary complex. J. Comp. Neurol., 84:141-219, 1946.

[†]Galambos, R.: Suppression of auditory nerve activity by stimulation of efferent fibers to cochlea. J. Neurophysiol., 19:424-437, 1956.

[‡]Culler, E. A.: Is there localization in the cochlea for low tones? Discussion from point of view of animal experiment. Ann. Otol. Rhinol. Laryngol., 44:807-813, 1935.

[§]Von Békésy, G.: Experiments in hearing (ed. by E. G. Wever). New York, McGraw-Hill Book Co., 1960.

ANATOMICAL DIAGRAM OF THE ACOUSTIC ACCOMMODATION

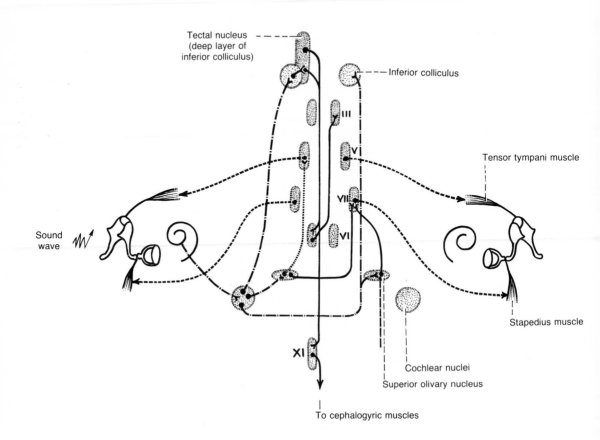

This anatomical diagram cannot take into consideration the conceptions of frequency and sound energy which are essential in the process of auditory accommodation. The contraction of the tensor tympani reduces the transmission of sounds which have a frequency inferior to 2000 c/s; that of stapedius lowers the transmission of those which have a frequency superior to 2000 c/s. Total relaxation is more favorable to transmission of low and weak sounds; total contraction is more efficient in transmission of high and intense sounds.*

*Stuhlman, O.: The correlation between cochlear microphonics and stapes motion. Physic. Rev., 59:911, 1941; Vallancien, B.: Acquisitions récentes sur la physiologie des organes de l'audition. Biologie médicale, 45:691-718, 1955.

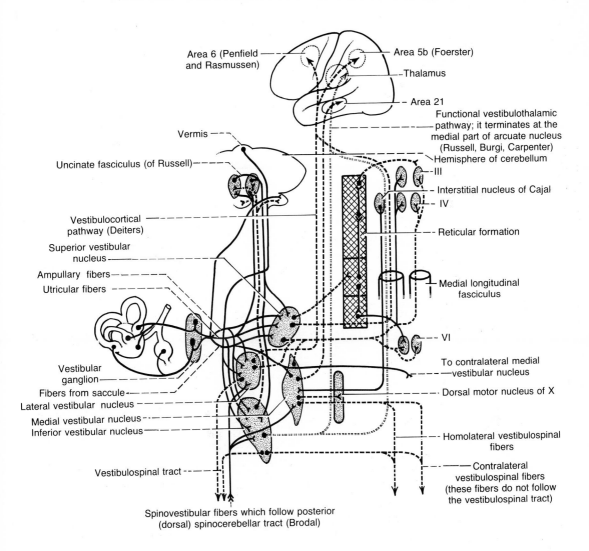

Area 6 (Penfield and Rasmussen)
Area 5b (Foerster)
Thalamus
Area 21
Functional vestibulothalamic pathway; it terminates at the medial part of arcuate nucleus (Russell, Burgi, Carpenter)
Vermis
Hemisphere of cerebellum
III
Uncinate fasciculus (of Russell)
Interstitial nucleus of Cajal
IV
Vestibulocortical pathway (Deiters)
Reticular formation
Superior vestibular nucleus
Ampullary fibers
Utricular fibers
Medial longitudinal fasciculus
VI
Vestibular ganglion
To contralateral medial vestibular nucleus
Fibers from saccule
Lateral vestibular nucleus
Dorsal motor nucleus of X
Medial vestibular nucleus
Inferior vestibular nucleus
Homolateral vestibulospinal fibers
Vestibulospinal tract
Contralateral vestibulospinal fibers (these fibers do not follow the vestibulospinal tract)
Spinovestibular fibers which follow posterior (dorsal) spinocerebellar tract (Brodal)

As in cochlear pathways, there are efferent fibers to the labyrinth which influence secretion of labyrinthine fluids; if vestibular accommodation exists, these efferent fibers could logically play a part.

Foerster, O.: The cerebral cortex in man. The Lancet, 2:309-312, 1931.
Penfield, W., and Rasmussen, T.: The Cerebral Cortex of Man. New York, The Macmillan Co., 1950.

Glossopharyngeal, Vagus, and Accessory Nerves

We have grouped these three nerves (sometimes called "mixed nerves") together because they have many points in common such as nuclei, emergence, course and distribution.

NUCLEI OF ORIGIN

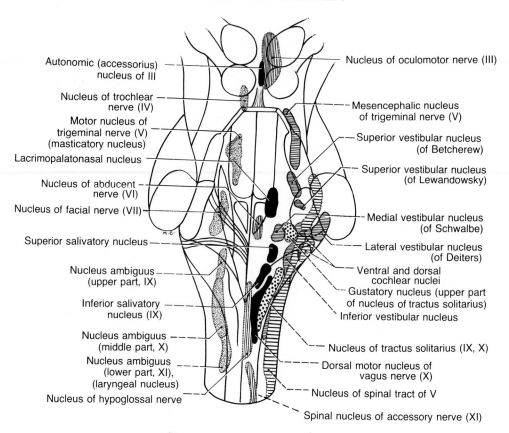

Autonomic (accessorius) nucleus of III
Nucleus of trochlear nerve (IV)
Motor nucleus of trigeminal nerve (V) (masticatory nucleus)
Lacrimopalatonasal nucleus
Nucleus of abducent nerve (VI)
Nucleus of facial nerve (VII)
Superior salivatory nucleus
Nucleus ambiguus (upper part, IX)
Inferior salivatory nucleus (IX)
Nucleus ambiguus (middle part, X)
Nucleus ambiguus (lower part, XI), (laryngeal nucleus)
Nucleus of hypoglossal nerve

Nucleus of oculomotor nerve (III)
Mesencephalic nucleus of trigeminal nerve (V)
Superior vestibular nucleus (of Betcherew)
Superior vestibular nucleus (of Lewandowsky)
Medial vestibular nucleus (of Schwalbe)
Lateral vestibular nucleus (of Deiters)
Ventral and dorsal cochlear nuclei
Gustatory nucleus (upper part of nucleus of tractus solitarius)
Inferior vestibular nucleus
Nucleus of tractus solitarius (IX, X)
Dorsal motor nucleus of vagus nerve (X)
Nucleus of spinal tract of V
Spinal nucleus of accessory nerve (XI)

SPINAL ORIGIN OF THE ACCESSORY NERVE (XI)

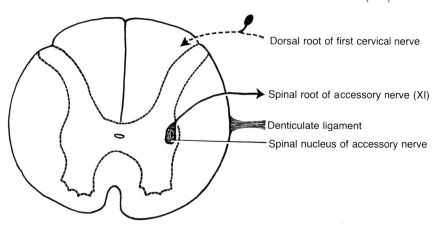

Dorsal root of first cervical nerve
Spinal root of accessory nerve (XI)
Denticulate ligament
Spinal nucleus of accessory nerve

EMERGENCE OF MIXED NERVES FROM
THE BRAIN STEM

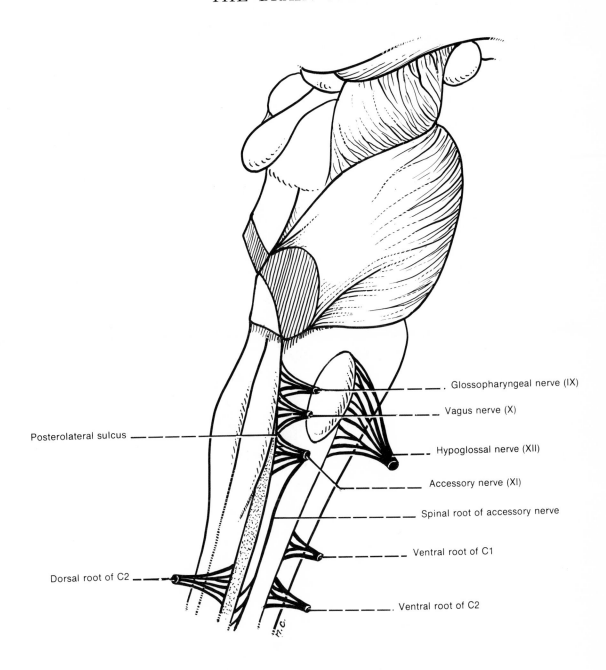

Lateral aspect of the medulla showing the posterolateral sulcus
where the glossopharyngeal, vagus and accessory nerves emerge.

Origins of the Accessory Nerve (XI)

(Posterior view of the medulla oblongata and the first spinal segments)

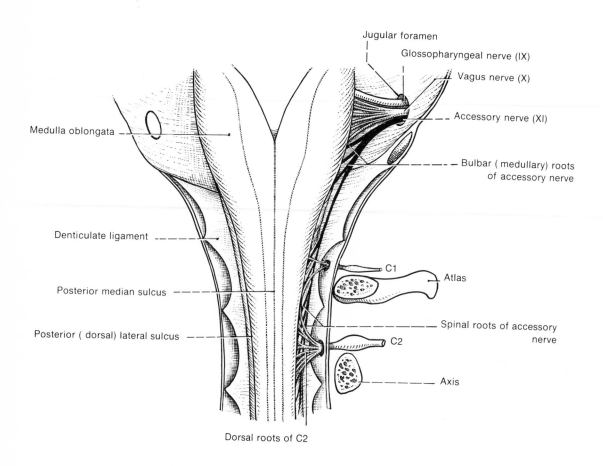

Jugular foramen

Glossopharyngeal nerve (IX)

Vagus nerve (X)

Accessory nerve (XI)

Bulbar (medullary) roots of accessory nerve

Medulla oblongata

Denticulate ligament

C1

Atlas

Posterior median sulcus

Spinal roots of accessory nerve

Posterior (dorsal) lateral sulcus

C2

Axis

Dorsal roots of C2

PASSAGE THROUGH THE SKULL

SAGITTAL SECTION OF THE POSTERIOR CRANIAL FOSSA

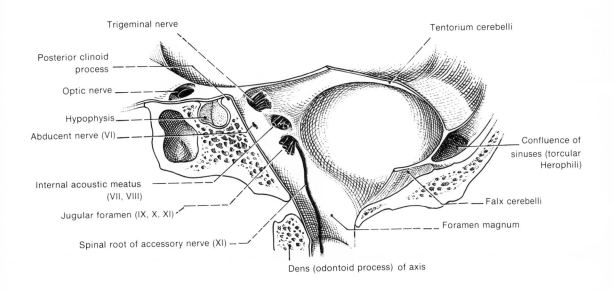

Trigeminal nerve

Tentorium cerebelli

Posterior clinoid process

Optic nerve

Hypophysis

Abducent nerve (VI)

Confluence of sinuses (torcular Herophili)

Internal acoustic meatus (VII, VIII)

Jugular foramen (IX, X, XI)

Spinal root of accessory nerve (XI)

Falx cerebelli

Foramen magnum

Dens (odontoid process) of axis

JUGULAR FORAMEN

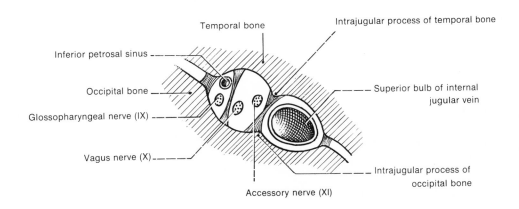

Temporal bone

Intrajugular process of temporal bone

Inferior petrosal sinus

Occipital bone

Glossopharyngeal nerve (IX)

Vagus nerve (X)

Superior bulb of internal jugular vein

Intrajugular process of occipital bone

Accessory nerve (XI)

RETROSTYLOID REGION

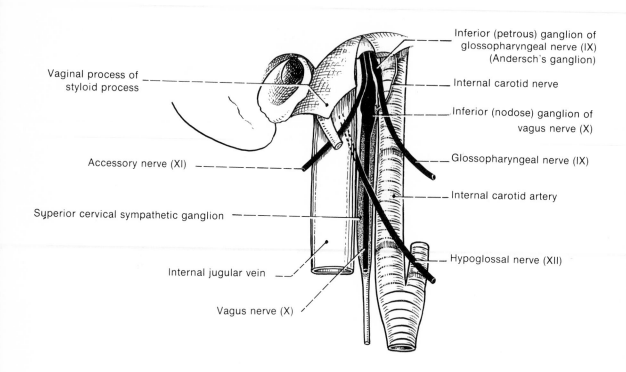

Vaginal process of styloid process

Accessory nerve (XI)

Superior cervical sympathetic ganglion

Internal jugular vein

Vagus nerve (X)

Inferior (petrous) ganglion of glossopharyngeal nerve (IX) (Andersch's ganglion)

Internal carotid nerve

Inferior (nodose) ganglion of vagus nerve (X)

Glossopharyngeal nerve (IX)

Internal carotid artery

Hypoglossal nerve (XII)

DISTRIBUTION OF THE GLOSSOPHARYNGEAL NERVE

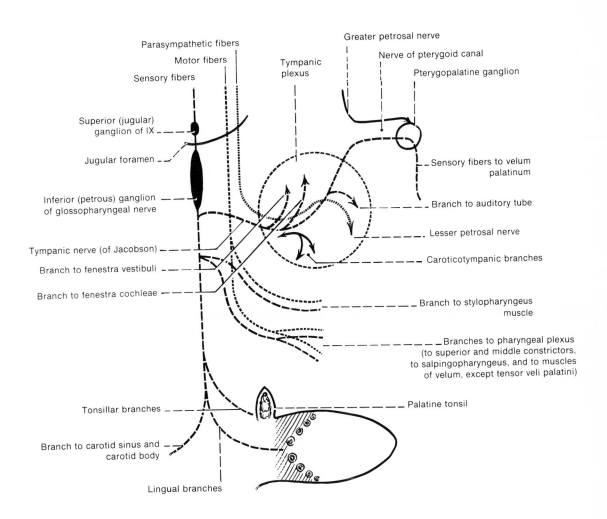

Parasympathetic fibers

Motor fibers

Sensory fibers

Greater petrosal nerve

Nerve of pterygoid canal

Pterygopalatine ganglion

Tympanic plexus

Superior (jugular) ganglion of IX

Jugular foramen

Inferior (petrous) ganglion of glossopharyngeal nerve

Tympanic nerve (of Jacobson)

Branch to fenestra vestibuli

Branch to fenestra cochleae

Sensory fibers to velum palatinum

Branch to auditory tube

Lesser petrosal nerve

Caroticotympanic branches

Branch to stylopharyngeus muscle

Branches to pharyngeal plexus (to superior and middle constrictors, to salpingopharyngeus, and to muscles of velum, except tensor veli palatini)

Tonsillar branches

Palatine tonsil

Branch to carotid sinus and carotid body

Lingual branches

DISTRIBUTION OF THE VAGUS NERVE

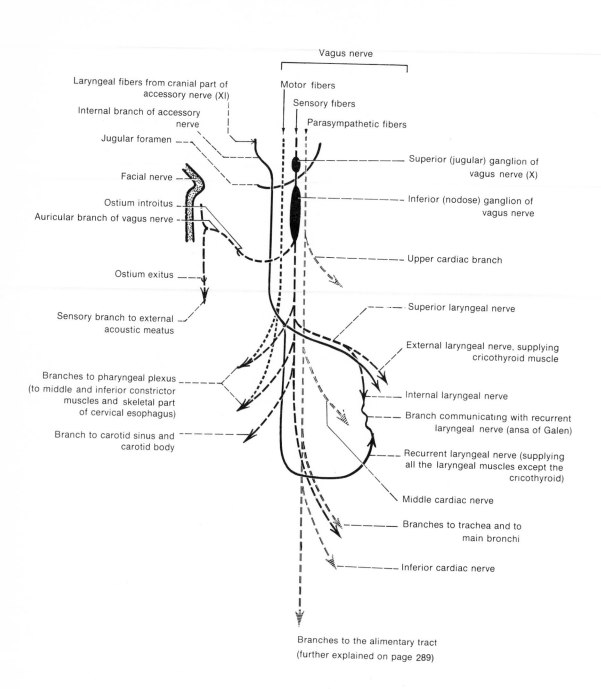

Vagus nerve

Motor fibers

Sensory fibers

Parasympathetic fibers

Laryngeal fibers from cranial part of accessory nerve (XI)

Internal branch of accessory nerve

Jugular foramen

Facial nerve

Ostium introitus

Auricular branch of vagus nerve

Ostium exitus

Sensory branch to external acoustic meatus

Branches to pharyngeal plexus (to middle and inferior constrictor muscles and skeletal part of cervical esophagus)

Branch to carotid sinus and carotid body

Superior (jugular) ganglion of vagus nerve (X)

Inferior (nodose) ganglion of vagus nerve

Upper cardiac branch

Superior laryngeal nerve

External laryngeal nerve, supplying cricothyroid muscle

Internal laryngeal nerve

Branch communicating with recurrent laryngeal nerve (ansa of Galen)

Recurrent laryngeal nerve (supplying all the laryngeal muscles except the cricothyroid)

Middle cardiac nerve

Branches to trachea and to main bronchi

Inferior cardiac nerve

Branches to the alimentary tract (further explained on page 289)

Vascular and Nervous Relationships at the Thoracic Inlet (Superior Thoracic Aperture)

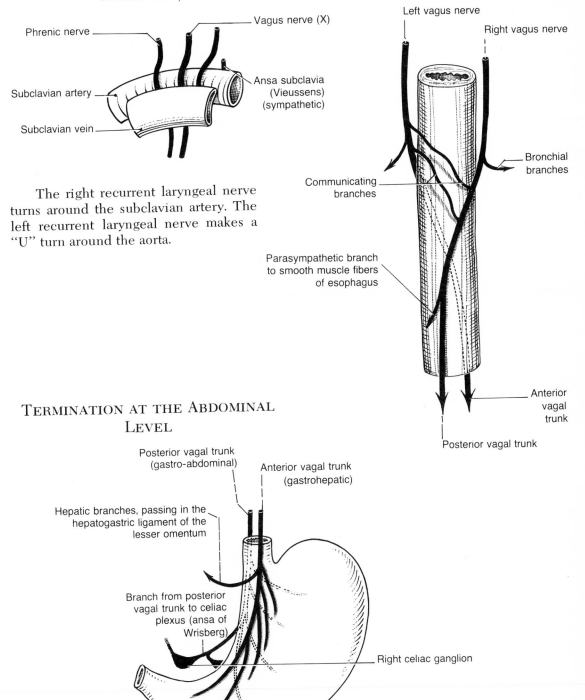

Phrenic nerve

Vagus nerve (X)

Subclavian artery

Ansa subclavia (Vieussens) (sympathetic)

Subclavian vein

The right recurrent laryngeal nerve turns around the subclavian artery. The left recurrent laryngeal nerve makes a "U" turn around the aorta.

Vagus Nerve in the Thorax (Posterior Aspect)

Left vagus nerve

Right vagus nerve

Communicating branches

Bronchial branches

Parasympathetic branch to smooth muscle fibers of esophagus

Anterior vagal trunk

Posterior vagal trunk

Termination at the Abdominal Level

Posterior vagal trunk (gastro-abdominal)

Anterior vagal trunk (gastrohepatic)

Hepatic branches, passing in the hepatogastric ligament of the lesser omentum

Branch from posterior vagal trunk to celiac plexus (ansa of Wrisberg)

Right celiac ganglion

Page 289

DISTRIBUTION OF THE ACCESSORY NERVE (XI)

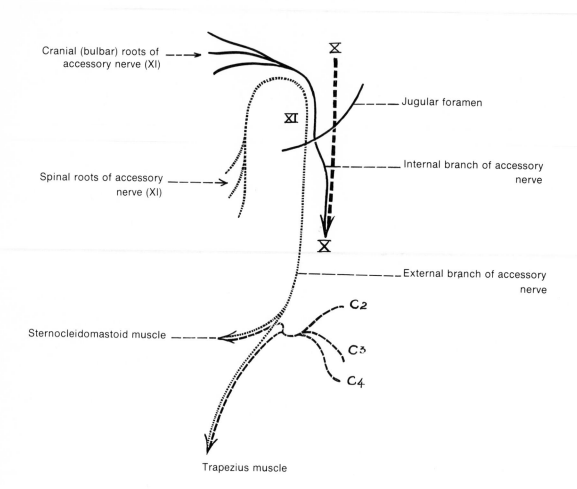

Cranial (bulbar) roots of
accessory nerve (XI)

Jugular foramen

XI

Internal branch of accessory
nerve

Spinal roots of accessory
nerve (XI)

External branch of accessory
nerve

C2

Sternocleidomastoid muscle

C3

C4

Trapezius muscle

External Branch of the Accessory Nerve

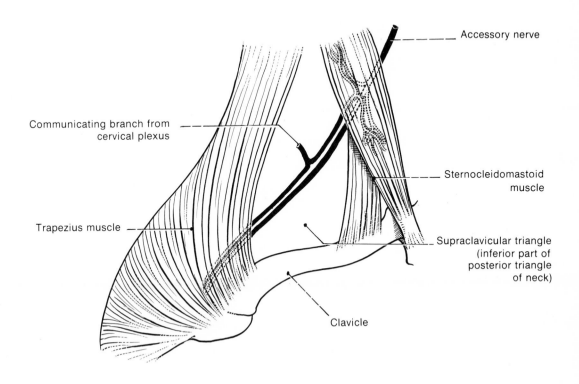

Accessory nerve

Communicating branch from cervical plexus

Sternocleidomastoid muscle

Trapezius muscle

Supraclavicular triangle (inferior part of posterior triangle of neck)

Clavicle

DIAGRAM OF THE IXth, Xth, AND XIth NERVES

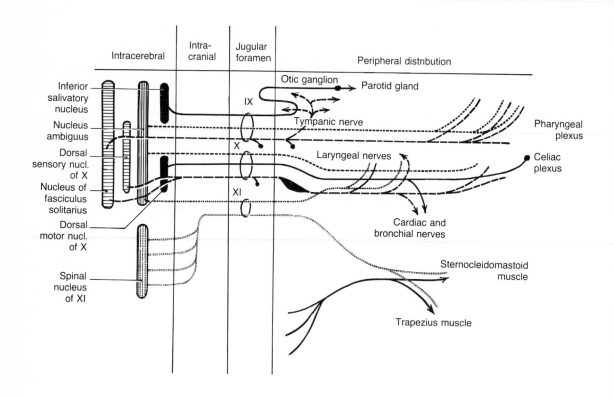

Hypoglossal Nerve

EMERGENCE FROM THE BRAIN STEM

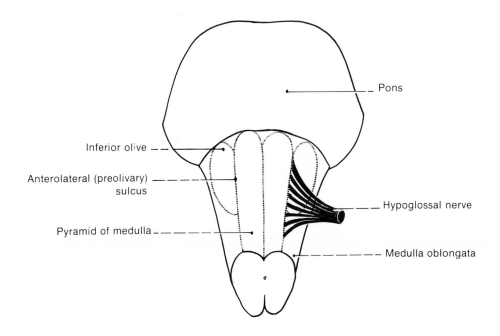

Pons

Inferior olive

Anterolateral (preolivary)
sulcus

Hypoglossal nerve

Pyramid of medulla

Medulla oblongata

NUCLEUS OF ORIGIN

See page 282.

BRANCHES OF THE HYPOGLOSSAL NERVE
AND ITS COMMUNICATIONS

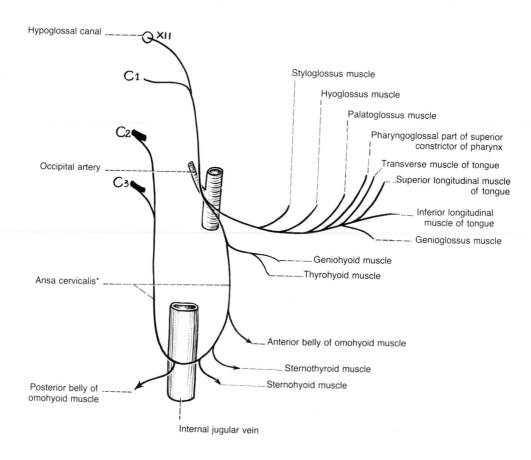

Hypoglossal canal

XII

C1

C2

Occipital artery

C3

Styloglossus muscle

Hyoglossus muscle

Palatoglossus muscle

Pharyngoglossal part of superior constrictor of pharynx

Transverse muscle of tongue

Superior longitudinal muscle of tongue

Inferior longitudinal muscle of tongue

Genioglossus muscle

Geniohyoid muscle

Thyrohyoid muscle

Ansa cervicalis*

Anterior belly of omohyoid muscle

Sternothyroid muscle

Sternohyoid muscle

Posterior belly of omohyoid muscle

Internal jugular vein

*Sometimes the ansa cervicalis may be located behind the internal jugular vein.

PASSAGE THROUGH THE SUBMANDIBULAR (DIGASTRIC) TRIANGLE

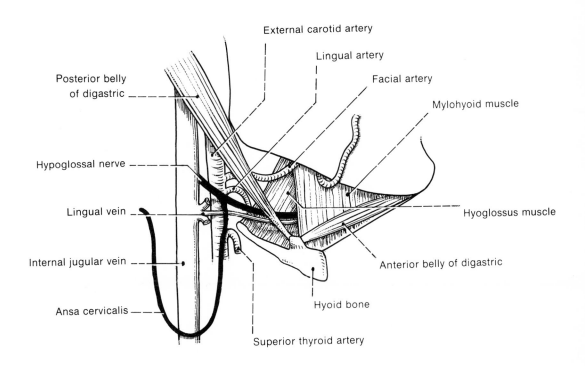

External carotid artery

Lingual artery

Facial artery

Mylohyoid muscle

Posterior belly of digastric

Hypoglossal nerve

Lingual vein

Internal jugular vein

Ansa cervicalis

Hyoglossus muscle

Anterior belly of digastric

Hyoid bone

Superior thyroid artery

The supradigastric triangle (Pirogoff) is bounded by the intervening tendon of the digastric muscle, the posterior border of the mylohyoid muscle and the hypoglossal nerve, which is accompanied by the lingual vein.

The infradigastric triangle (Béclard) is located below the intervening tendon of the digastric muscle. Its two other boundaries are the greater horn of the hyoid bone and the hypoglossal nerve.

DIAGRAM OF THE HYPOGLOSSAL NERVE

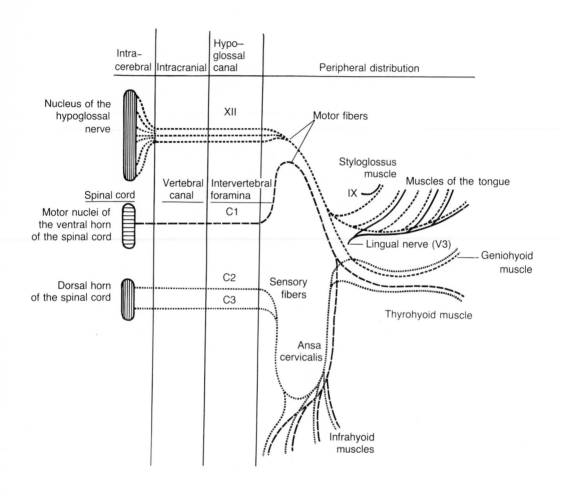

Pathways and Centers of Phonation

CORTICAL CENTERS OF PHONATION

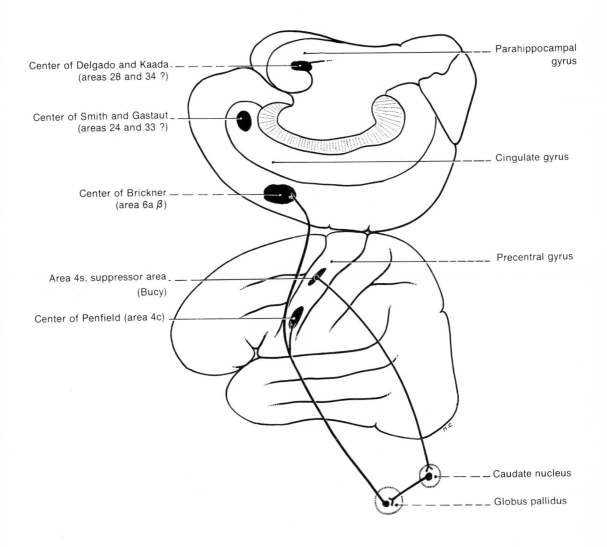

Center of Delgado and Kaada
(areas 28 and 34 ?)

Center of Smith and Gastaut
(areas 24 and 33 ?)

Center of Brickner
(area 6a β)

Area 4s, suppressor area
(Bucy)

Center of Penfield (area 4c)

Parahippocampal
gyrus

Cingulate gyrus

Precentral gyrus

Caudate nucleus

Globus pallidus

According to Husson,* the hierarchy of cortical centers, in decreasing order of importance, is as follows:
rhinencephalic centers (cingulate and parahippocampal gyri)
neocortical center of Brickner (origin of extrapyramidal pathways)
neocortical center of Penfield (origin of direct fibers)
The suppressor area acts on the areas 6aβ and 4c.

*From Husson, R.: Physiologie de la Phonation. Paris, Masson et Cie., 1962, pp. 201-202.

PATHWAYS OF PHONATION

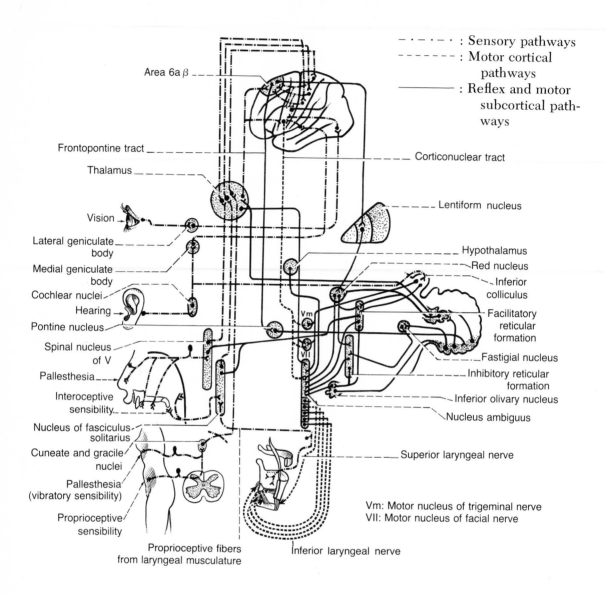

— · — · — · : Sensory pathways
— — — — — : Motor cortical
            pathways
——————— : Reflex and motor
            subcortical path-
            ways

Area 6a β

Frontopontine tract
Thalamus
Vision
Lateral geniculate
    body
Medial geniculate
    body
Cochlear nuclei
Hearing
Pontine nucleus
Spinal nucleus
    of V
Pallesthesia
Interoceptive
    sensibility
Nucleus of fasciculus
    solitarius
Cuneate and gracile
    nuclei
Pallesthesia
(vibratory sensibility)
Proprioceptive
    sensibility

Corticonuclear tract
Lentiform nucleus
Hypothalamus
Red nucleus
Inferior
    colliculus
Facilitatory
    reticular
    formation
Fastigial nucleus
Inhibitory reticular
    formation
Inferior olivary nucleus
Nucleus ambiguus
Superior laryngeal nerve

Vm
VII

Vm: Motor nucleus of trigeminal nerve
VII: Motor nucleus of facial nerve

Proprioceptive fibers
from laryngeal musculature

Inferior laryngeal nerve

(From the works of Eyriès, Husson, Goerttler, Krmpotic, and Szentagothaï.)

CORTICAL CENTERS OF VERBAL EXPRESSION

CENTERS OF LANGUAGE*

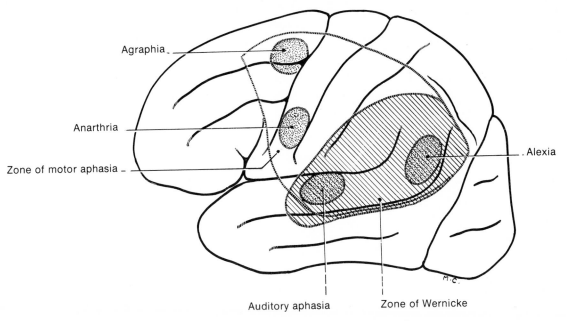

The frontal lobe contains the zones responsible for expressive (motor) aphasia when damaged; the temporo-parieto-occipital region gives rise to receptive (sensory) aphasia when damaged.

MAP OF LOCATION OF VARIOUS LANGUAGE ACTIVITIES†

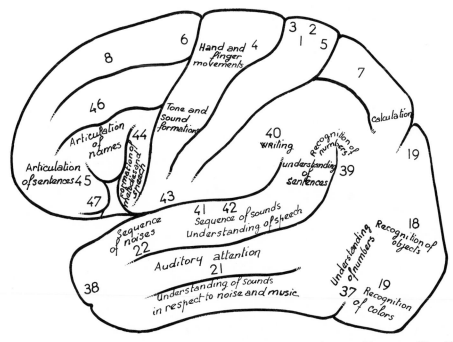

*From Delmas, J., and Delmas, A.: Voies et Centres Nerveux, 8th ed. Paris, Masson et Cie., 1969, p. 240.
†From Kleist, cited by De Ajuriaguerra, J., and Hécaen, H.: Le Cortex Cérébral, 2nd ed. Paris, Masson et Cie., 1960, p. 4.

Taste Pathways and Centers

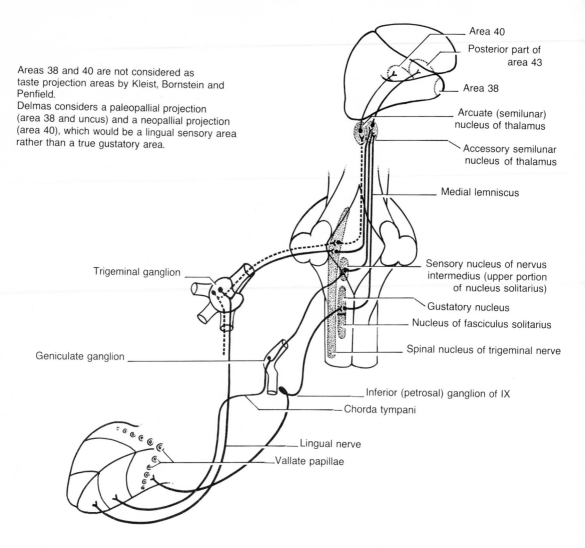

Areas 38 and 40 are not considered as taste projection areas by Kleist, Bornstein and Penfield.
Delmas considers a paleopallial projection (area 38 and uncus) and a neopallial projection (area 40), which would be a lingual sensory area rather than a true gustatory area.

Area 40

Posterior part of area 43

Area 38

Arcuate (semilunar) nucleus of thalamus

Accessory semilunar nucleus of thalamus

Medial lemniscus

Sensory nucleus of nervus intermedius (upper portion of nucleus solitarius)

Gustatory nucleus

Nucleus of fasciculus solitarius

Spinal nucleus of trigeminal nerve

Inferior (petrosal) ganglion of IX

Chorda tympani

Lingual nerve

Vallate papillae

Geniculate ganglion

Trigeminal ganglion

STRUCTURE OF A TASTE BUD

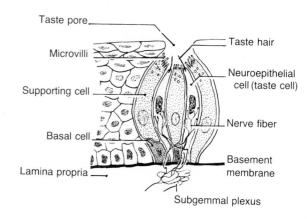

Taste pore

Microvilli

Supporting cell

Basal cell

Lamina propria

Taste hair

Neuroepithelial cell (taste cell)

Nerve fiber

Basement membrane

Subgemmal plexus

Taste buds may be also found in the mucous membrane of palate and oropharynx.

Part Five

Autonomic Nervous System

Cephalic and Cervical Segments of the Autonomic Nervous System

CERVICAL SYMPATHETIC TRUNK

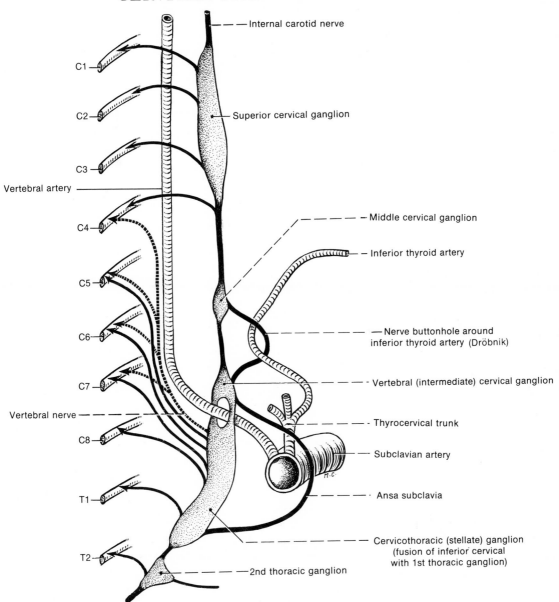

Claude Bernard-Horner's Syndrome

Interruption of the fibers passing through the ansa subclavia and the cervical part of the sympathetic trunk give rise to a syndrome characterized by:

Miosis (i.e., contraction of the pupil)

Ptosis (i.e., drooping of the upper eyelid)

Enophthalmos (i.e., recession of eye)

Vasodilatation (i.e., redness and increased temperature of the skin)

Anhidrosis (i.e., absence of sweating)

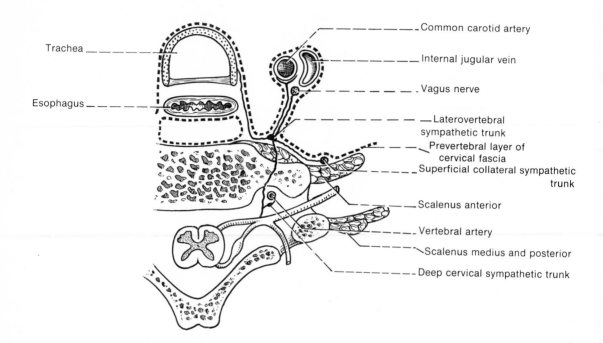

The deep and superficial collateral sympathetic trunks are easily visible in embryos and fetuses, but they are reduced to vestigial remains in the adult.

The deep cervical sympathetic trunk is located in the transverse canal behind the vertebral artery. It originates in the superior vertebral plexus (C3 and C4) and terminates in the first two thoracic ganglia.

The superficial collateral sympathetic trunk is composed of 3 or 4 ganglia lying on the scalenus anterior; it extends from the cervicothoracic ganglion to the superior cervical ganglion, each ganglion being related to a spinal nerve by a ramus perforating the scalenus anterior. (Delmas, J., and Laux, G.: Le Système Nerveux Sympathique. Paris, Masson et Cie., 1952.)

SUPERIOR CERVICAL GANGLION

Topography of the Superior Cervical Ganglion

(It extends from 2 cm. below the lower end of the carotid canal
to the angle of the mandible)

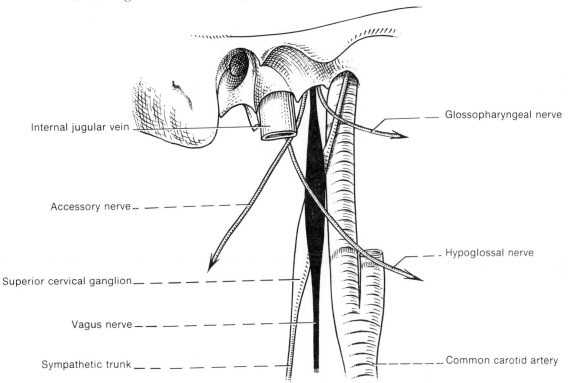

Internal jugular vein

Accessory nerve

Superior cervical ganglion

Vagus nerve

Sympathetic trunk

Glossopharyngeal nerve

Hypoglossal nerve

Common carotid artery

Branches of Superior Cervical Ganglion

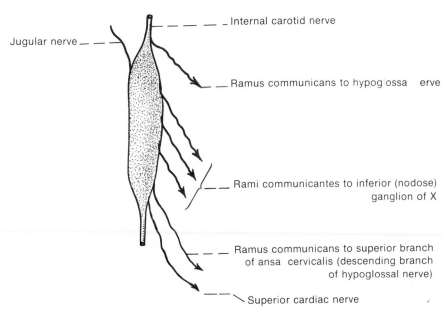

Jugular nerve

Internal carotid nerve

Ramus communicans to hypoglossa   erve

Rami communicantes to inferior (nodose)
ganglion of X

Ramus communicans to superior branch
of ansa cervicalis (descending branch
of hypoglossal nerve)

Superior cardiac nerve

INTERNAL CAROTID PLEXUS AND ITS BRANCHES

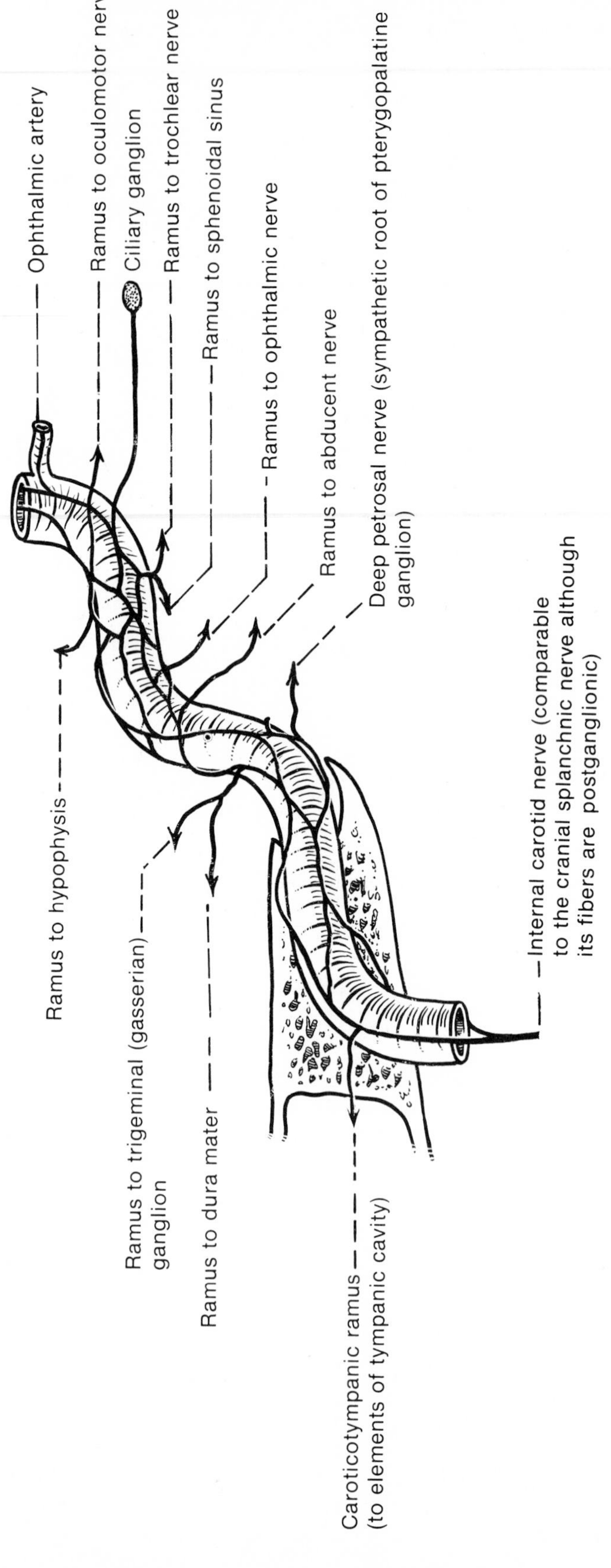

Ophthalmic artery

Ramus to oculomotor nerve

Ciliary ganglion

Ramus to trochlear nerve

Ramus to sphenoidal sinus

Ramus to ophthalmic nerve

Ramus to abducent nerve

Deep petrosal nerve (sympathetic root of pterygopalatine ganglion)

Internal carotid nerve (comparable to the cranial splanchnic nerve although its fibers are postganglionic)

Ramus to hypophysis

Ramus to trigeminal (gasserian) ganglion

Ramus to dura mater

Caroticotympanic ramus (to elements of tympanic cavity)

Page 306

The middle cervical ganglion is macroscopically inconstant (50 per cent). Usually, it is found at the level of the carotid tubercle; it is always related to the inferior thyroid artery and sometimes forms a loop (Dröbnik) around this artery, either in front of or behind it. It gives rise to rami to the phrenic nerve and to the inferior (recurrent) laryngeal nerve.

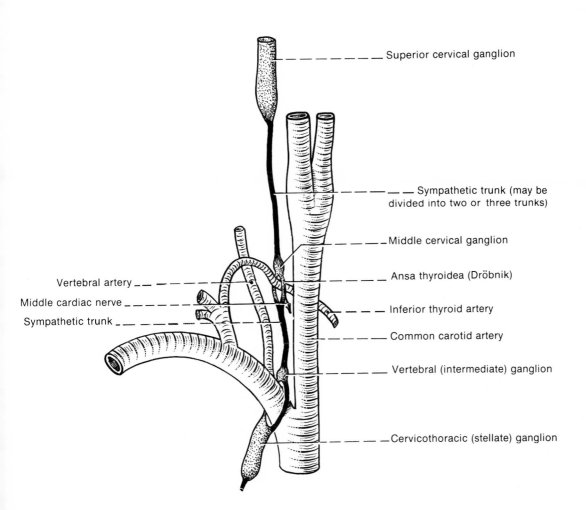

Superior cervical ganglion

Sympathetic trunk (may be divided into two or three trunks)

Middle cervical ganglion

Ansa thyroidea (Dröbnik)

Inferior thyroid artery

Common carotid artery

Vertebral (intermediate) ganglion

Cervicothoracic (stellate) ganglion

Vertebral artery

Middle cardiac nerve

Sympathetic trunk

Cervicothoracic (or Stellate) Ganglion

Morphology and Branches

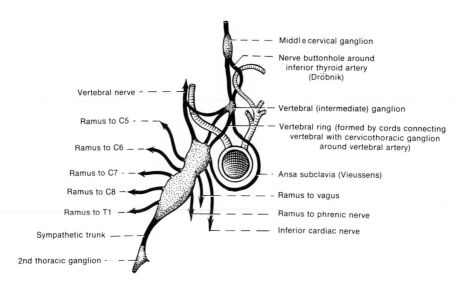

Vertebral nerve

Ramus to C5

Ramus to C6

Ramus to C7

Ramus to C8

Ramus to T1

Sympathetic trunk

2nd thoracic ganglion

Middle cervical ganglion

Nerve buttonhole around inferior thyroid artery (Dröbnik)

Vertebral (intermediate) ganglion

Vertebral ring (formed by cords connecting vertebral with cervicothoracic ganglion around vertebral artery)

Ansa subclavia (Vieussens)

Ramus to vagus

Ramus to phrenic nerve

Inferior cardiac nerve

Relations of the Cervicothoracic Ganglion

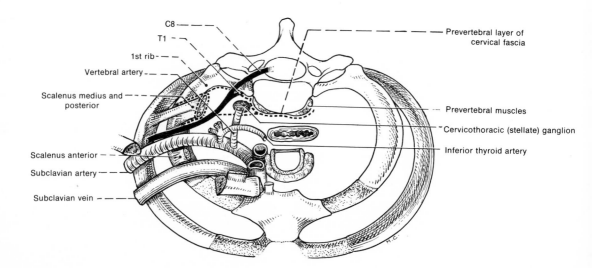

C8

T1

1st rib

Vertebral artery

Scalenus medius and posterior

Scalenus anterior

Subclavian artery

Subclavian vein

Prevertebral layer of cervical fascia

Prevertebral muscles

Cervicothoracic (stellate) ganglion

Inferior thyroid artery

Lateral aspect

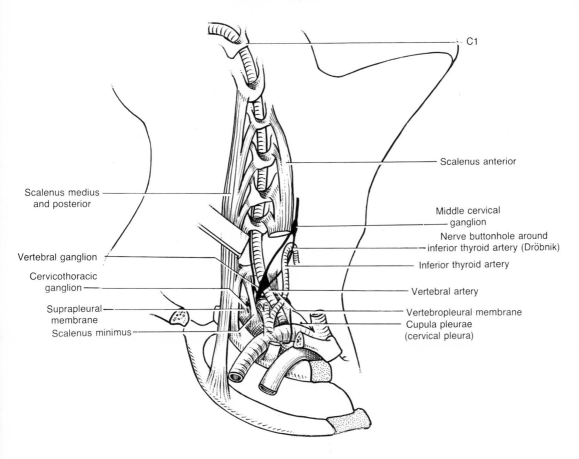

C1

Scalenus anterior

Scalenus medius
and posterior

Middle cervical
ganglion

Nerve buttonhole around
inferior thyroid artery (Dröbnik)

Inferior thyroid artery

Vertebral ganglion

Cervicothoracic
ganglion

Vertebral artery

Suprapleural
membrane

Vertebropleural membrane

Cupula pleurae
(cervical pleura)

Scalenus minimus

Sagittal section of cavum of cervicothoracic ganglion
(supraretropleural fossula)

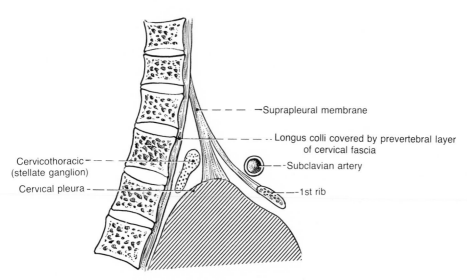

Suprapleural membrane

Longus colli covered by prevertebral layer
of cervical fascia

Cervicothoracic
(stellate ganglion)

Subclavian artery

Cervical pleura

1st rib

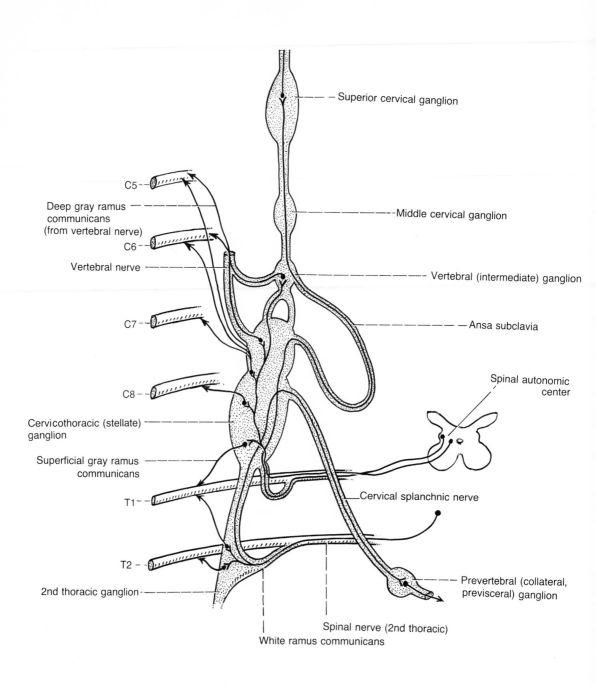

Superior cervical ganglion

C5

Deep gray ramus
communicans
(from vertebral nerve)

C6

Vertebral nerve

Middle cervical ganglion

Vertebral (intermediate) ganglion

C7

Ansa subclavia

C8

Spinal autonomic
center

Cervicothoracic (stellate)
ganglion

Superficial gray ramus
communicans

Cervical splanchnic nerve

T1

T2

Prevertebral (collateral,
previsceral) ganglion

2nd thoracic ganglion

Spinal nerve (2nd thoracic)

White ramus communicans

CEPHALIC PART OF THE PARASYMPATHETIC ELEMENTS AND GANGLIA

(These ganglia may be considered as the equivalents of the prevertebral [collateral, previsceral] ganglia.)

DIAGRAM OF CILIARY GANGLION

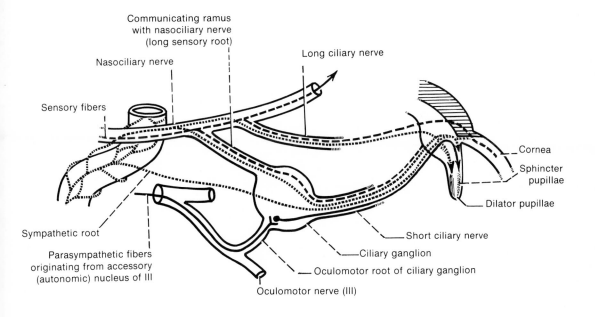

Communicating ramus with nasociliary nerve (long sensory root)

Long ciliary nerve

Nasociliary nerve

Sensory fibers

Cornea

Sphincter pupillae

Dilator pupillae

Sympathetic root

Short ciliary nerve

Parasympathetic fibers originating from accessory (autonomic) nucleus of III

Ciliary ganglion

Oculomotor root of ciliary ganglion

Oculomotor nerve (III)

- - - - - Sensory fibers
··········· Sympathetic fibers
———— Parasympathetic fibers

DIAGRAM OF THE PTERYGOPALATINE (SPHENOPALATINE) GANGLION

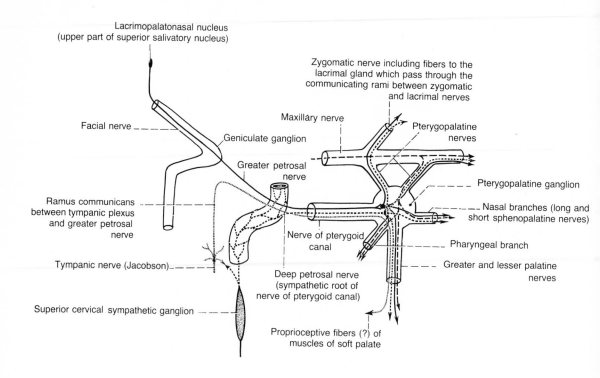

Lacrimopalatonasal nucleus
(upper part of superior salivatory nucleus)

Zygomatic nerve including fibers to the
lacrimal gland which pass through the
communicating rami between zygomatic
and lacrimal nerves

Maxillary nerve

Facial nerve

Pterygopalatine
nerves

Geniculate ganglion

Greater petrosal
nerve

Pterygopalatine ganglion

Ramus communicans
between tympanic plexus
and greater petrosal
nerve

Nasal branches (long and
short sphenopalatine nerves)

Nerve of pterygoid
canal

Pharyngeal branch

Tympanic nerve (Jacobson)

Greater and lesser palatine
nerves

Deep petrosal nerve
(sympathetic root of
nerve of pterygoid canal)

Superior cervical sympathetic ganglion

Proprioceptive fibers (?) of
muscles of soft palate

Diagram of the Submandibular Ganglion and Nerve Supply of the Submandibular and Sublingual Glands

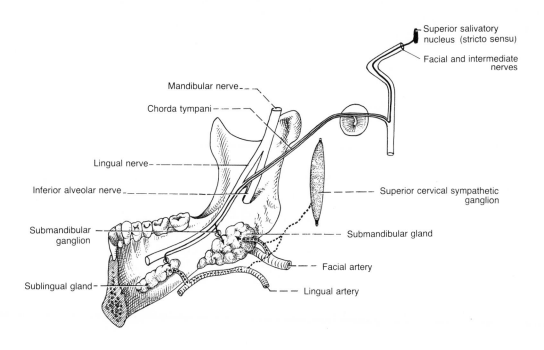

Superior salivatory nucleus (stricto sensu)

Facial and intermediate nerves

Mandibular nerve

Chorda tympani

Lingual nerve

Inferior alveolar nerve

Superior cervical sympathetic ganglion

Submandibular ganglion

Submandibular gland

Facial artery

Sublingual gland

Lingual artery

Diagram of the Otic Ganglion

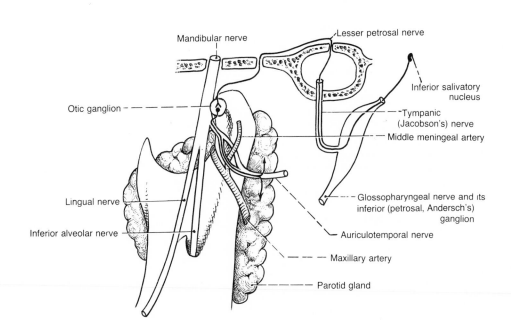

Mandibular nerve

Lesser petrosal nerve

Inferior salivatory nucleus

Otic ganglion

Tympanic (Jacobson's) nerve

Middle meningeal artery

Lingual nerve

Glossopharyngeal nerve and its inferior (petrosal, Andersch's) ganglion

Inferior alveolar nerve

Auriculotemporal nerve

Maxillary artery

Parotid gland

Thoracic Part of the Autonomic Nervous System

THORACIC LATEROVERTEBRAL TRUNK
AND ITS RAMI COMMUNICANTES

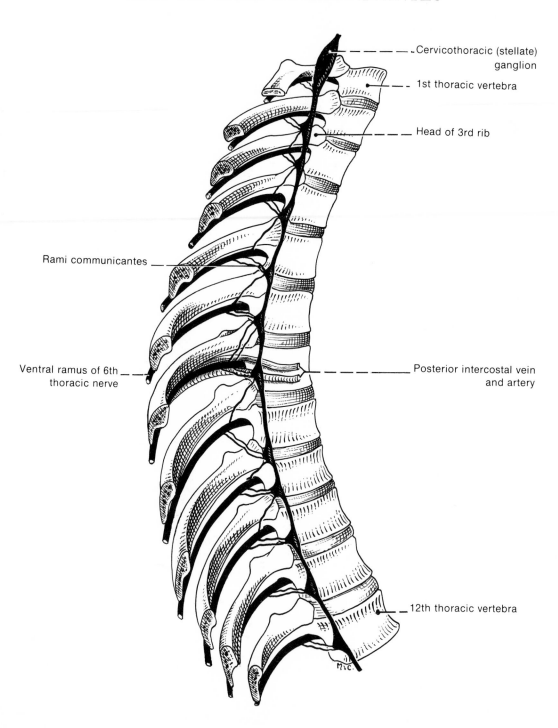

Cervicothoracic (stellate) ganglion

1st thoracic vertebra

Head of 3rd rib

Rami communicantes

Ventral ramus of 6th thoracic nerve

Posterior intercostal vein and artery

12th thoracic vertebra

SPLANCHNIC NERVES ORIGINATING FROM THORACIC SYMPATHETIC TRUNK

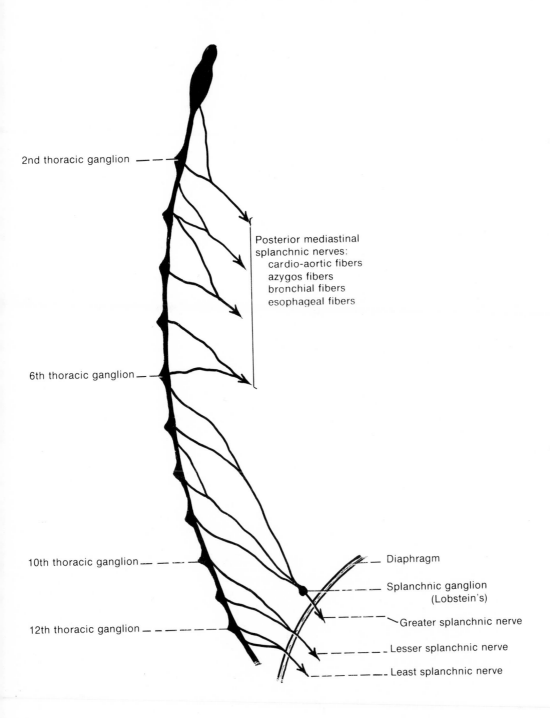

2nd thoracic ganglion ———

Posterior mediastinal
splanchnic nerves:
   cardio-aortic fibers
   azygos fibers
   bronchial fibers
   esophageal fibers

6th thoracic ganglion ——

10th thoracic ganglion ——

12th thoracic ganglion ——

— Diaphragm

— Splanchnic ganglion
  (Lobstein's)

— Greater splanchnic nerve

— Lesser splanchnic nerve

— Least splanchnic nerve

THORACIC PART OF THE PARASYMPATHETIC ELEMENTS AND THE PREVERTEBRAL (COLLATERAL, PREVISCERAL) GANGLIA

The visceral autonomic nervous system of the thorax may be divided into three parts:

Anterosuperior part

Related to the thymus and adjacent formations; the nerve supply comes only from cervical elements.

Middle part

Composed of the heart, the great vessels, the trachea and the main bronchi; the nerves arrive from cervical and thoracic parts of the autonomic nervous system.

From each side of the neck, the heart and the adjacent great vessels receive three nerves of the cervical sympathetic trunk and three nerve of the vagus nerve or its branches.

The cardiac ganglia may be divided as follows:

> superior (arterial) center, located in the subaortic recess; this center may appear as a ganglion applied against the inferior aspect of the aorta (cardiac ganglion of Wrisberg), or as a macroscopic or microscopic disseminated form.

> inferior (venous) center; located in the wall of the right atrium, which is a more or less conglomerated ganglionic mass (Perman).

These two centers are opposed to each other by their position originating from their relation to the primitive cardiac tube. One of them is anterosuperior, arterial, or cranial, receiving primarily the left cardiac nerves; the other is posteroinferior, atriosinusal, or venous, or caudal, and receives mainly the right cervical and the thoracic cardiac nerves.

The pulmonary previsceral ganglia are represented by a disseminated or conglomerated mass (ganglion supremum thoraci of Kondratjew), remnants of the thoracic collateral sympathetic trunk. Visceral nerves originate from these, and along their pathways there are small ganglionic groups; these latter correspond to intraparietal ganglia.

The pulmonary parasympathetic fibers leave the vagus nerve behind the homolateral main bronchus.

Posteroinferior part

This part includes the esophagus, the thoracic aorta and the azygos veins. The previsceral centers of this region are represented by the internal collateral trunk, extending from the cervicothoracic (stellate) ganglion to the abdominal splanchnic nerves. From this trunk the visceral and vascular nerves form the periaortic, periesophageal and periazygos longitudinal plexuses, in which there are ganglionic groups corresponding to intraparietal ganglia.

This division according to the outflow of autonomic fibers does not agree with the usual division of the thoracic mediastinum. As a matter of fact, a plane passing from the fourth thoracic vertebra to the lower extremity of the manubrium sterni bounds the superior mediastinum caudally; therefore, this phase includes the most important portion of the anterosuperior part, a quarter of the middle part, and a small amount of the posteroinferior part.

OUTFLOW OF AUTONOMIC FIBERS TO THE THORAX

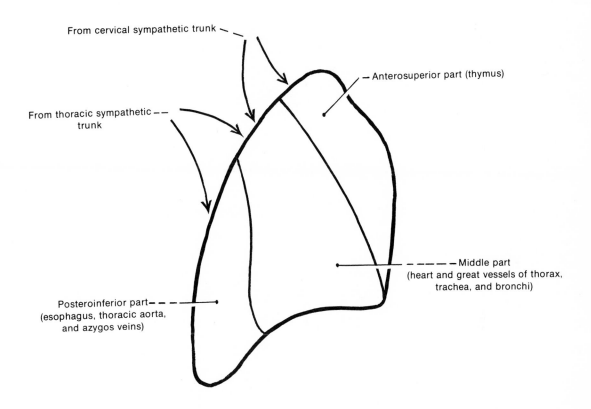

LUMBAR LATEROVERTEBRAL SYMPATHETIC TRUNK AND ITS RAMI COMMUNICANTES

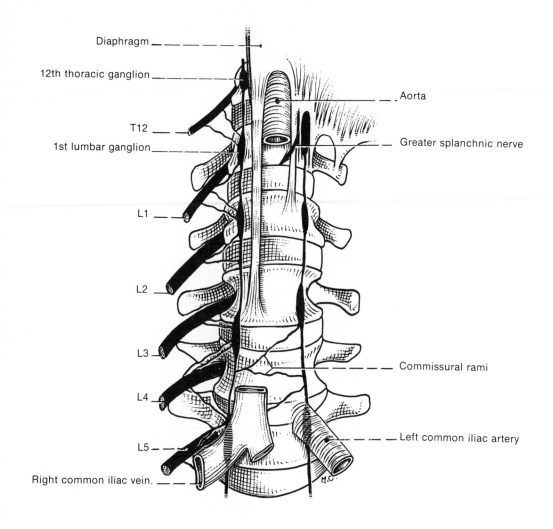

Diaphragm

12th thoracic ganglion

Aorta

T12

1st lumbar ganglion

Greater splanchnic nerve

L1

L2

L3

Commissural rami

L4

L5

Left common iliac artery

Right common iliac vein.

SPLANCHNIC NERVES ORIGINATING FROM LUMBAR SYMPATHETIC TRUNKS

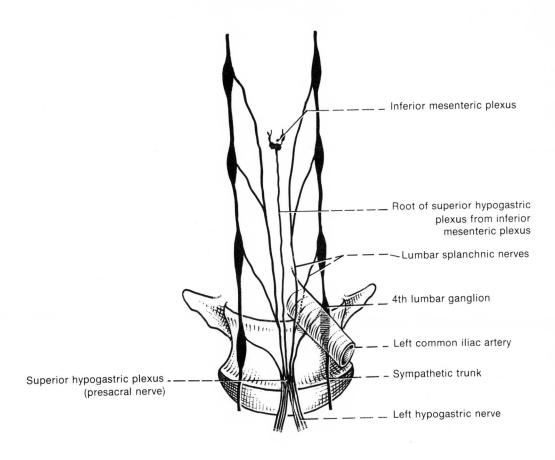

Inferior mesenteric plexus

Root of superior hypogastric plexus from inferior mesenteric plexus

Lumbar splanchnic nerves

4th lumbar ganglion

Left common iliac artery

Sympathetic trunk

Left hypogastric nerve

Superior hypogastric plexus (presacral nerve)

ABDOMINAL PART OF THE PARASYMPATHETIC ELEMENTS AND THE PREVERTEBRAL (COLLATERAL, PREVISCERAL) GANGLIA

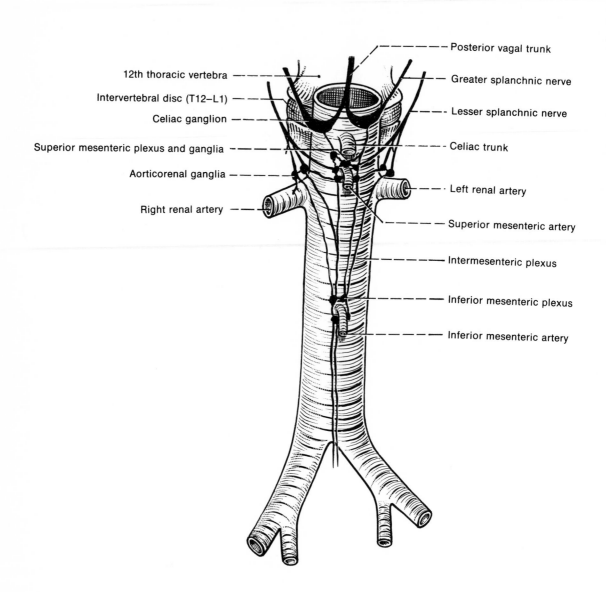

12th thoracic vertebra

Intervertebral disc (T12–L1)

Celiac ganglion

Superior mesenteric plexus and ganglia

Aorticorenal ganglia

Right renal artery

Posterior vagal trunk

Greater splanchnic nerve

Lesser splanchnic nerve

Celiac trunk

Left renal artery

Superior mesenteric artery

Intermesenteric plexus

Inferior mesenteric plexus

Inferior mesenteric artery

Besides the visceral components, an important vascular plexus exists around the aorta. This aortic plexus is connected with the lumbar sympathetic trunk and with the abdominal visceral plexuses.

Pelvic Part of the Autonomic Nervous System

SACRAL SYMPATHETIC TRUNK

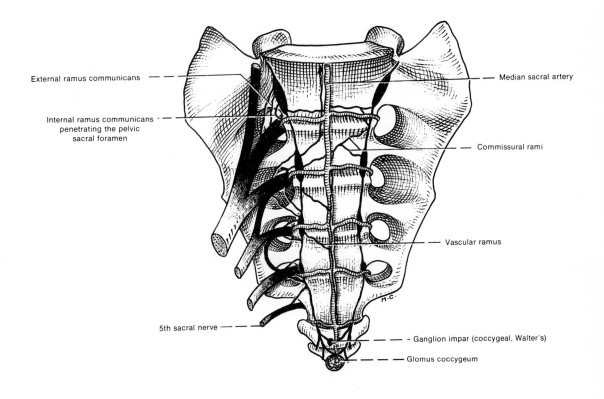

External ramus communicans

Internal ramus communicans penetrating the pelvic sacral foramen

Median sacral artery

Commissural rami

Vascular ramus

5th sacral nerve

Ganglion impar (coccygeal, Walter's)

Glomus coccygeum

The Different Kinds of Rami Communicantes of S2

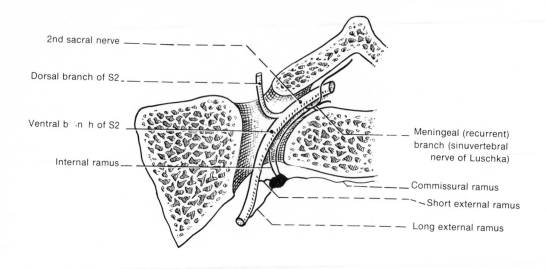

2nd sacral nerve

Dorsal branch of S2

Ventral b n h of S2

Internal ramus

Meningeal (recurrent) branch (sinuvertebral nerve of Luschka)

Commissural ramus

Short external ramus

Long external ramus

Types of Termination of the Laterovertebral Sympathetic Trunk

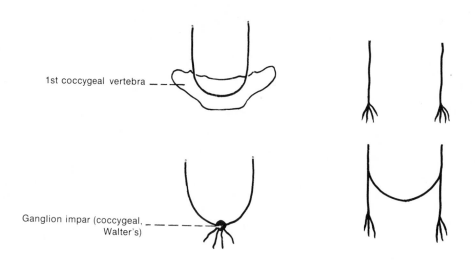

1st coccygeal vertebra

Ganglion impar (coccygeal, Walter's)

PELVIC PART OF THE PARASYMPATHETIC ELEMENTS AND THE PREVERTEBRAL (OR COLLATERAL, OR PREVISCERAL) GANGLIA

INFERIOR HYPOGASTRIC PLEXUS AND PELVIC ORGANS IN THE FEMALE
(The dotted line indicates the parasympathetic fibers)

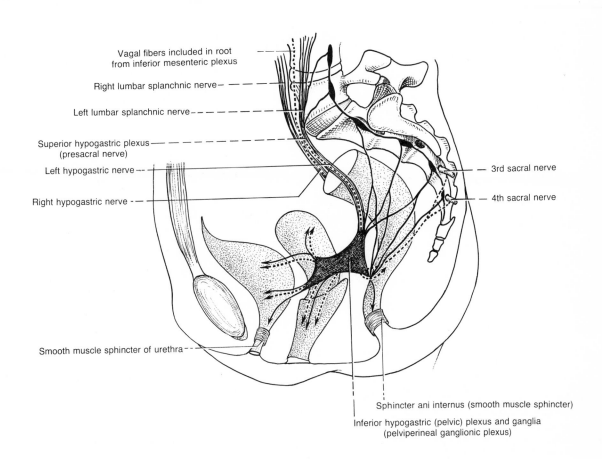

Vagal fibers included in root from inferior mesenteric plexus

Right lumbar splanchnic nerve

Left lumbar splanchnic nerve

Superior hypogastric plexus (presacral nerve)

Left hypogastric nerve

Right hypogastric nerve

3rd sacral nerve

4th sacral nerve

Smooth muscle sphincter of urethra

Sphincter ani internus (smooth muscle sphincter)

Inferior hypogastric (pelvic) plexus and ganglia (pelviperineal ganglionic plexus)

INFERIOR HYPOGASTRIC PLEXUS IN THE MALE
(The dotted line indicates the parasympathetic fibers)

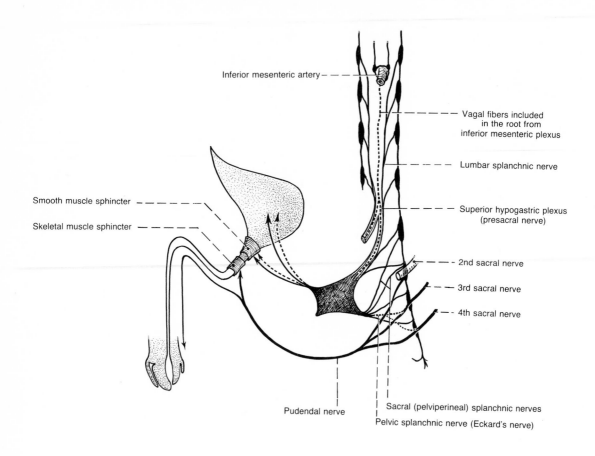

Inferior mesenteric artery

Vagal fibers included in the root from inferior mesenteric plexus

Lumbar splanchnic nerve

Smooth muscle sphincter

Superior hypogastric plexus (presacral nerve)

Skeletal muscle sphincter

2nd sacral nerve

3rd sacral nerve

4th sacral nerve

Pudendal nerve

Sacral (pelviperineal) splanchnic nerves

Pelvic splanchnic nerve (Eckard's nerve)

Central Pathways and Centers of the Autonomic Nervous System

AUTONOMIC CENTERS OF THE SPINAL CORD

Schematic Transverse Section of the Spinal Cord Showing the Autonomic Columns in the Intermediate Gray Matter

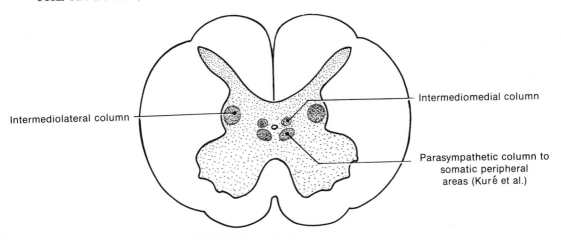

Intermediolateral column

Intermediomedial column

Parasympathetic column to somatic peripheral areas (Kuré et al.)

Sacral Autonomic Nucleus (Intermedioventral Column)

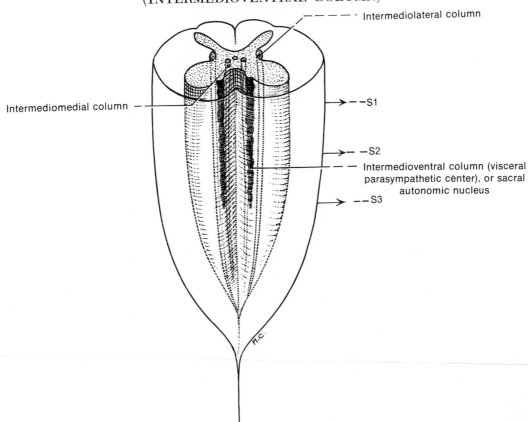

Intermediolateral column

Intermediomedial column

S1

S2

Intermedioventral column (visceral parasympathetic center), or sacral autonomic nucleus

S3

Kuré, K., Yese, M., Merimasa, T., Kensaku, S., and Suyenaga: Demonstration of special parasympathetic nerve fibers in the dorsal portion of the lumbar cord. Quart. J. Exp. Physiol., 18:333-334, 1928.

Page 325

TABLE OF THE SPINAL AUTONOMIC CENTERS

Spinal segments	Somatic sympathetic centers			Visceral sympathetic centers	Parasympathetic centers	
	Pilomotor & sudomotor	Vaso-constrictor	Vaso-dilator		Somatic	Visceral
C1						
2						
3						
4		?			?	
5						
6				Cardiac accelerator center		
7						
8						
T1	Face & neck					
2						
3		Upper thorax		Poster. medias. viscer.	Ciliospinal center	
4	Upper limb					
5	Mammary gland	Areola mammae		Abdominal viscera		
6						
7				Inhibitor: small intestine		
8					Secretion of adrenaline	
9						
10		Scrotal reflex				
11						
12	Lower limb			Pelvic viscera		
L1						X nucleus (of Onuf)
2				Colon, rectum & urinary bladder		
3						Intermedioventral column
4						
5						
S1						
2		?				
3						
4						
5						
Co1						

CRANIAL PARASYMPATHETIC OUTFLOW

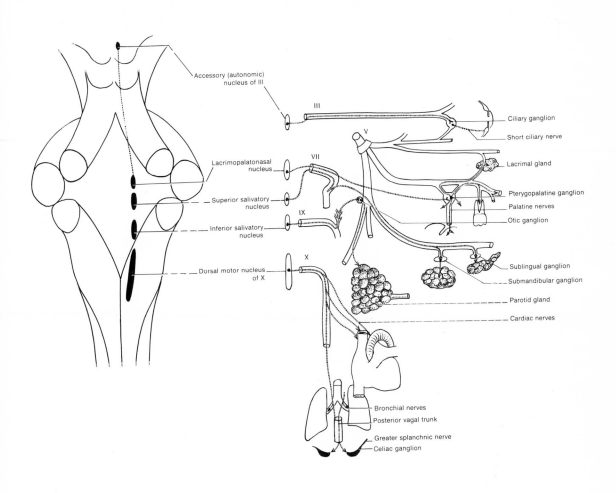

Accessory (autonomic) nucleus of III

III

Ciliary ganglion

Short ciliary nerve

V

Lacrimopalatonasal nucleus

VII

Lacrimal gland

Pterygopalatine ganglion

Palatine nerves

Superior salivatory nucleus

Otic ganglion

IX

Inferior salivatory nucleus

Sublingual ganglion

Submandibular ganglion

Dorsal motor nucleus of X

X

Parotid gland

Cardiac nerves

Bronchial nerves

Posterior vagal trunk

Greater splanchnic nerve

Celiac ganglion

DIAGRAM OF THE INNERVATION OF THE HYPOPHYSIS
(PITUITARY GLAND)

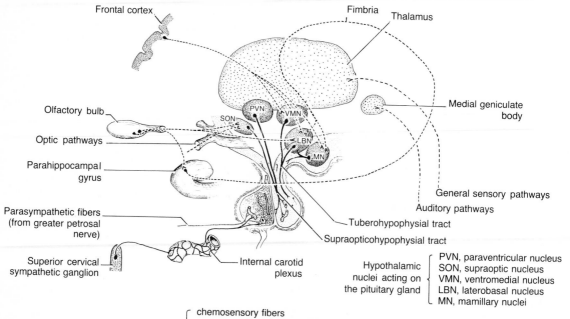

Frontal cortex

Fimbria

Thalamus

Olfactory bulb

Optic pathways

Parahippocampal gyrus

Parasympathetic fibers (from greater petrosal nerve)

Superior cervical sympathetic ganglion

SON

PVN

VMN

LBN

MN

Medial geniculate body

General sensory pathways

Auditory pathways

Tuberohypophysial tract

Supraopticohypophysial tract

Internal carotid plexus

Hypothalamic nuclei acting on the pituitary gland

PVN, paraventricular nucleus
SON, supraoptic nucleus
VMN, ventromedial nucleus
LBN, laterobasal nucleus
MN, mamillary nuclei

The <u>sensory intrinsic innervation</u> includes:
- chemosensory fibers
- sensory endings in the ependymal epithelium
- end-feet in stalk and neurohypophysis
- fibers of Hagen in the adenohypophysis

The <u>sensory extrinsic innervation</u> includes: free and encapsulated nerve endings in the capsule

SCHEME OF THE BLOOD SUPPLY OF THE PITUITARY GLAND

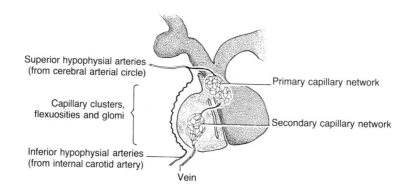

Superior hypophysial arteries (from cerebral arterial circle)

Capillary clusters, flexuosities and glomi

Inferior hypophysial arteries (from internal carotid artery)

Primary capillary network

Secondary capillary network

Vein

HYPOTHALAMIC NUCLEI

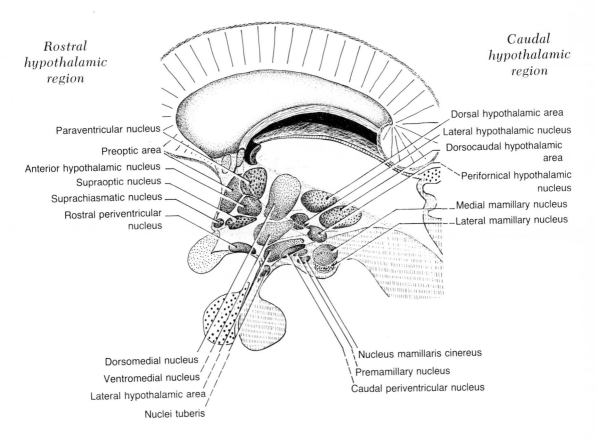

Rostral hypothalamic region

Caudal hypothalamic region

Paraventricular nucleus

Preoptic area

Anterior hypothalamic nucleus

Supraoptic nucleus

Suprachiasmatic nucleus

Rostral periventricular nucleus

Dorsal hypothalamic area

Lateral hypothalamic nucleus

Dorsocaudal hypothalamic area

Perifornical hypothalamic nucleus

Medial mamillary nucleus

Lateral mamillary nucleus

Dorsomedial nucleus

Ventromedial nucleus

Lateral hypothalamic area

Nuclei tuberis

Nucleus mamillaris cinereus

Premamillary nucleus

Caudal periventricular nucleus

Intermediate (tuberalis) hypothalamic region

AUTONOMIC CORTICAL AREAS
(Brodmann's chart)

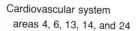

Cardiovascular system
areas 4, 6, 13, 14, and 24

Respiratory system
areas 6, 13, 14, and 24

Digestive system
areas 4, 6, and 13

Urinary system
areas 4, 6, and
orbital cortex(?)

Genital system
areas 4 and 6
(especially in their
medial parts)

Glandular organs
prefrontal cortex;
area 6 to lacrimal gland;
motor centers of face and
tongue to salivary glands

Pupillary system
myosis, areas 6 and 19;
mydriasis, areas 8 and 24

Pilomotor system
areas 8 and 24

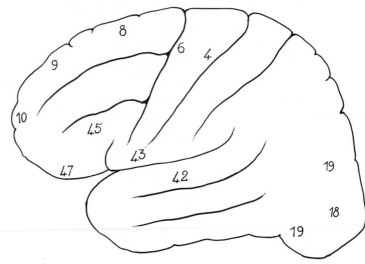

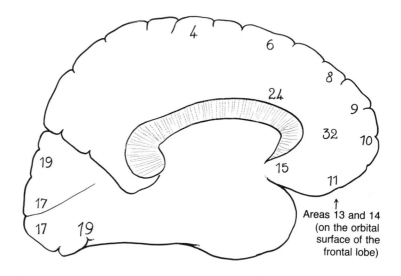

It seems possible that area 24, which is a powerful suppressor area, opposes the activating areas of the premotor cortex (area 6 and adjoining areas).

MAIN CEREBRAL PATHWAYS OF THE AUTONOMIC NERVOUS SYSTEM

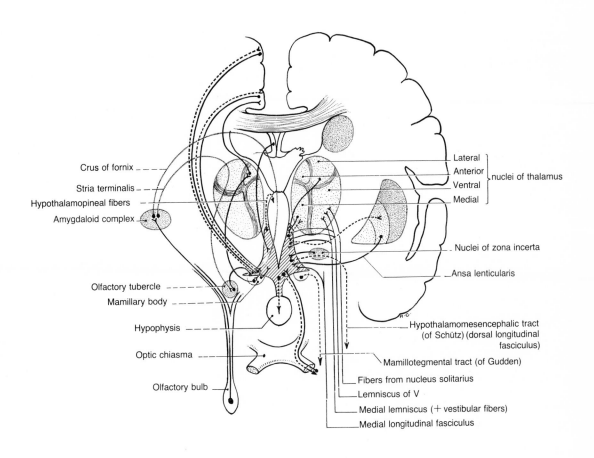

Crus of fornix

Stria terminalis

Hypothalamopineal fibers

Amygdaloid complex

Lateral
Anterior
Ventral ⎱ nuclei of thalamus
Medial

Nuclei of zona incerta

Ansa lenticularis

Olfactory tubercle

Mamillary body

Hypophysis

Optic chiasma

Olfactory bulb

Hypothalamomesencephalic tract
(of Schütz) (dorsal longitudinal
fasciculus)

Mamillotegmental tract (of Gudden)

Fibers from nucleus solitarius

Lemniscus of V

Medial lemniscus (+ vestibular fibers)

Medial longitudinal fasciculus

Autonomic Innervation of the Organs

ORGANS		PERIPHERAL CENTERS		PERIPHERAL PATHWAYS		PLEXUS AND SPECIAL ARRANGEMENTS
		Sympathetic Trunk	Prevertebral Ganglion	Sympathetic	Parasympathetic	
Cephalic organs	Eyeball		Ciliary ganglion	Internal carotid plexus	Oculomotor n. (III)	The communicating ramus with the nasociliary nerve includes sensory and sympathetic fibers
	Lacrimal gl., nasal, buccal & nasophar. mucous membrane		Pterygopalat. g.		Greater petrosal n.	The parasympathetic fibers to the lacrimal gland follow the zygomatic nerve
	Submandib. and subling. glands	Superior cervical ganglion	Submandib. g.	External carotid plexus	Chorda tympani & lingual n.	The sympathetic fibers reach the glands by the perivascular plexuses
	Parotid gland		Otic ganglion		Lesser petrosal n. & auriculotemp. n.	
	External ear			Sup. temporal art. & post. auric. art. plexuses; tympanic plexus	Auriculotemp. n.; n. intermedius; auricul. branch. of X	
	Middle ear			Middle mening. art., tympanic art. & stylomast. art. plex.; caroticotympanic n.	Tympanic n. & auricular br. of X	
	Internal ear			Perivascular plexuses (internal audit., maxill. & int. carot. arteries)	VIII, VII & n. intermedius	Autonomic fibers follow VIII directly
Viscera of neck	Larynx	Sup. & inf. cerv. ganglia	Inf. g. of X	Rami communicantes with laryngeal nerves	Laryngeal nerves	
	Pharynx	Sup. cerv. g.	Pterygopalatine & inf. g. of X	Rami communicates between X & sympat. trunks	Pharyngeal nerves & pharyng. br. of pterygopalatine g.	
Card. vasc. syst.	Heart & great vessels	Superior, middle & inf. cervical g.; T2 to T5 ganglia	Cardiac ganglia	Sup. middle and inf. cardiac n.; upper splanch. thorac. nn.	3 cardiac rami from X or laryngeal nerves	
Resp. syst.	Trachea	Inf. cerv. g.			Inf. laryngeal n.	
	Bronchi & lungs	Cervicothoracic g. & T2 ganglion			X (bronchial pulmonary branches)	Anterior and posterior bronchial plexuses
Digestive system	Esophagus	T5 & T6 ganglia			Sup. & inf. laryng. nn.; rami from vagal trunks	Esophageal plexus
	Stomach	T6 to T10 g.	Celiac ganglion	Greater & lesser splanchnic nn.	Ant. and post. vagal trunks	Esophageal plexus; perivascular plexuses; anterior hepatic plexus
	Duodenum	T10 to T12 g.	Sup. mes. g.		Posterior vagal trunk	Superior mesenteric plexus
	Jejunum & ileum	T10 to L3 g.	Inf. mes. g.			Inferior mesenteric plexus
	Large intestine					
	Rectum & anal	L2 to L5 ganglia (S1 & S2 ?)	Pelvic ganglion	Perivascular plex. (hemorrhoid art.) & sacral splanch. n.	Pelvic splanchnic nerve (Eckard)	Inferior hypogastric plexus
	Liver & gallbladder	T6 to T12 g.	Celiac ganglion	Greater splanch. n.	Posterior vagal trunk	Anterior & posterior hepatic plexuses; perivascular plexus
	Pancreas	T6 to T10 g.				Usually rami do not follow the arteries

Category	Organ	Spinal ganglia	Prevertebral / terminal ganglia	Splanchnic nerves	Parasympathetic	Plexus
Urinary organs	Kidney	T10 to T12 g.	Celiac, sup. mes. & aorticorenal g.	Lesser & least splanchnic nn.	Post. vagal tr.	Renal plexus
	Ureters	T10 to T12, L1 to L5 & S1 to S3 g.	Gangl. of renal plex. & hypogastric plexuses	Lesser, lumbar & pelvic splanchnic nn.	Post. vagal tr. & pelvic spl. nn. (Eckard)	Inferior hypogastric plexus
	Urinary bladder	L1 to S4	Pelvic g.	Lumbar & pelvic splanchnic nn.	Pelvic splanch. n. (Eckard)	Inferior hypogastric plexus
Male reproduct. organs	Testes	T10 to L1				Spermatic and perivascular plexuses
	Epididymis & ductus deferens					Interspermatico-deferential plexus
	Seminal vesicles		Pelvic ganglion		Pelvic splanchnic n. (Eckard)	Perivascular plexuses
	Prostrate gl. & ejaculatory duct.	T10 to T12				
	Penis	L1 to L5 & S1 to S4				
Female reprod. organs	Ovaries & uterine tubes	T10 to L1				Utero-ovarian plexus
	Uterus	T10 to T12 & S1 to S3	Pelvic ganglion			Utero-ovarian plexus & cervico-isthmic pedicle
	Vagina					
	Female ext. genitalia		Pelvic ganglion	Perivascular plexuses	Pudendal n.	
Endocrine glands	Hypophysis	Sup. cerv. g.		Int. carot. plex.	Hypothalamo-hypophysial tract.	
	Thyroid & parathyroid gl.	Sup., middle & inf. cerv. g.		Cerv. splanch. n.	Sup. & inf. laryngeal n.	
	Thymus	Middle & inf. cerv. ganglia		Inf. cerv. splanchnic nn.	Inferior laryngeal n.	
	Suprarenal gland	T6 to T10	Celiac ganglion	Greater splanch. n.	Post. vagal trunk	
Hemat. organs	Spleen	T6 to T10	Celiac ganglion	Lumbar splanchnic n.		Perivascular plexus
	Bone marrow	Sup. cerv. ganglion				Perivascular plexuses and bone nerves to bone
Paraganglia	Aortic paraganglia	Sup. cerv. ganglion			IX & X	Aortic plexus
	Carotid body	Sup. cerv. ganglion	Ganglion impar (Walter)		Tympanic n.	
	Tympanic organ				Pelvic splanchnic nerve (Eckard)	
	Coccygeal body	Sacral g.				
Vessels	Somatic	Vertebral g.	Prevertebral g.	Adjoining cranial and spinal nn.		
	Visceral			Vascular plexuses		
Somatic organs	Head & neck	Cervical ganglia Cervicothoracic ganglion		Rami communicates	Cranial & spinal nn.	
	Upper limb & shoulder girdle					
	Thorax	Thoracic ganglia				
	Ant. & medial region of thigh	Lumbar g.				
	Gluteal region; post region of thigh; leg & foot	Sacral g.				

INDEX

Numbers set in *italics* indicate principal illustrations.

Cavity(ies), nasal (skeleton and mucous membrane), 201, 202
  of brain, 158
  pneumatic, annexed to middle ear, 262
  tympanic, 261, 262, 263, 264
Cell, air (mastoid, petrous, tympanic), 269
  amacrine (retina), 218
  association (cerebellum), 137
  autonomic (central autonomic centers), 6, 117
  basal (olfactory epithelium), 205
  basket (cerebellum), 137
  bipolar, 8, 218
  ependymal, 34, 117
  funicular, 117
  fusiform (cerebral cortex), 155
  ganglionic, 8
    primitive, 5
  glial, 9, 28
  granule, cerebellum, 137
    cerebral cortex, 155, 165
    primitive (allocortex), 155
  hair, of cochlea, 275, 276
    of maculae and cristae ampullares, 276
  horizontal, cerebral cortex, 155
    retina, 218
  internuncial, cerebellum, 127
  interstitial, 31, 33
  marginal, 110
  microglia, 34, 137
  mitral, 6, 206
  nerve, 5. See also Neuron.
    of spinal cord, 117
  neurosecretory, 5
  of Bergmann (cerebellum), 137
  of Cajal, types I and II, 14
  of Fañanas, 137
  of Golgi, types I and II, 117
  of Henson, 275
  of Martinotti, 155, 165
  of Müller (retina), 218
  of Renshaw, 117
  of spinal ganglion, 6, 14
  olfactory, 26, 205
  pigmented (eye), 212, 215
  pseudosensory, 28
  Purkinje, 6, 137
  pyramidal (cerebral cortex), 5, 155, 165
  radicular, 117
  satellite, 14
  stellate, large and superficial, 137
  supporting, 28, 300
    of Deiters (cochlea), 275, 276
    of olfactory epithelium (or sustentacular), 205
  taste, 300
  tufted, 208
Center(s), 156
  auditory, 279
  cardiac (spinal cord), 326
  ciliospinal, of Budge, 239, 326
  motor nuclear, of eye, 235
  oculocephalogyric, 236
  of autonomic nervous system, 324
  of spinal cord, autonomic, 25, 110, 113, 310, 325, 326
    motor, 111, 112
    sensory, 110, 112
  of vision, 237
  of visual accommodation, 239
  phonation and verbal expression, 297, 299
  taste, 300
  vestibular, 281

Centrifugal fiber, 3
Centripetal fiber, 3
Centrum medianum (thalamus), 144, 146, 147
  semiovale, 152, 195
Cerebellum, 22, 133, 148, 151, 281
  divisions of, 136
Chain, neuronic, 8
Chiasma, optic, 21, 118, 139, 140, 148, 155, 193, 195, 207, 229, 237, 331
Chorda tympani, 248, 249, 251, 254, 255, 258, 262, 264, 265, 300, 313
Cingulum, 153, 189, 194
Cistern, subarachnoid, 180
Claustrum, 146, 152, 160, 162-164
Cleft, of Schmidt-Lanterman, 5
  synaptic, 9, 30
Cochlea, 254, 263, 271, 272, 274
Cold, area of sensibility to, 114
Colliculus, facial, 121
  inferior, 120, 143, 147, 171, 186, 195, 229, 279, 280, 298
  superior, 119, 120, 143, 147, 186, 195, 229, 237, 238, 239
Colon, 332
Column, cell, 21, 110
    dorsal gray of spinal cord, 22, 110, 117
    intermediolateral, 25, 110, 113, 115, 325
    intermediomedial, 110, 113, 325
    intermedioventral, 110, 113, 325
    ventral gray, 22, 110, 111
  fundamental. See Fasciculus proprii.
  of fornix, 140, 146, 154, 160, 161, 162, 191, 192, 193, 194, 209
Commissure(s), 189, 190
  anterior, 139, 140, 146, 148, 152, 161, 162, 189, 191, 192, 193, 195, 207
  hypothalamic (of Ganser), 193, 194, 195
  habenular, 190
  of fornix, 154, 189, 193
  of inferior colliculus, 131
  posterior, 139, 140, 189, 191
    hypothalamic, 190, 193
    subthalamic (of Forel), 189
  supramamillary. See Commissure(s), posterior, hypothalamic.
  supra-optic, dorsal (of Meynart), 189, 195
    ventral (of Gudden), 189, 195
Complex, amygdaloid, 141, 163, 191, 192, 194, 208, 331
  oculomotor nuclear. See Nucleus, of medulla oblongata, of cranial nerves, III.
Concha of external ear, 261
Conduction, antidromic, 7
Confluence of dural venous sinuses. See Sinus(es), dural venous.
Conjunctiva, 212, 221
Conus medullaris, 19, 109
Cord, of brachial plexus, 47, 62, 66-68
  spinal, 4, 7, 22, 109
Core, inner, 28, 29
Cornea, 212, 213
  limbus of, 214
Corona radiata, 151, 152, 161, 163, 182
Corpus callosum, 139, 140, 141, 143, 146, 148, 154, 158, 159, 160, 161, 162, 163, 164, 189, 194, 195, 209
Corpuscle, cylindrical, 27
  of Golgi-Mazzoni, 26, 29
  of Krause, 26
  of Meissner, 26, 29
  of Ruffini, 26, 29
  Pacinian, 26, 27, 29, 181

Facilitation, spatial, 8
Falx cerebelli, *179*, 285
  cerebri, 179
Fascia(s), orbital, 225
Fascicle, nerve, 14
Fasciculus, 21
  arcuate, 151, 153, *154*, 189
  association, 189
  central tegmental, 128, 129, 130, 131
  cuneatus, 109, 114, 116, 119, 121, 127, 128, 132, 186
  dorsolateralis. See *Zone, marginal, of Lissauer.*
  gracilis, *109*, 114, 116, 119, 121, *127*, 128, 132, *186*
  interfascicularis, 116
  lenticular, 146
  longitudinal, dorsal, 127, *130*, *190*, 331
      inferior, *153*, 189, 195
      medial, 127, 128, 129, 130, 131, *190*, 191, 228, 238, 281, 331
      superior, *153*, *154*, 159, 161, 162, 163, 189, 238
  mamilloparaoptic, 192
  mamillotectal (of Gudden), 192
  mamillothalamic, 192
  paraoptic, 192
  proprii, 189, 190
  septomarginal, 116
  septothalamic, 192
  solitarius, 128
  thalamic, 146
  triangularis of Philippe-Gombault, 116
  uncinate, of hemisphere, 154, 161, 189, 195
      of Russell. See *Tract, fastigiobulbar.*
Fat, orbital, 225
Fenestra cochleae, *254*, 264, 265, 271, 274
  vestibuli, *254*, 264, 265, 271, 274
Fiber(s), afferent, 3, 7
  arcuate, *127*, 128, 129, 189
  association, 189
      cerebellum, 165
      hemisphere, 153, 154
      spinal cord, 116
  centrifugal, 3
  centripetal, 3
  cerebelloreticular, 188
  cerebroretinal, *218*, *238*
  climbing, cerebellum, 137
  cochleosaccular, 277
  commissural, of spinal cord, 189
  corticopontine, *182*, 184, 187
  efferent, 3, 7
      to cochlea, 278, 279
  excitosecretory, 31, 53
  flocculovestibular, 188
  glandular, 31
  hypothalamopineal, 331
  intersegmental, of spinal cord. See *Fasciculus proprii.*
  mossy, cerebellum, 137
  α-motor, 32
  γ-motor, 32
  muscle, extra- and intrafusal, 29
  nerve, 5, 14, 16, 23, 214
  oculocephalogyric, 131, *182*
      of Hagen, 328
  of Müller, retina, 218
  of Perroncito, 30
  of retina, 218
  olfactory, 205
  olivocerebellar, 128, 187

Fiber(s) *(Continued)*
  parallel, cerebellum, 137
  parapyramidal, 182
  parasympathetic, from autonomic nucleus of III, 311
      of VII and VIIbis, 252, 255
      of IX, 287
      of X, 288
      pelvic, 323
  pontocerebellar, 184, 187
  postganglionic, 13, 33
  preganglionic, 13
  projection, 21
      of cerebellum, 165
  proprioceptive, 186
  reticulocerebellar, 187
  retinohypothalamic, 238
  retinomesencephalic, 239
  rubrocerebellar, 187
  sensory, 33
  spinospinal. See *Fasciculus proprii.*
  spinotectal, 127
  spinovestibular, 281
  tactile, 186
  thalamofugal and thalamopetal, 147
  thalamospinal, 184
  thermoalgesic, 186
  transcallosal, 194
  transverse pontine, 130, 228
  trophic, 26
  vestibulocerebellar, 187
Field, tegmental, of Forel, H1 and H2, 146
  visual, 237
Filum terminale, 19, 109
Fimbria, *154*, 157, 159, 164, *193*, 208, 209, 328
Fissure(s), 148
  calcarine, 237
  cerebral transverse, 139, *140*, 143, 180
  choroidea, 143, 157
  Glaserian, 255
  interhemispheric, 163
  of cerebellum, horizontal, 134, 136
      postcentral, 133, 134
      posterolateral, 134
      postpyramidal, 134
      prenodular, 134
      primary, 133, 134, 136
      secondary, 134
  orbital, superior and inferior, 210, *211*, 231, 232, 243, 245
  palpebral, 221
  petrotympanic, 255
  retinal, 212
  rhinal, 150
Flocculus, 134, 136
Floss of ventricle IV, 121
Fluid, cerebrospinal, 176
  otic. See *Endolymph.*
  periotic. See *Perilymph.*
Fold(s), junctional, 30
  neural, 10
Folium(a), cerebellar, 135
  vermis, 133, 134, 136
Foot, end, 9, 31
  perivascular, of astrocyte, 34, 175
Foramen, cecum, 179
  infraorbital, 245
  interventricular, *139*, 143, 154, *158*
  intervertebral, 15, 18

Page 340

Helicotrema, 272, 274
Hemisphere, cerebral, 22
    external features, 148-151
Henle's sheath, 3, 5, 6, 14, 30
Hindbrain, 20, *118*
Horn, gray, of spinal cord, dorsal (or posterior), 109,
        110, 296
        lateral, 109, *110*
        ventral (or anterior), 109, *110*, 168, 296
    of lateral ventricle, anterior (or frontal), 158
        inferior (or temporal), 158, 159, 162, 164
        posterior (or occipital), 158, 159
Humor, aqueous, 220
Hypophysis, 139, 179, 230, 231, 285, *328*, 333
    stalk of, *242*
Hypothalamus, 138, *140*, 147, 193, 298, *329*

Ileum and jejunum, 332
Incisure, of Schmidt-Lantermann, 5
    tentorial, 178
Incus, 266, 267
Indusium griseum, *157*, 195, *208*, 209
Infundibulum, 138, 179
Innervation, gland, 33
    motor, segmental, 105
    muscle, cardiac, 31
        skeletal, 32
        smooth, 31
    of cornea, 214
    of hypophysis, 328
    organ, 32
        autonomic, 332, 333
    pelvic organs, female, 323
        male, 324
    sensory, of external ear, 260
        peripheral and segmental, 103, 104
    viscera, 33, 113
Insula, 141, *151*, 161, 163, 191
Intestine, large, 332
Iris, *215*, 219, 244
Isocortex, 155

Jejunum and ileum, 332
Junction, sclerocorneal, 214
    synaptic, 9

Kidney, 333
Koniocortex, 155

Labyrinth, membranous, 273
    osseous, 271, 273
Lambda, 179
Lamina affixa, 143
    cribrosa of sclera, 217
    epidural, 18
    medullary, of thalamus, 146, 189
    terminalis, 139, 140, 148
Language, 299
Larynx, 332
Layers, of cerebellar cortex, 137
    of cerebral cortex, 155, 165
    of olfactory bulb, 206
    of retina, 218

Lemniscus, 21
    lateral, 130-132
    medial, *128*, 129, 130, 131, 132, 147, *186*, 331
    of V, *147*, *331*
Lens, 214, 220
Leptomeninx, 177
Ligament, denticulate, 18, *177*, 282, 284
    of incus, 266, 267
    of malleus, 264, 265, 266, 267, 268
    of stapes, 266
    palpebral, 223
Limbus of cornea, 214
Limen insulae, 154
Lingula of cerebellum, 120, 122, *133*, 134, 136
Liver, 332
Lobe, ansiform, 126. See also *Lobule.*
    frontal, 149, 151
        flocculonodular, 136
    limbic, of Broca, 209
    occipital, 149, 151, 191
    parietal, 149, 151
    temporal, 149, *151*, 279
Lobule, biventral, 134, 136
    central, *133*, 134, 136
    gracile, 134, 136
    hippocampal, 150, 154
    paracentral, 149
    quadrangular, 133, 134, 136
    semilunar, inferior, 134, 136
        superior, 133, 136
    simplex, 133, 134
Locus coeruleus, 121, 130
Loop, of atlas, 41, 45
    of Dröbnik, *303*, 307, 308, 309
    of pectoral nerves, 47, 48
Lungs, 332
Lymphatic drainage of external ear, 260

Macroglia, 34
Macula lutea, 217, 237
    utriculi and sacculi, 27, *273*, 276, 277
Malleus, 262, 266, 267
Marrow, bone, 333
Mater, dura. See *Dura mater.*
    pia. See *Pia mater.*
Matter, gray. See *Gray matter.*
    white. See *White matter.*
Meatus, acoustic, external, *261*, 263, 264, 265
    internal, 230, *253*, 254, 255, 265, 272, 285
Meckel's cave, 242
Media dioptric, of eye, 220
Medulla oblongata, *118*, 278, 284, 293
Melanocyte, pia mater, 181
Membrane, basilar, cochlea, 274, 275
    hyaloid, 219
    limiting, glial, brain, 117, 175, 181
        cerebellum, 137
    of retina, 218
    mucous, nasal, buccal and nasopharyngeal, 332
        of olfactory area, 205
        of tympanic cavity, 268
    of Reissner, 274, 275
    of Shrapnell, 261, *262*, 266, 267
    otolithic, 276
    pre- and postsynaptic, 9, 30
    reticular, cochlea, 275

Nervous system (Continued)
  organization of, 7
  peripheral, 4, 13
  spinal, 4, 13, 35
Network, arterial, of spinal cord, 167, 168
  capillary, of hypophysis, 328
  papillary, peritrichial, 28
  subcervical, peritrichial, 28
Neuroepithelium, olfactory, 205
Neurofilament, 6
Neuroglia, 34
  cerebellar cortex, 137
  retina, 218
  spinal cord, 117
Neurolemma, 5, 6, 14, 30
Neuron(s), 5-7
  α-motor, 115
  polarity of, 3
  thalamocortical, 22
Neurokeratin, 5
Neuropore, 10
Neurotubule, 6
Neurovesicle, 9, 30, 31, 275, 276
Nissl bodies, 5
Node of Ranvier, 5, 6
Nodulus, 133, 134, 136
Nose, external, 199, 200
Nostrils, 192
Notch, preoccipital, 149
Nucleus(i), 21
  caudate, 138, 140, 141, 143, 146, 151, 152, 157, 158, 160, 161, 162, 163, 164, 182, 194, 297
  habenular, 145, 146, 192, 208
  hypothalamic, 329
    anterior, 329
    dorsal, 329
    dorsocaudal, 329
    dorsomedial, 329
    lateral, 329
    laterobasal, 328
    paraventricular, 140, 164, 328, 329
    perifornical, 329
    periventricular, 329
    reuniens, 140
    suprachiasmatic, 329
    supraoptic, 140, 208, 328, 329
    tuberis, 140, 208, 329
    ventromedial, 140, 328, 329
  lenticular, 138, 141, 147, 158, 182, 185, 191, 298
  mamillary, 194, 328, 329
  median, of olfactory bulb, 206
  of cerebellum, dentate, 135, 183, 188
    emboliform, 135, 188
    fastigial, 135, 188, 298
    globose, 135, 188
  of medulla oblongata, of cranial nerves, 20, 22, 123
    III, 25, 123, 131, 191, 227, 228, 234, 235, 238, 239, 251, 281, 282, 327
    IV, 123, 131, 227, 228, 234, 235, 281
    V, 123, 127, 128, 129, 130, 131, 186, 187, 241, 251, 282, 298, 300
    VI, 123, 227, 228, 234, 235, 252, 279, 280, 281, 282
    VII and VIIbis, 123, 129, 252, 258, 282, 298, 300
    VIII, 123, 128, 129, 147, 184, 187, 188, 190, 279, 280, 281, 282, 298
    IX, X and XI, 25, 123, 127, 128, 281, 282, 292, 298, 327

Nucleus(i) (Continued)
  of medulla oblongata, of cranial nerves, XI, spinal, 123, 127, 236, 282, 292
    XII, 123, 128, 282, 296
    gustatory, 123, 252, 258, 282, 300
    lacrimopalatonasal, 21, 123, 227, 247, 251, 252, 258, 282, 312, 327
    fasciculus solitarius, 123, 128, 147, 186, 187, 250, 282, 292, 298, 331
    salivatory, superior and inferior, 25, 123, 129, 250, 251, 252, 258, 282, 292, 313, 327
   unsegmental formations, 124
    arcuate, 124, 128, 129
    colliculus, inferior, 124, 131, 228
     superior, 124, 131, 190, 191
    cuneatus, 124, 127, 128, 186, 187
     accessory, 124, 127, 128
    gracilis, 124, 127, 128, 186, 187
    intercalatus, 124, 128
    interpeduncular, 124, 130, 131, 145, 192
    interpositus, 135, 185
    interstitial of Cajal, 124, 190, 191, 281
    of Darkschewitsch, 124
    of lateral lemniscus, 130, 279
    of median raphe, 124, 128, 129
    of posterior commissure, 124, 190, 191
    of trapezoid body, 130, 279
    olivary, inferior, 124, 127, 128, 129, 298
     superior, 129, 279, 280
    paramedian, dorsal, 124, 128, 129, 130
    pontine, 124, 130, 182, 183, 298
    red, 124, 131, 146, 183, 184, 185, 192, 228, 278, 298
    reticular, lateral, 124, 127, 128, 185
    tectal, 131, 147, 184, 185, 280
    tegmental, dorsal, 124
  of spinal cord, cornu commissuralis, 110
    posteromarginalis, 110
    proprius cornu dorsalis, 110
    sacral autonomic, 325
    thoracicus of Clarke, 110
    X of Onuf, 326
  of zona incerta, 140, 220
  septal, 191, 193, 208
  subthalamic (of Luys), 140, 145, 146, 147, 163, 164, 185
    thalamic, 144, 145, 147, 164, 188, 194, 300, 331
     nuclear group, 142

Obex, 121
Olfaction, 27, 199
Oligodendrocyte, 5, 34, 117
Oligodendroglia, 34
Olive, inferior, 118, 119, 184, 185, 187, 229, 293
Operculum, frontoparietal, 161, 163, 191
Ora serrata, 215, 217, 219
Orbit, 210
Organ, neurotendinous, of Golgi, 27, 32
  somatic, innervation, 333
  special sense, 27, 197
  special, of Corti, 273, 274, 275, 276
  tympanic, 333
Organization of nervous system, 7
Organogenesis, of central nervous system, 10, 11
  of commissural fibers, 139
  of diencephalon, 139
  of eye, 212

Organogenesis *(Continued)*
    of tela choroidea of ventricle IV, *125*
Orifice, scleral, for optic nerve, 214
Ossicles, auditory, *266*
Outflow, cranial parasympathetic, *327*
    of autonomic fibers to thorax, *317*
Ovaries, 333

Pachymeninx, *177*
Pain, 27, 114
Paleocerebellum, *136*, 188
Pallesthesia. See *Sensibility, vibratory.*
Pallidum. See *Globus pallidus.*
Pancreas, 332
Papilla, circumvallate, 300
    of eye, 217
Paraflocculus, *136*
Paraganglia, aortic, 333
Parasympathetic components of nervous system, 24
Pathway, 21, 22, 182
    auditory, *279*, 328
    autonomic, central, 325, *331*
    cerebellar, 22, *187*, 188
    corticobulbar, 22, *182*
    corticonuclear, 22, *182*
    corticorubrospinal, *183*
    corticospinal, 22, *182*
    extrapyramidal, *184*
    final common, 32, 115, *182*, 183
    oculocephalogyric, *236*
    of phonation, *298*
    of vision (optic), *237*, 328
    of visual accommodation, *239*
    olfactory, *208*
    somesthetic, general, 22, *186*, 328
    switching, 8
    taste, 300
    trigeminal, secondary, *241*
    vestibular, 281
Peduncle(s), cerebellar, *119*, *120*, 121, 122, 130, 131, *132*, 135, 147, 185, 229
    cerebral, *278*
    mamillary, *194*
    septal, *209*
Penis, 100, 333
Perception, olfactory, *209*
Perilymph, *273*, 274
Perineurium, 3, *14*
Period, refractory, 8
Pharynx, 332
Photoreceptors, *218*
Pia mater, 18, 20, 125, 139, 175, *177*, *178*, *181*
Pigment, lipochrome, 5
    yellowish, 205
Plate, cerebellar, 125
    end, motor, *29*, *30*
    sole, 30
Platysma, 256
Plexus, autonomic, ganglionic, 24, 33
        cardiac and pulmonary, 25
        carotid, internal, 244, *306*, 328
        celiac, 25, *319*
        hypogastric, inferior, 25, *323*, *324*
            superior, 319, *323*, *324*
        mesenteric, 25, *319*, *320*
        pelviperineal, *323*

Plexus *(Continued)*
    autonomic, ganglionic, perivascular, 320
    basilar, venous, *173*
    choroid, *176*
        of lateral ventricle, 140, *141*, 143, 160, 164
        of ventricle IV, *122*, 125
        structure, 125, *175*
    nerve, 13, 15, 24
        brachial, 17, *47*, 48, 49, *68*, 103, 104
        cervical, *41*, 42, 43, *46*, 103, 104, 225, 258
            posterior, 37
        intraepithelial, cornea, 214
        lumbar, 74, 75, *83*, 103, 104
        patellar, 81, 83
        sacral, *84*, 85, 97, 103, 104
            posterior, 37
        subepithelial, cornea, *214*
            skin, *26*
        subgemmal, *300*
        subsartorial, *81*, 83
        tympanic, 264, 287
Polarity of neurons, 3
Pole, frontal, occipital and temporal, 148, 149, 155
Pons, *118*, *129*, 135, 148, *183*, 278, 293
Position of eyeball, 211
Pouch, of Kretschmann, 264, 265, 266, *268*
    of Prussak, 266, *268*
    of Tröltsch, *268*
Precuneus, 149, *194*
Process, clinoid, *178*, 230, 231, 242, 285
    mastoid, 254
Promontory, 264
Protection of central nervous system, *176*
Ptosis, 303
Pulvinar, 120, *143*, 144, 146, 147, 192
Pupil of eye, 214, 219
Putamen, *146*, 152, 160, 161, 162, 163, 164
Pyramid, of medulla, *118*, 119, *182*, 229, 293
    of middle ear, *254*, *263*, 264, *267*
    of nose, skeleton of, *199*
Pyramis, of cerebellum, *133*, *134*, *136*

Radiation(s), of corpus callosum, 195
    optic, *159*, 237, 238
Ramus, commissural, *318*, 321, 322
    communicans, 11, 23, 25
        gray, 13, 16, *25*, 40, 310
        to cranial nerves, *305*, *306*
        to spinal nerves, brachial plexus, *68*, *308*
            cervical plexus, 45
            lumbar plexus, 75
            sacral, *321*, 322
            thoracic, *314*
        white, 13, 16, *25*, 310
        connecting, 13
    meningeal, of cranial nerves, 245, 249, 306
        of spinal nerves, 15, *16*, 18, 20, *40*, 70, 322
    of spinal nerves, dorsal and ventral, *15*, 16, *37*, 39
Receptor, 3, *28*
Recess, epitympanic, 264, 265, 266, *268*
    lateral, of ventricle IV, *120*, 121, *122*
    tympanic, anterior and posterior, 268
        superior, 266, *268*
Rectum, 332
Reflex, axon, 7
    monosynaptic (or single), 7

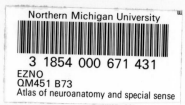

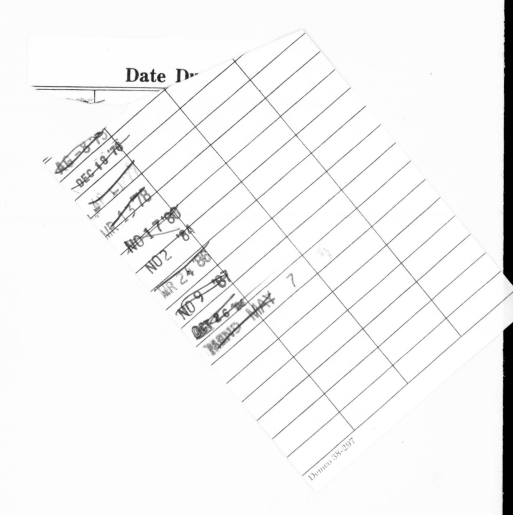

Date Du

AG 3 '73
DEC 18 '74
JA 2 '77
JE 1 5 78
NO 1 7 80
NO2 '8
MR 24 '85
NO 9 '87
OG 26
MANG MAY

7

Demco 38-297